INDIANA

GLENCOE

MATH

AUTHORS
Carter • Cuevas • Day • Malloy
Kersaint • Reynosa • Silbey • Vielhaber

Mc
Graw
Hill
Education

connectED.mcgraw-hill.com

STEM McGraw-Hill is committed to providing instructional materials in Science, Technology, Engineering, and Mathematics (STEM) that give all students a solid foundation, one that prepares them for college and careers in the 21st century.

Send all inquiries to:
McGraw-Hill Education
8787 Orion Place
Columbus, OH 43240

ISBN: 978-0-07-672094-1 (*Volume 2*)
MHID: 0-07-672094-2

Printed in the United States of America.

4 5 6 7 8 9 LMN 22 21 20 19 18 17

CONTENTS IN BRIEF

Units

Indiana Glencoe Math is organized into units based on groups of related standards. The Standards for **PS** Process Standards are embedded throughout the course.

PROCESS STANDARDS HANDBOOK

Tetra Images/Getty Images

UNIT 1

Richard Drury/Photodisc/Getty Images

UNIT 2

Gerald Nowak/Westend61/Photolibrary

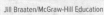

UNIT 3

Jill Braaten/McGraw-Hill Education

UNIT 4

©Photo by Scott Bauer/USDA

UNIT 5

Back in the Pack dog portraits/Flickr/Getty Images

Everything you need,

anytime, anywhere.

With ConnectED, you have instant access to all of your study materials—anytime, anywhere. From homework materials to study guides—it's all in one place and just a click away. ConnectED even allows you to collaborate with your classmates and use mobile apps to make studying easy.

Resources built for you—available 24/7:

- Your eBook available wherever you are

- Personal Tutors and Self-Check Quizzes to help your learning

- An Online Calendar with all of your due dates

- eFlashcard App to make studying easy

- A message center to stay in touch

Go Mobile!

Visit mheonline.com/apps to get entertainment, instruction, and education on the go with ConnectED Mobile and our other apps available for your device.

Go Online!

connectED.mcgraw-hill.com

your Username

your Password

Vocab

Learn about new vocabulary words.

Watch

Watch animations and videos.

Tutor

See and hear a teacher explain how to solve problems.

Tools

Explore concepts with virtual manipulatives.

Sketchpad

Discover concepts using The Geometer's Sketchpad®.

Check

Check your progress.

eHelp

Get targeted homework help.

Worksheets

Access practice worksheets.

UNIT 1 Ratios and Proportional Relationships

UNIT PROJECT PREVIEW
page 2

Chapter 1
Ratios and Proportional Reasoning

Essential Question

HOW can you show that two objects are proportional?

Real World
p. 45

vi

Chapter 2
Percents

Real World
p. 121

Essential Question

HOW can percent help you understand situations involving money?

UNIT PROJECT 183

Become a Travel Expert

UNIT 2 The Number System

UNIT PROJECT PREVIEW
page 185

Chapter 3
Integers

Essential Question

WHAT happens when you add, subtract, multiply, and divide integers?

Real World
p. 233

Chapter 4
Rational Numbers

Real World
p. 319

ⓔ Essential Question

WHAT happens when you add, subtract, multiply, and divide fractions?

UNIT PROJECT 341

Explore the Ocean Depths

UNIT 3 Expressions and Equations

UNIT PROJECT PREVIEW
page 344

Chapter 5
Expressions

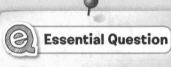

Essential Question

HOW can you use numbers and symbols to represent mathematical ideas?

p. 387

x

Chapter 6
Equations and Inequalities

Real World
p. 437

Essential Question

WHAT does it mean to say two quantities are equal?

Stand Up and Be Counted!

xi

UNIT 4 Geometry

UNIT PROJECT PREVIEW
page 530

Chapter 7
Geometric Figures

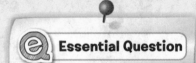

Essential Question

HOW does geometry help us
describe real-world objects?

Real World
p. 535

Chapter 8
Measure Figures

 Essential Question

HOW do measurements help
you describe real-world
objects?

Real World
p. 623

UNIT PROJECT 703

Turn Over a New Leaf

UNIT 5 Statistics and Probability

UNIT PROJECT PREVIEW
page 706

Chapter 9 Probability

Essential Question

HOW can you predict the outcome of future events?

Real World
p. 733

Chapter 10
Statistics

Real World
p. 813

Essential Question

HOW do you know which type
of graph to use when displaying
data?

UNIT PROJECT 853

Math Genes

Indiana Glencoe Math, Grade 7

Indiana Glencoe Math, Course 2, focuses on four critical areas: (1) developing understanding of and applying proportional relationships; (2) operations with rational numbers and working with expressions and linear equations; (3) solving problems involving scale drawings, geometric constructions, and surface area, and volume; and (4) drawing inferences about populations.

Unit Overview

Ratios and Proportional Relationships
- Analyze proportional relationships and use them to solve real-world and mathematical problems.

The Number System
- Apply and extend previous understandings of operations with fractions to add, subtract, multiply, and divide rational numbers.

Expressions and Equations
- Use properties of operations to generate equivalent expressions.
- Solve real-life and mathematical problems using numerical and algebraic expressions and equations.

Geometry
- Draw, construct and describe geometrical figures and describe the relationships between them.
- Solve real-life and mathematical problems involving angle measure, area, surface area, and volume.

Statistics and Probability
- Use random sampling to draw inferences about a population.
- Draw informal comparative inferences about two populations.
- Investigate chance processes and develop, use, and evaluate probability models.

PS Process Standards

1   Make sense of problems and persevere in solving them.
2   Reason abstractly and quantitatively.
3   Construct viable arguments and critique the reasoning of others.
4   Model with mathematics.
5   Use appropriate tools strategically.
6   Attend to precision.
7   Look for and make use of structure.
8   Look for and express regularity in repeated reasoning.

Track Your Progress

These pages list the key ideas that you should be able to understand by the end of the year. You will rate how much you know about each one. Don't worry if you have no clue **before** you learn about them. Watch how your knowledge grows as the year progresses!

☹ I have no clue.　　😐 I've heard of it.　　😊 I know it!

	Before			After		
NUMBER SENSE	☹	😐	😊	☹	😐	😊
7.NS.1 Find the prime factorization of whole numbers and write the results using exponents.						
7.NS.2 Understand the inverse relationship between squaring and finding the square root of a perfect square integer. Find square roots of perfect square integers.						
7.NS.3 Know there are rational and irrational numbers. Identify, compare, and order rational and common irrational numbers ($\sqrt{2}$, $\sqrt{3}$, $\sqrt{5}$, Π) and plot them on a number line.						

	Before			After		
COMPUTATION	☹	😐	😊	☹	😐	😊
7.C.1: Understand $p + q$ as the number located a distance $\lvert q \rvert$ from p, in the positive or negative direction, depending on whether q is positive or negative. Show that a number and its opposite have a sum of 0 (are additive inverses). Interpret sums of rational numbers by describing real-world contexts.						
7.C.2: Understand subtraction of rational numbers as adding the additive inverse, $p - q = p + (-q)$. Show that the distance between two rational numbers on the number line is the absolute value of their difference, and apply this principle in real-world contexts.						
7.C.3: Understand that multiplication is extended from fractions to rational numbers by requiring that operations continue to satisfy the properties of operations, particularly the distributive property, leading to products such as $(-1)(-1) = 1$ and the rules for multiplying signed numbers.						
7.C.4: Understand that integers can be divided, provided that the divisor is not zero, and that every quotient of integers (with non-zero divisor) is a rational number. Understand that if p and q are integers, then $-(p/q) = (-p)/q = p/(-q)$.						
7.C.5: Compute unit rates associated with ratios of fractions, including ratios of lengths, areas and other quantities measured in like or different units.						
7.C.6: Use proportional relationships to solve ratio and percent problems with multiple operations, such as the following: simple interest, tax, markups, markdowns, gratuities, commissions, fees, conversions within and across measurement systems, percent increase and decrease, and percent error.						
7.C.7: Compute with rational numbers fluently using a standard algorithmic approach.						
7.C.8: Solve real-world problems with rational numbers by using one or two operations.						

	Before			After		
ALGEBRA AND FUNCTIONS	☹	😐	🙂	☹	😐	🙂
7.AF.1: Apply the properties of operations (e.g., identity, inverse, commutative, associative, distributive properties) to create equivalent linear expressions, including situations that involve factoring (e.g., given $2x - 10$, create an equivalent expression $2(x - 5)$). Justify each step in the process.						
7.AF.2: Solve equations of the form $px + q = r$ and $p(x + q) = r$ fluently, where p, q, and r are specific rational numbers. Represent real-world problems using equations of these forms and solve such problems.						
7.AF.3: Solve inequalities of the form $px + q$ (> or ≥) r or $px + q$ (< or ≤) r, where p, q, and r are specific rational numbers. Represent real-world problems using inequalities of these forms and solve such problems. Graph the solution set of the inequality and interpret it in the context of the problem.						
7.AF.4: Define slope as vertical change for each unit of horizontal change and recognize that a constant rate of change or constant slope describes a linear function. Identify and describe situations with constant or varying rates of change.						
7.AF.5: Graph a line given its slope and a point on the line. Find the slope of a line given its graph.						
7.AF.6: Decide whether two quantities are in a proportional relationship (e.g., by testing for equivalent ratios in a table or graphing on a coordinate plane and observing whether the graph is a straight line through the origin).						
7.AF.7: Identify the unit rate or constant of proportionality in tables, graphs, equations, and verbal descriptions of proportional relationships.						
7.AF.8: Explain what the coordinates of a point on the graph of a proportional relationship mean in terms of the situation, with special attention to the points (0, 0) and (1, r), where r is the unit rate.						
7.AF.9: Identify real-world and other mathematical situations that involve proportional relationships. Write equations and draw graphs to represent proportional relationships and recognize that these situations are described by a linear function in the form $y = mx$, where the unit rate, m, is the slope of the line.						

	Before			After		

GEOMETRY AND MEASUREMENT

7.GM.1: Draw triangles (freehand, with ruler and protractor, and using technology) with given conditions from three measures of angles or sides, and notice when the conditions determine a unique triangle, more than one triangle, or no triangle.

7.GM.2: Identify and describe similarity relationships of polygons including the angle-angle criterion for similar triangles, and solve problems involving similarity.

7.GM.3: Solve real-world and other mathematical problems involving scale drawings of geometric figures, including computing actual lengths and areas from a scale drawing. Create a scale drawing by using proportional reasoning.

7.GM.4: Solve real-world and other mathematical problems that involve vertical, adjacent, complementary, and supplementary angles.

7.GM.5: Understand the formulas for area and circumference of a circle and use them to solve real-world and other mathematical problems; give an informal derivation of the relationship between circumference and area of a circle.

7.GM.6: Solve real-world and other mathematical problems involving volume of cylinders and three-dimensional objects composed of right rectangular prisms.

7.GM.7: Construct nets for right rectangular prisms and cylinders and use the nets to compute the surface area; apply this technique to solve real-world and other mathematical problems.

	Before			After		
DATA ANALYSIS AND STATISTICS	☹	😐	🙂	☹	😐	🙂
7.DSP.1: Understand that statistics can be used to gain information about a population by examining a sample of the population and generalizations about a population from a sample are valid only if the sample is representative of that population. Understand that random sampling tends to produce representative samples and support valid inferences.						
7.DSP.2: Use data from a random sample to draw inferences about a population. Generate multiple samples (or simulated samples) of the same size to gauge the variation in estimates or predictions.						
7.DSP.3: Find, use, and interpret measures of center (mean and median) and measures of spread (range, interquartile range, and mean bsolute deviation) for numerical data from random samples to draw comparative inferences about two populations.						
7.DSP.4: Make observations about the degree of visual overlap of two numerical data distributions represented in line plots or box plots. Describe how data, particularly outliers, added to a data set may affect the mean and/or median.						
7.DSP.5: Understand that the probability of a chance event is a number between 0 and 1 that expresses the likelihood of the event occurring. Understand that a probability near 0 indicates an unlikely event, a probability around 1/2 indicates an event that is neither unlikely nor likely, and a probability near 1 indicates a likely event. Understand that a probability of 1 indicates an event certain to occur and a probability of 0 indicates an event impossible to occur.						
7.DSP.6: Approximate the probability of a chance event by collecting data on the chance process that produces it and observing its relative frequency from a large sample.						
7.DSP.7: Develop probability models that include the sample space and probabilities of outcomes to represent simple events with equally likely outcomes. Predict the approximate relative frequency of the event based on the model. Compare probabilities from the model to observed frequencies; evaluate the level of agreement and explain possible sources of discrepancy.						

UNIT 3
Expressions and Equations

 Essential Question

HOW can you communicate mathematical ideas effectively?

Chapter 5
Expressions

Algebraic expressions can be used to represent real-world situations. In this chapter, you will apply the properties of operations to simplify and evaluate algebraic expressions.

Chapter 6
Equations and Inequalities

An equation is a mathematical sentence stating that two expressions are equal. In this chapter, you will use the properties of equality to solve equations algebraically. Then you will apply what you learn to solve inequalities.

Unit Project Preview

Stand Up and Be Counted! The U.S. Census is a survey of the American people that is taken every 10 years. The census is used to collect data about the United States population and to determine the number of House of Representatives for each state.

Conduct your own mini-census. Survey twenty students about the typical way they come to school: by school bus, by car, on foot, or by some other means. Then make a circle graph of the data.

At the end of Chapter 6, you'll complete a project to find how the U.S. population affects the House of Representatives. This adventure will appeal to your "census."

Ways to Come to School

Chapter 5
Expressions

Essential Question

HOW can you use numbers and symbols to represent mathematical ideas?

Indiana Academic Standards
7.AF.1, 7.AF.2

PS Process Standards
1, 2, 3, 4, 5, 6, 7

Math in the Real World

Meerkats live in burrows. Because meerkats have sharp claws, they are able to dig at a rate of 1 foot per second.

Suppose a meerkat digs for 3 seconds. Cross out the expression that does not represent the underground distance dug by the meerkat.

$(-1) + (-1) + (-1)$

$3(-1) + 1$

$3(-1)$

FOLDABLES
Study Organizer

Cut out the Foldable on page FL3 of this book.

Place your Foldable on page 426.

3 Use the Foldable throughout this chapter to help you learn about expressions.

What Tools Do You Need?

 Vocabulary

Additive Identity Property	define a variable	Multiplicative Property
algebra	Distributive Property	of Zero
algebraic expression	equivalent expressions	property
arithmetic sequence	factor	sequence
Associative Property	factored form	simplest form
coefficient	like terms	term
Commutative Property	linear expression	variable
constant	monomial	
counterexample	Multiplicative Identity Property	

Review Vocabulary

Order of Operations The order of operations is a four-step process used to evaluate numerical expressions.

1. Evaluate the expressions inside grouping symbols.
2. Evaluate all powers.
3. Multiply and divide in order from left to right.
4. Add and subtract in order form left to right.

Use the order of operations to evaluate $3 + 5^2(4 + 4)$. Write each step in the organizer below.

What Do You Already Know?

Read each statement. Decide whether you agree (A) or disagree (D). Place a checkmark in the appropriate column and then justify your reasoning.

Expressions			
Statement	A	D	Why?
Like terms are terms that contain different variables.			
When addition or subtraction signs separate an algebraic expression into parts, each part is called a term.			
An algebraic expression is in simplest form if it has no like terms and no parentheses.			
A property is an example that shows that a conjecture is false.			
When you use the Distributive Property to combine like terms, you are simplifying the expression.			
Equivalent expressions have the same value.			

When Will You Use This?

Here are a few examples of how expressions are used in the real world.

Activity 1 Do you or your parents have a texting plan? If so, how much does it cost per text or per month? Ask your parents to help you research different texting plans. Then compare and contrast each plan.

_____

_____

Activity 2 Go online at **connectED.mcgraw-hill.com** to read the graphic novel **Too Many Texts**. How many text messages are

included in Dario's texting plan? _____

Hiroshi, Caitlyn, and Dario in

Too Many Texts

Oh, NO! What's THIS going to cost me?

Your plan: 250 text messages = $5.00

Messages sent to date: 275

Are You Ready?

Try the Quick Check below.
Or, take the Online Readiness Quiz.

Check ✓

Quick Review

Example 1

Evaluate 2^5.

$$2^5 = 2 \cdot 2 \cdot 2 \cdot 2 \cdot 2$$
$$= 32$$

Example 2

Write $3 \cdot 3 \cdot 3 \cdot 3 \cdot 3 \cdot 3 \cdot 3$ in exponential form.

3 is the base. It is used as a factor 7 times. So, the exponent is 7.

$$3 \cdot 3 \cdot 3 \cdot 3 \cdot 3 \cdot 3 \cdot 3 = 3^7$$

Example 3

Find $4(-2)$.

$$4(-2) = -8$$

The integers have different signs.
The product is negative.

Example 4

Find $-5(-8)$.

$$-5(-8) = 40$$

The integers have the same signs.
The product is positive.

Quick Check

Exponents Evaluate each expression.

1. $2^4 =$ _____

2. $3^3 =$ _____

3. $4^2 =$ _____

Show your work.

4. Write $4 \cdot 4 \cdot 4 \cdot 4$ in exponential form. _____

Integer Operations Multiply.

5. $5(-10) =$ _____

6. $-9(-4) =$ _____

7. $-5^2 =$ _____

How Did You Do?

Which problems did you answer correctly in the Quick Check?
Shade those exercise numbers below.

① ② ③ ④ ⑤

Algebraic Expressions

Vocabulary Start-Up

A **variable** is a symbol that represents an unknown quantity. An **algebraic expression**, such as $n + 2$, is an expression that contains variables, numbers, and at least one operation.

Variable $\cdots\!\!\rightarrow$ **$n + 2$**

Write each of the following phrases in the correct section of the Venn diagram: *contains an operation, has variables and numbers, has only numbers.*

Characteristics of Expressions

numerical expression   algebraic expression

 Essential Question

HOW can you use numbers and symbols to represent mathematical ideas?

Vocabulary

variable
algebraic expression
algebra
coefficient
define a variable

Indiana Academic Standards
Preparation for 7.AF.1, 7.AF.2

PS Process Standards
1, 2, 3, 4

Real-World Link

The expression $(F - 32) \times \frac{5}{9}$ can be used to convert a temperature from Fahrenheit to Celsius. In this algebraic expression, the variable _____ represents the temperature in degrees Fahrenheit.

Brrr...!

Which PS **Process Standards** did you use?
Shade the circle(s) that applies.

1. Persevere with Problems
2. Reason Abstractly
3. Construct an Argument
4. Model with Mathematics

5. Use Math Tools
6. Attend to Precision
7. Make Use of Structure
8. Use Repeated Reasoning

Evaluate an Algebraic Expression

The branch of mathematics that involves expressions with variables is called **algebra**. In algebra, the multiplication sign is often omitted.

6d — 6 times *d*

9st — 9 times *s* times *t*

mn — *m* times *n*

a³ — *a* times *a* times *a*

The numerical factor of a multiplication expression that contains a variable is called a **coefficient**. So, 6 is the coefficient of 6*d*.

Expressions like $\frac{y}{2}$ can be written as $y \div 2$ or $y \times \frac{1}{2}$.

Order of Operations

1. Evaluate the expressions inside grouping symbols.
2. Evaluate all powers.
3. Multiply and divide in order from left to right.
4. Add and subtract in order from left to right.

Examples

Watch **Tutor**

1. **Evaluate 2(n + 3) if n = −4.**

$$2(n + 3) = 2(-4 + 3)$$ Replace *n* with −4.
$$= 2(-1)$$ Evaluate inside the parentheses.
$$= -2$$ Multiply.

2. **Evaluate 8w − 2v if w = 5 and v = 3.**

$$8w - 2v = 8(5) - 2(3)$$ Replace *w* with 5 and *v* with 3.
$$= 40 - 6$$ Do all of the multiplication first.
$$= 34$$ Subtract 6 from 40.

3. **Evaluate 4y³ + 2 if y = 3.**

$$4y^3 + 2 = 4(3)^3 + 2$$ Replace *y* with 3.
$$= 4(27) + 2$$ Evaluate the power.
$$= 110$$ Multiply, then add.

 Show your work.

Got It? Do these problems to find out.

Evaluate each expression if c = 8 and d = −5.

a. $c - 3$ b. $15 - c$ c. $3(c + d)$

d. $2c - 4d$ e. $d - c^2$ f. $2d^2 + 5d$

a. _____

b. _____

c. _____

d. _____

e. _____

f. _____

Example

Tutor

4. Athletic trainers use the formula $\frac{3(220 - a)}{5}$, where a is a person's age, to find their minimum training heart rate. Find Latrina's minimum training heart rate if she is 15 years old.

$$\frac{3(220 - a)}{5} = \frac{3(220 - 15)}{5} \qquad \text{Replace } a \text{ with 15.}$$

$$= \frac{3(205)}{5} \qquad \text{Subtract 15 from 220.}$$

$$= \frac{615}{5} \qquad \text{Multiply 3 and 205.}$$

$$= 123 \qquad \text{Divide 615 by 5.}$$

Latrina's minimum training heart rate is 123 beats per minute.

Fractions
The fraction bar is a grouping symbol. Evaluate the expressions in the numerator and denominator separately before dividing.

Got It? Do this problem to find out.

g. To find the area of a triangle, use the formula $\frac{bh}{2}$, where b is the base and h is the height. What is the area in square inches of a triangle with a height of 6 inches and base of 8 inches?

Show your work.

9. _____

Write Expressions

To translate a verbal phrase into an algebraic expression, the first step is to define a variable. When you **define a variable**, you choose a variable to represent an unknown quantity.

Examples

Tutor

5. Marisa wants to buy a DVD player that costs $150. She already saved $25 and plans to save an additional $10 each week. Write an expression that represents the total amount of money Marisa has saved after any number of weeks.

Words	savings of $25 plus ten dollars each week

Variable   Let w represent the number of weeks.

Expression   25   +   10 · w

$25 + 10w$ represents the total saved after any number of weeks.

6. Refer to Example 5. Will Marisa have saved enough money to buy the **$150 DVD player in 11 weeks? Use the expression 25 + 10w.**

$$25 + 10w = 25 + 10(11) \qquad \text{Replace } w \text{ with 11.}$$
$$= 25 + 110 \qquad \text{Multiply.}$$
$$= 135 \qquad \text{Add.}$$

Marisa will have saved $135 after 11 weeks. Since $135 < $150, Marisa will not have enough money to buy the DVD player.

Got It? Do this problem to find out.

h. _____

h. An MP3 player costs $70 and song downloads cost $0.85 each. Write an expression that represents the cost of the MP3 player and *x* number of downloaded songs. Then find the total cost if 20 songs are downloaded.

Guided Practice

Check ✓

Evaluate each expression if *m* = 2, *n* = 6, and *p* = −4. (Examples 1–4)

1. $3m + 4p$ _____

2. $n^2 + 5$ _____

3. $6p^3$ _____

4. A Web site charges $0.99 to download a game and a $12.49 membership fee. Write an expression that gives the total cost in dollars to download *g* games. Then find the cost of downloading 6 games. (Examples 5 and 6)

_____

5. ⓔ **Building on the Essential Question** Tell whether the statement below is *sometimes*, *always*, or *never* true. Justify your reasoning.

The expressions x − 3 and y − 3 represent the same value.

_____

_____

_____

Extra Practice

Evaluate each expression if $d = 8$, $e = 3$, $f = 4$, and $g = -1$.

20. $10 - e$ 7

$10 - e$

$10 - 3 = 7$

Homework Help ➡

21. $\frac{16}{f}$ 4

$\frac{16}{f}$

$\frac{16}{4} = 4$

22. $4e^2$ _____

23. $8g - f$ _____

24. $\frac{(5 + g)^2}{2}$ _____

25. $e^2 - 4$ _____

26. The expression $\frac{w}{30}$, where w is a person's weight in pounds, is used to find the approximate number of quarts of blood in the person's body. How many quarts of blood does a 120-pound person have?

_____

27. (PS) **Model with Mathematics** Refer to the graphic novel frame below. Let n represent the number of text messages. Evaluate the expression

$0.15(n - 250) + 5$ to find the cost of 275 text messages. _____

Price Guide:

Number of Text Messages Sent	Cost
250	$5.00
252	$5.30
254	$5.60
256	$5.90

Caitlin is helping Dario figure out what his text messaging bill will be this month.

28. Tonya has x quarters, y dimes, and z nickels in her pocket. Select the appropriate operations to complete the expression that represents the total amount of change Tonya has in her pocket.

($0.25 $\boxed{}$ x) $\boxed{}$ ($0.1 $\boxed{}$ y) $\boxed{}$ ($0.05 $\boxed{}$ z)

Evaluate the expression for $x = 3$, $y = 5$, and $z = 2$. What does this value represent?

29. The prices of magazines and books at the school book fair are shown in the table. Determine if each statement is true or false.

School Book Fair Prices	
Item	Cost
Magazines	$4.95
Paperback books	$7.95

a. The expression $7.95b + 4.95m$ represents the cost of buying b books and m magazines. ☐ True ☐ False

b. The expression $12.90(b + m)$ represents the cost of buying b books and m magazines. ☐ True ☐ False

c. The total cost of buying 3 books and 4 magazines is $43.65. ☐ True ☐ False

Spiral Review

Define a variable and write each phrase as an algebraic expression.

30. 8 feet less than the height _____

31. Sarah worked 8 more hours than Paida. _____

32. Kumar has twice the number of goals as Jacob. _____

33. Addison is 3 years younger than Nathan. _____

34. The table shows the costs of different camping activities. Over the summer, Maura canoed 4 times and fished 3 times. Write and evaluate an expression that represents the total cost Maura spent canoeing and fishing.

Camping Activity Costs	
Activity	Cost
Canoeing	$8
Fishing	$5

Sequences

Vocabulary Start-Up

A **sequence** is an ordered list of numbers. Each number in a sequence is called a **term**. In an **arithmetic sequence**, each term is found by adding the same number to the previous term.

Complete the graphic organizer below.

arithmetic sequences

Numbers

Continue each sequence.

1, 3, 5, 7, ☐ , ...

1, 1.5, 2, ☐ , ☐ , ☐ , ...

Words

Describe each sequence.

Add ☐ to the previous term.

_____

Essential Question

HOW can you use numbers and symbols to represent mathematical ideas?

 Vocabulary

sequence
term
arithmetic sequence

Indiana Academic Standards
Preparation for 7.AF.1, 7.AF.2

PS Process Standards
1, 2, 3, 4

Real-World Link

Horseback Riding The number of students who went on each horseback riding trip is shown. Do the numbers represent the terms of an arithmetic sequence? Explain.

Trip	1	2	3	4	5
Number of Students	15	16	18	21	25

_____

_____

Which **PS** Process Standards did you use?
Shade the circle(s) that applies.

① Persevere with Problems   ⑤ Use Math Tools

② Reason Abstractly   ⑥ Attend to Precision

③ Construct an Argument   ⑦ Make Use of Structure

④ Model with Mathematics   ⑧ Use Repeated Reasoning

Describe and Extend Sequences

In an arithmetic sequence, the terms can be whole numbers, fractions, or decimals.

Examples

Tutor

1. Describe the relationship between the terms in the arithmetic sequence **8, 13, 18, 23, ...** Then write the next three terms in the sequence.

8, 13, 18, 23, ...
+5   +5   +5

Each term is found by adding 5 to the previous term.

Continue the pattern to find the next three terms.

$23 + 5 = 28$ $28 + 5 = 33$ $33 + 5 = 38$

The next three terms are 28, 33, and 38.

2. Describe the relationship between the terms in the arithmetic sequence **0.4, 0.6, 0.8, 1.0, ...** Then write the next three terms in the sequence.

0.4, 0.6, 0.8, 1.0, ...
+0.2 +0.2 +0.2

Each term is found by adding 0.2 to the previous term.

Show your work.

Continue the pattern to find the next three terms.

$1.0 + 0.2 = 1.2$ $1.2 + 0.2 = 1.4$ $1.4 + 0.2 = 1.6$

The next three terms are 1.2, 1.4, and 1.6.

Got It? Do these problems to find out.

Describe the relationship between the terms in each arithmetic sequence. Then write the next three terms in the sequence.

a. 0, 13, 26, 39, ...

b. 4, 7, 10, 13, ...

c. 1.0, 1.3, 1.6, 1.9, ...

d. 2.5, 3.0, 3.5, 4.0, ...

a. _____

b. _____

c. _____

d. _____

Write an Algebraic Expression

In a sequence, each term has a specific position within the sequence. Consider the sequence 2, 4, 6, 8,...

| 1st position | | 3rd position |
| 2nd position | **2, 4, 6, 8,...** | 4th position |

Notice that as the position number increases by 1, the value of the term increases by 2.

Position	Operation	Value of Term
1	$1 \cdot 2 = 2$	2
2	$2 \cdot 2 = 4$	4
3	$3 \cdot 2 = 6$	6
4	$4 \cdot 2 = 8$	8

+1 ... +2

You can also write an algebraic expression to represent the relationship between any term in a sequence and its position in the sequence. In this case, if n represents the position in the sequence, the value of the term is $2n$.

> **Arithmetic Sequences**
>
> When looking for a pattern between the position number and each term in the sequence, it is often helpful to make a table.

Example

Tutor

3. The greeting cards that Meredith makes are sold in boxes at a gift store. The first week, the store sold 5 boxes. Each week, the store sells five more boxes. The pattern continues. What algebraic expression can be used to find the total number of boxes sold at the end of the 100th week? What is the total?

Position	Operation	Value of Term
1	$1 \cdot 5$	5
2	$2 \cdot 5$	10
3	$3 \cdot 5$	15
n	$n \cdot 5$	$5n$

Each term is 5 times its position. So, the expression is $5n$.

$5n$ Write the expression.

$5(100) = 500$ Replace n with 100.

At the end of 100 weeks, 500 boxes will have been sold.

STOP and Reflect

Suppose Figure 1 had 3 circles, Figure 2 had 5 circles, and Figure 3 had 7 circles. What algebraic expression represents this situation?

e. _____

Got It? Do this problem to find out.

e. If the pattern continues, what algebraic expression can be used to find the number of circles used in any figure? How many circles will be in the 50th figure?

Figure 1   Figure 2   Figure 3

Guided Practice

Describe the relationship between the terms in each arithmetic sequence. Then write the next three terms in each sequence. (Examples 1 and 2)

1. 0, 9, 18, 27, ...

2. 4, 9, 14, 19, ...

3. 1, 1.1, 1.2, 1.3, ...

4. Hannah has a doll collection. The table shows the total number of dolls in her collection for three years. Suppose this pattern continues. Write an algebraic expression to find the number of dolls in her collection after n years. How many dolls will Hannah have after 25 years? (Example 3)

Year	Number of Dolls
1	6
2	12
3	18

5. 🅠 **Building on the Essential Question** Explain why the following sequence is considered an arithmetic sequence.

5, 9, 13, 17, 21,...

Rate Yourself!

How confident are you about sequences? Check the box that applies.

For more help, go online to access a Personal Tutor.

Independent Practice

Go online for Step-by-Step Solutions

Describe the relationship between the terms in each arithmetic sequence. Then write the next three terms in each sequence. (Examples 1 and 2)

1. 0, 7, 14, 21, ...

 Show your work.

2. 1, 7, 13, 19, ...

3. 26, 34, 42, 50, ...

4. 0.1, 0.4, 0.7, 1.0, ...

5. 2.4, 3.2, 4.0, 4.8, ...

6. 2.0, 3.1, 4.2, 5.3, ...

7. Refer to the table shown. If the pattern continues, what algebraic expression can be used to find the plant's height for any month? What will be the plant's height at 12 months? (Example 3)

Month	Height (in.)
1	3
2	6
3	9

8. (PS) **Model with Mathematics** Explain how the number of text messages Dario sent and the cost form an arithmetic sequence. Then write an expression to find Dario's text messaging bill if he sends *n* text messages over 250.

9. **PS** **Multiple Representations** Kendra is stacking boxes of tissues for a store display. She stacks 3 boxes in the first minute, 6 boxes by the end of the second minute, and 9 boxes by the end of the third minute. Suppose the pattern continues for parts **a–d**.

a. **Table** Make a table of values for 1, 2, 3, 4, and 5 minutes.

b. **Symbols** Write an expression to find the *n*th term in the sequence.

c. **Graph** Graph the table of values from part **a** on the coordinate plane. Let *x* represent the number of minutes and *y* represent the number of boxes. Then describe the graph.

d. **Numbers** How many boxes will be displayed after 45 minutes?

H.O.T. Problems Higher Order Thinking

10. **PS** **Justify Conclusions** Write five terms of an arithmetic sequence and describe the rule for finding the terms.

PS **Persevere with Problems** Not all sequences are arithmetic. But, there is still a pattern. Describe the relationship between the terms in each sequence. Then write the next three terms in the sequence.

11. 1, 2, 4, 7, 11, ...

12. 0, 2, 6, 12, 20, ...

13. **PS** **Persevere with Problems** Use an arithmetic sequence to find the number of multiples of 6 between 41 and 523. Justify your reasoning.

Extra Practice

Describe the relationship between the terms in each arithmetic sequence. Then write the next three terms in each sequence.

14. 19, 31, 43, 55, ...

12 is added to the previous
term; 67, 79, 91

Homework Help

15. 6, 16, 26, 36, ...

10 is added to the previous
term; 46, 56, 66

16. 33, 38, 43, 48, ...

_____

_____

17. 4.5, 6.0, 7.5, 9.0, ...

_____

_____

18. 1.2, 3.2, 5.2, 7.2, ...

_____

_____

19. 4.6, 8.6, 12.6, 16.6, ...

_____

_____

20. 18, 33, 48, 63, ...

_____

_____

21. 20, 45, 70, 95, ...

_____

_____

22. 38, 61, 84, 107, ...

_____

_____

23. **PS** **Reason Abstractly** Refer to the figures for parts **a** and **b**.

Figure 1   Figure 2   Figure 3

a. Describe the relationship between the figures and the number of

rectangles shown. _____

b. If the pattern continues, how many rectangles will be in the next

2 figures? _____

The terms of an arithmetic sequence can be related by subtraction. Write the next three terms of each sequence.

24. 32, 27, 22, 17, ...

_____

_____

25. 45, 42, 39, 36, ...

_____

_____

26. 10.5, 10, 9.5, 9, ...

_____

_____

27. The table shows the first 5 terms of a sequence. Determine if each statement is true or false.

Position	1	2	3	4	5	n
Value of Term	2	5	10	17	26	■

    a. The expression $n^2 + 1$ can be used to find the nth term of the sequence.   ☐ True   ☐ False

    b. The 8th term of the sequence is 65.   ☐ True   ☐ False

    c. The table represents an arithmetic sequence.   ☐ True   ☐ False

28. Katie is putting photos in an album. She puts five pictures on the first page. Each page after that contains five pictures. Suppose the pattern continues. Complete the table of values for 1, 2, 3, 4, and 5 pages. Then graph the table of values on the coordinate plane. Let x represent the number of pages and y represent the total number of photos.

Number of Pages	Total Photos
1	
2	
3	
4	
5	

How many photos will Katie have on 20 pages? [____]

Spiral Review

Evaluate.

29. $1^4 =$ _____

30. $3^3 =$ _____

31. $8^2 =$ _____

32. $10^4 =$ _____

33. $5^1 =$ _____

34. $7^5 =$ _____

35. Jayden goes to the batting cage. He purchases three tokens and rents a helmet. If he spends a total of $6.50, how much is each token?

Batting Cage Prices	
Tokens	■
Helmet Rental	$2

Inquiry Lab

Sequences

 Indiana Academic Standards
Preparation for 7.AF.1, 7.AF.2

PS **Process Standards**
1, 3

A fencing company uses 4 planks of wood for one section of fencing, 7 planks for two sections, and 10 planks of wood for three sections. The fence sections are represented using the toothpicks shown. Determine how many planks would be used to create 5 sections of fencing.

1 Section   2 Sections   3 Sections

Hands-On Activity

Step 1   Find a pattern in the table. Then fill in the number of planks that would be in 4 and 5 sections of fencing.

Number of Sections	Number of Planks
1	4
2	7
3	10
4	
5	

Step 2   Check your work by using toothpicks to show 5 fence sections. Draw the result in the space below.

So, there will be ⬚ planks in 5 sections of fencing.

Work with a partner. Complete the table. You can use toothpicks to continue each pattern if needed.

1.

Figure 1   Figure 2

Figure 3

Figure Number	Number of Toothpicks
1	6
2	11
3	16
4	
5	

2. Refer to Exercise 1. Write an expression that could be used to find the number of toothpicks that would be needed for any figure.

_____

3. Use your expression from Exercise 2 to find the number of toothpicks that would be needed to create Figure 10. Explain.

_____

_____

Create

On Your Own

4. (PS) **Reason Abstractly** Refer to the activity. Write an expression that could be used to find the number of planks in any number of sections.

_____

5. (PS) **Justify Conclusions** Use the expression in Exercise 4 to find the number of planks that would be needed to create 10 sections of fencing. Explain.

_____

_____

6. (Inquiry) HOW can geometric figures be used to model numerical patterns?

_____

_____

_____

Properties of Operations

 Real-World Link

Driving Miss Ricardo drives up and down her street to complete different errands. Some of the places on her street are shown below. The number of blocks between the places are also shown.

2 blocks | 1 block | 3 blocks

1. Suppose Miss Ricardo drives from home to the game store and back. Write an expression for each distance.

   from home to   from the game
   the game store: _____ store to home: _____

2. Circle the property that is illustrated in Exercise 1.

   Commutative   Associative

3. On Monday, Miss Ricardo drives from home, stops at the library, and then drives to the football field. On Tuesday, she drives from home, stops at the game store, and then drives to the football field. Write an expression for each distance.

   Monday: _____   Tuesday: _____

4. Circle the property that is illustrated in Exercise 3.

   Commutative   Associative

 Essential Question

HOW can you use numbers and symbols to represent mathematical ideas?

Vocabulary

commutative property
associative property
property
additive identity property
multiplicative identity property
multiplicative property of zero
counterexample

Indiana Academic Standards
7.AF.1, 7.AF.2

PS Process Standards
1, 3, 4, 5, 7

Which PS Process Standards did you use?
Shade the circle(s) that applies.

① Persevere with Problems   ⑤ Use Math Tools

② Reason Abstractly   ⑥ Attend to Precision

③ Construct an Argument   ⑦ Make Use of Structure

④ Model with Mathematics   ⑧ Use Repeated Reasoning

Properties of Operations

Watch

Words   The **Commutative Property** states that the order in which numbers are added or multiplied does not change the sum or product.

	Addition	Multiplication
Symbols	$a + b = b + a$	$a \cdot b = b \cdot a$
Examples	$6 + 1 = 1 + 6$	$7 \cdot 3 = 3 \cdot 7$

Words   The **Associative Property** states that the way in which numbers are grouped when they are added or multiplied does not change the sum or product.

	Addition	Multiplication
Symbols	$a + (b + c) = (a + b) + c$	$a \cdot (b \cdot c) = (a \cdot b) \cdot c$
Examples	$2 + (3 + 8) = (2 + 3) + 8$	$3 \cdot (4 \cdot 5) = (3 \cdot 4) \cdot 5$

A **property** is a statement that is true for any number. The following properties are also true for any numbers.

Property	Words	Symbols	Examples
Additive Identity	When 0 is added to any number, the sum is the number.	$a + 0 = a$ $0 + a = a$	$9 + 0 = 9$ $0 + 9 = 9$
Multiplicative Identity	When any number is multiplied by 1, the product is the number.	$a \cdot 1 = a$ $1 \cdot a = a$	$5 \cdot 1 = 5$ $1 \cdot 5 = 5$
Multiplicative Property of Zero	When any number is multiplied by 0, the product is 0.	$a \cdot 0 = 0$ $0 \cdot a = 0$	$8 \cdot 0 = 0$ $0 \cdot 8 = 0$

Example

Tutor

1. **Name the property shown by the statement**
   $2 \cdot (5 \cdot n) = (2 \cdot 5) \cdot n$.

   The order of the numbers and variable did not change, but their grouping did. This is the Associative Property of Multiplication.

Show your work.

Got It?   Do these problems to find out.

a. _____

b. _____

   a. $42 + x + y = 42 + y + x$ **b.** $3x + 0 = 3x$

You may wonder if any of the properties apply to subtraction or division. If you can find a **counterexample**, an example that shows that a conjecture is false, the property does not apply.

Example

2. State whether the following conjecture is *true* or *false*. If *false*, provide a counterexample.

> *Division of whole numbers is commutative.*

Write two division expressions using the Commutative Property.

$15 \div 3 \overset{?}{=} 3 \div 15$ State the conjecture.

$5 \neq \dfrac{1}{5}$ Divide.

The conjecture is false. We found a counterexample. That is, $15 \div 3 \neq 3 \div 15$. So, division is *not* commutative.

Got It? Do this problem to find out.

c. The difference of two different whole numbers is always less than both of the two numbers.

c. _____

Example

3. Alana wants to buy a sweater that costs $38, sunglasses that costs $14, a pair of jeans that costs $22, and a T-shirt that costs $16. Use mental math to find the total cost before tax.

Write an expression for the total cost. You can rearrange the numbers using the properties of math. Look for sums that are multiples of ten.

$38 + 14 + 22 + 16$

$= 38 + 22 + 14 + 16$ Commutative Property of Addition

$= (38 + 22) + (14 + 16)$ Associative Property of Addition

$= 60 + 30$ Add.

$= 90$ Simplify.

The total cost of the items is $90.

Got It? Do this problem to find out.

d. Lance made four phone calls from his cell phone today. The calls lasted 4.7, 9.4, 2.3, and 10.6 minutes. Use mental math to find the total amount of time he spent on the phone.

d. _____

Examples

Simplify each expression. Justify each step.

4. $(7 + g) + 5$

$(7 + g) + 5 = (g + 7) + 5$	Commutative Property of Addition
$= g + (7 + 5)$	Associative Property of Addition
$= g + 12$	Simplify.

5. $(m \cdot 11) \cdot m$

$(m \cdot 11) \cdot m = (11 \cdot m) \cdot m$	Commutative Property of Multiplication
$= 11 \cdot (m \cdot m)$	Associative Property of Multiplication
$= 11m^2$	Simplify.

 Show your work.

Got It? Do this problem to find out.

e. _____

e. $4 \cdot (3c \cdot 2)$

Guided Practice

 Check ✓

Name the property shown by each statement. (Example 1)

1. $3m \cdot 0 \cdot 5m = 0$ _____

2. $7c + 0 = 7c$ _____

3. State whether the following conjecture is *true* or *false*. If *false*, provide a counterexample. (Example 2)

Subtraction of whole numbers is associative.

_____

4. Simplify $9c + (8 + 3c)$. Justify each step. (Examples 3–5)

_____

_____

_____

5. ⓔ **Building on the Essential Question** Explain the difference between the Commutative and Associative Properties. _____

_____

_____

Rate Yourself!

Are you ready to move on? Shade the section that applies.

YES   ?   NO

For more help, go online to access a Personal Tutor. Tutor

Independent Practice

Go online for Step-by-Step Solutions

Name the property shown by each statement. (Example 1)

1. $a + (b + 12) = (b + 12) + a$

_____

2. $(5 + x) + 0 = 5 + x$

_____

3 $16 + (c + 17) = (16 + c) + 17$

_____

4. $d \cdot e \cdot 0 = 0$

_____

5. **PS** **Use a Counterexample** State whether the conjecture is *true* or *false*. If *false*, provide a counterexample. (Example 2)

Division of whole numbers is associative.

_____

6. Darien ordered a soda for $2.75, a sandwich for $8.50, and a dessert for $3.85. Sales tax was $1.15. Use mental math to

find the total amount of the bill. Explain. (Example 3) _____

_____

_____

Simplify each expression. Justify each step. (Examples 4 and 5)

7. $15 + (12 + 8a)$

_____

_____

_____

_____

8. $(5n \cdot 9) \cdot 2n$

_____

_____

_____

_____

9 $3x \cdot (7 \cdot x)$

_____

_____

_____

_____

10. $(4m \cdot 2) \cdot 5m$

_____

_____

_____

_____

11. Simplify the expression $(7 + 47 + 3)[5 \cdot (2 \cdot 3)]$. Use properties to justify each step.

H.O.T. Problems Higher Order Thinking

12. (PS) **Model with Mathematics** Write about something you do every day that is commutative. Then write about another situation that is not commutative.

13. (PS) **Find the Error** Blake is simplifying $4 \cdot (5 \cdot m)$. Find his mistake and correct it.

$4 \cdot (5 \cdot m) = 20 \cdot 5m$
$= 100m$

14. (PS) **Identify Structure** Does the Associative Property *always*, *sometimes*, or *never* hold for subtraction? Explain your reasoning using examples and counterexamples.

15. (PS) **Persevere with Problems** If you take any two whole numbers and add them together, the sum is always a whole number. This is the Closure Property for Addition. The set of whole numbers is *closed* under addition.

a. Is the set of whole numbers closed under subtraction? If not, give a counterexample.

b. Suppose you had a very small set of numbers that contained only 0 and 1. Would this set be closed under addition? If not, give a counterexample.

Extra Practice

Name the property shown by each statement.

16. $9(ab) = (9a)b$

Associative (X)

17. $y \cdot 7 = 7y$

_____

18. $1 \times c = c$

_____

19. $5 + (a + 8) = (5 + a) + 8$

_____

20. State whether the conjecture is *true* or *false*. If *false*, provide a counterexample.

Subtraction of whole numbers is commutative.

_____

21. **Use Math Tools** The times for each leg of a relay for four runners are shown. Use mental math to find the total time for the relay team. Explain.

Runner	Time (s)
Jamal	12.4
Kenneth	11.8
Bryce	11.2
Jorge	12.6

_____

_____

Simplify each expression. Justify each step.

22. $(22 + 19b) + 7$

_____

_____

23. $18 + (5 + 6m)$

_____

_____

24. $11s(4)$

_____

_____

_____

25. $10y(7)$

_____

_____

_____

26. $(9 + 31 + 5)[(7 \cdot 5) \cdot 4]$

_____

_____

_____

_____

27. The table shows the cost of different items at a bakery. Yolanda buys 2 doughnuts, a muffin, and 2 cookies. Which of the following expressions represents the total cost? Select all that apply.

Item	Cost ($)
Cookie	2.21
Doughnut	2.29
Muffin	2.50
Roll	1.15

☐ $2(2.29) + 2(2.21) + 2.50$

☐ $2(2.29) + 2.50 + 2(2.21)$

☐ $2(2.29 + 2.21 + 2.50)$

☐ $2.50 + 2(2.21 + 2.29)$

28. Determine if the two expressions in each pair are equivalent. If they are equivalent, select the property that is illustrated.

| Commutative Property |
| Identity Property |
| Associative Property |
| Multiplicative Property of Zero |

	Equivalent?	Property
$9 \cdot 4 \div 20 = 9 \cdot 20 \div 4$		
$3b \cdot 0 \cdot c = 0$		
$35 + 2m + n = 35 + n + 2m$		
$12t \cdot 3v + 0 = 12t \cdot 3v$		

Spiral Review

Evaluate each expression if $a = 6$, $b = 15$, and $c = 9$.

29. $a + 2b$ _____

30. $c^2 - 5$ _____

31. $10 + a^3$ _____

32. $8c - 9 + 25$ _____

33. $14 + 8b \div 2$ _____

34. $3^3 \div (3a)$ _____

35. A package of pencils costs $1.25. A new eraser costs $0.45. Write an expression to find the total cost of 3 packages of pencils and 2 erasers. Then find the total cost.

_____

The Distributive Property

Real-World Link

School Supplies Jordan buys three notebooks that cost $5 each. He also buys three packages of pens for $6 each.

1. Write an expression that shows the cost of three notebooks added to the cost of three packages of pens.

   $\boxed{} \cdot 5 + \boxed{} \cdot 6$

2. Write an expression that shows three times the cost of one notebook and one package of pens.

   $\boxed{}\left(\boxed{} + \boxed{}\right)$

3. Evaluate both expressions. What do you notice?

   _____

   _____

4. Suppose Jordan buys five notebooks that cost $3 each and five packages of pens that cost $1 each. Circle the expressions that represent Jordan's purchases.

   $5 \cdot 3 + 5 \cdot 1$ $5 \cdot 3 \cdot 5 \cdot 1$ $5(3 + 1)$

5. Suppose Jordan buys two rulers that cost $1 each and two folders that cost $1.50 each. Circle the expressions that represent Jordan's purchases.

   $2 + 1 + 2 + 1.50$ $2(1 + 1.50)$ $2 \cdot 1 + 2 \cdot 1.50$

Essential Question

HOW can you use numbers and symbols to represent mathematical ideas?

Vocabulary

distributive property
equivalent expressions

Indiana Academic Standards
7.AF.1, 7.AF.2

PS Process Standards
1, 3, 4, 5, 7

Which PS **Process Standards** did you use?
Shade the circle(s) that applies.

1. Persevere with Problems
2. Reason Abstractly
3. Construct an Argument
4. Model with Mathematics
5. Use Math Tools
6. Attend to Precision
7. Make Use of Structure
8. Use Repeated Reasoning

Use the Distributive Property

Watch   Tools

Work Zone

Words   The **Distributive Property** states that to multiply a sum or difference by a number, multiply each term inside the parentheses by the number outside the parentheses.

Symbols $a(b + c) = ab + ac$ $a(b − c) = ab − ac$

Examples $4(6 + 2) = 4 \cdot 6 + 4 \cdot 2$ $3(7 − 5) = 3 \cdot 7 − 3 \cdot 5$

You can model the Distributive Property with algebraic expressions using algebra tiles. The expression $2(x + 2)$ is modeled below.

Model $x + 2$ using algebra tiles.

Double the amount of tiles to represent $2(x + 2)$.

Rearrange the tiles by grouping together the ones with the same shapes.

$$2(x + 2) = 2(x) + 2(2) \qquad \text{Distributive Property}$$
$$= 2x + 4 \qquad \text{Multiply.}$$

The expressions $2(x + 2)$ and $2x + 4$ are **equivalent expressions**. No matter what x is, these expressions have the same value.

Example

Tutor

Show your work.

1. Use the Distributive Property to evaluate $8(−9 + 4)$.

$$8(−9 + 4) = 8(−9) + 8(4) \qquad \text{Expand using the Distributive Property.}$$
$$= −72 + 32 \text{ or } −40 \qquad \text{Multiply. Then add.}$$

Got It? Do these problems to find out.

a. $5(−9 + 11)$ **b.** $7(10 − 5)$ **c.** $(12 − 8)9$

a. _____

b. _____

c. _____

Examples

Use the Distributive Property to rewrite each expression.

2. $4(x + 7)$

$$4(x + 7) = 4(x) + 4(7) \qquad \text{Expand using the Distributive Property.}$$
$$= 4x + 28 \qquad \text{Simplify.}$$

3. $6(p - 5)$

$$6(p - 5) = 6[p + (-5)] \qquad \text{Rewrite } p - 5 \text{ as } p + (-5).$$
$$= 6(p) + 6(-5) \qquad \text{Expand using the Distributive Property.}$$
$$= 6p + (-30) \qquad \text{Simplify.}$$
$$= 6p - 30 \qquad \text{Definition of subtraction}$$

4. $-2(x - 8)$

$$-2(x - 8) = -2[x + (-8)] \qquad \text{Rewrite } x - 8 \text{ as } x + (-8).$$
$$= -2(x) + -2(-8) \qquad \text{Expand using the Distributive Property.}$$
$$= -2x + 16 \qquad \text{Simplify.}$$

5. $5(-3x + 7y)$

$$5(-3x + 7y) = 5(-3x) + 5(7y) \qquad \text{Expand using the Distributive Property.}$$
$$= -15x + 35y \qquad \text{Simplify.}$$

6. $\frac{1}{3}(x - 6)$

$$\frac{1}{3}(x - 6) = \frac{1}{3}[x + (-6)] \qquad \text{Rewrite } x - 6 \text{ as } x + (-6).$$
$$= \frac{1}{3}(x) + \left(\frac{1}{3}(-6)\right) \qquad \text{Expand using the Distributive Property.}$$
$$= \frac{1}{3}x + (-2) \qquad \text{Simplify.}$$
$$= \frac{1}{3}x - 2 \qquad \text{Definition of subtraction}$$

Got It? Do these problems to find out.

d. $6(a + 4)$

e. $(m + 3n)8$

f. $-3(y - 10)$

g. $\frac{1}{2}(w - 4)$

d. _____

e. _____

f. _____

g. _____

Example

7. Mr. Ito needs to buy batting helmets for the baseball team. The helmets he plans to buy are $19.95 each. Find the total cost if Mr. Ito needs to buy 9 batting helmets for the team.

Rename $19.95 as $20.00 − $0.05. Then use the Distributive Property to find the total cost mentally.

$$9(\$20.00 - \$0.05) = 9(\$20.00) - 9(\$0.05) \quad \text{Distributive Property}$$
$$= \$180 - \$0.45 \quad \text{Multiply.}$$
$$= \$179.55 \quad \text{Subtract.}$$

The total cost of the helmets is $179.55.

Show your work.

Got It? Do this problem to find out.

h. A sports club rents dirt bikes for $37.50 each. Find the total cost for the club to rent 20 bikes. Justify your answer by using the Distributive Property.

h. _____

Guided Practice

Check ✓

Use the Distributive Property to evaluate or rewrite each expression. (Examples 1–6)

1. $(8 + 11)(-3) =$ _____

Show your work.

2. $-5(2x + 4y) =$ _____

3. $\frac{1}{5}(g - 10) =$ _____

4. A housefly can fly about 6.4 feet per second. At this rate, how far can it fly in 25 seconds? Justify your answer by using the Distributive Property. (Example 7)

_____

5. **Building on the Essential Question** Describe how the formula to find the perimeter of a rectangle is an application of the Distributive Property. _____

_____

_____

_____

Rate Yourself!

How confident are you about the Distributive Property? Check the box that applies.

For more help, go online to access a Personal Tutor.
Tutor

Independent Practice

 eHelp
Go online for Step-by-Step Solutions

Use the Distributive Property to evaluate each expression. (Example 1)

1. $3(5 + 6) =$ _____

2. $(6 + 4)(-12) =$ _____

3 $-6(9 - 4) =$ _____

Show your work.

4. $5(-6 + 4) =$ _____

5. $4(8 - 7) =$ _____

6. $(5 - 7)(-3) =$ _____

PS Identify Structure **Use the Distributive Property to rewrite each expression.** (Examples 2–6)

7. $3(-4x + 8) =$ _____

8. $4(x - 6y) =$ _____

9. $6(5 - q) =$ _____

10. $\frac{1}{2}(c - 8) =$ _____

11. $-3(5 - b) =$ _____

12. $(d + 2)(-7) =$ _____

13 Amelia bought roast beef for $6.85 per pound. Find the total cost if Amelia bought 4 pounds of roast beef. Justify your answer by using the Distributive Property. (Example 7)

_____

_____

14. The table shows the different prices of items at a movie theater.
   a. Suppose Mina and two of her friends go to the movies. Write an expression that could be used to find the total cost for them to go to the movies and buy one of each item.

   _____

   b. What is the total cost for all three people?

   _____

Movie Theater Prices	
Item	**Cost ($)**
box of candy	2.25
drink	3.25
popcorn	4.50
ticket	7.50

PS **Use Math Tools** Find each product mentally. Justify your answer.

15. $9 \cdot 35 =$ _____

16. $8 \cdot 28 =$ _____

17. $112 \cdot 6 =$ _____

18. $85 \cdot 8 =$ _____

19. $4 \cdot 122 =$ _____

20. $12 \cdot 64 =$ _____

 H.O.T. Problems Higher Order Thinking

21. **PS** **Reason Abstractly** Write an expression that when using the Distributive Property can be simplified to $12a + 18b - 6c$.

_____

22. **PS** **Identify Structure** Use the Distributive Property to rewrite the expression $7bx + 7by$ as an equivalent expression.

_____

23. **PS** **Persevere with Problems** Use the Distributive Property to write an equivalent expression for the expression $(a + b)(2 + y)$.

_____

24. **PS** **Find the Error** Julia is using the Distributive Property to simplify $3(x + 2)$. Find her mistake and correct it.

$$3(x + 2) = 3x + 2$$

_____

_____

25. **PS** **Persevere with Problems** Is $3 + (x \cdot y) = (3 + x) \cdot (3 + y)$ a true statement? If so, explain your reasoning. If not, give a counterexample.

_____

Extra Practice

Use the Distributive Property to evaluate each expression.

26. $(3 + 6)(-8) =$ ___−72___

$3 \cdot (-8) + 6 (-8) =$

$-24 + (-48) = -72$

Homework Help →

27. $4(11 - 5) =$ _____

28. $(12 - 4)(-5)$ _____

Use the Distributive Property to rewrite each expression.

29. $-8(a + b) =$ _____

30. $(2b + 8)5 =$ _____

31. $(p + 7)(-2) =$ _____

32. **PS Justify Conclusions** Theresa is planning on making a fleece blanket for her nephew. She learns that the fabric she wants to use is $7.99 per yard. Find the total cost of 4 yards of fabric. Justify your answer by using the Distributive Property.

_____

_____

33. You are ordering T-shirts with your school's mascot printed on them. Each T-shirt costs $4.75. The printer charges a setup fee of $30 and $2.50 to print each shirt. Write two expressions to represent the total cost of printing n T-shirts.

_____

_____

Use the Distributive Property to rewrite each expression.

34. $0.5x(y - z)$

$=$ _____

35. $-6a(2b + 5c)$

$=$ _____

36. $-4m(3n - 6p)$

$=$ _____

37. $3(2y + 4z)$

$=$ _____

38. $-2(3a - 2b)$

$=$ _____

39. $-6(12p - 8n)$

$=$ _____

40. Write two equivalent expressions for the area of the figure.

_____

$x + 4$

16

41. A group of 3 seniors, 3 adults, and 3 children bought tickets to the aquarium.

Fill in the boxes to model the total amount spent with an expression.

Type of Ticket	Cost ($)
Adult	18.95
Senior	14.95
Child	9.95

[　　　　] × ([　　　　] + [　　　　] + [　　　　])

How much did the group spend on tickets altogether? How does applying the Distributive Property make it easier to find this amount?

42. Celeste is going to summer camp. The table shows the cost of items she will need to purchase with the camp logo. She needs to buy four of each item.

Which of the following expressions represents the total cost of the items? Select all that apply.

Item	Cost ($)
T-shirt	8.00
Shorts	4.50
Socks	2.25

☐ 4(14.75)

☐ 4(8.00) + 4.50 + 2.25

☐ 4(8) + 4(4.50) + 4(2.25)

☐ 4(8.00 + 4.50 + 2.25)

Spiral Review

Evaluate each expression if $x = 9$ and $y = 3$.

43. $x + y - 58$ _____

44. $y^3 + x^3$ _____

45. $y^4 - 128 =$ _____

46. In the expression below, identify the coefficient and the variable.

$$4x + 450$$

coefficient: _____   variable: _____

Problem-Solving Investigation
Make a Table

Case #1 Mountain Biking

Hoshi wants to purchase a membership to a bike park.
The cost depends on the number of people on the membership.
It costs $55 for 5 people, $65 for 6 people, and $75 for 7 people.

Find the cost of a membership that includes 8 people.

Indiana Academic Standards
7.AF.1

Process Standards
1, 3, 4

 Understand *What are the facts?*

The cost of a membership depends on the number of people included on the membership.

Plan *What is your strategy to solve this problem?*

Make a table that shows the number of people and the cost.

Solve *How can you apply the strategy?*

Make a table. Find the cost for 8 people.

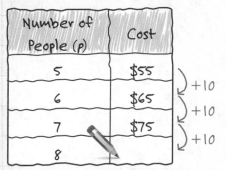

So, the cost for 8 people is ⬚.

Check *Does the answer make sense?*

The expression $10p + 5$ can be used to represent the situation.

Since $\$10(8) + \$5 = \$85$, the solution is reasonable.

Analyze the Strategy

Justify Conclusions Hoshi wants to purchase a membership for four people. Explain how the table would change and then solve.

_____

_____

Case #2 Financial Literacy

Latoya is saving money to buy a saxophone. After 1 month, she has $75. After 2 months, she has $120. After 3 months, she has $165. She plans to keep saving at the same rate.

How long will it take Latoya to save enough money to buy a saxophone that costs $300?

 Understand

Read the problem. What are you being asked to find?

I need to find _____

_____

<u>Underline</u> **key words and values. What information do you know?**

After 1 month, Latoya has [   ]. After 2 months, she has [   ].

After 3 months, she has [   ]. She continues to save at the same rate.

Is there any information that you do *not* need to know?

I do not need to know _____ .

 Plan

Choose a problem-solving strategy.

I will use the _____ strategy.

 Solve

Use your problem-solving strategy to solve the problem.

Months	1	2	3	4	5	6
Amount Saved ($)	75	120	165			

+45 +45 +45   +45 +45

Latoya will have $300 saved in _____ .

 Check

Use information from the problem to check your answer.

_____

_____

Work with a small group to solve the following cases.
Show your work on a separate piece of paper.

Case #3 Carnivals

For a carnival game, containers are arranged in a triangular display. The top row has 1 container. The second row has 2 containers. The third row has 3 containers. The pattern continues until the bottom row, which has 10 containers.

A contestant knocks down 29 containers on the first throw. How many containers remain?

Case #4 Budget

Tamara earns $2,050 each month. She spends 65% of the amount she earns. The rest of the money is equally divided and deposited into two separate accounts.

How many months until Tamara has deposited more than $2,500 in one of her accounts?

Case #5 Toothpicks

Write an expression that can be used to find the number of toothpicks needed to make any figure. Then find the number of toothpicks needed to make the eighth figure.

Figure 1   Figure 2   Figure 3

Use any strategy!

Case #6 Diving

A diver descends to −15 feet after 1 minute, −30 feet after 2 minutes, and −45 feet after 3 minutes.

If the diver keeps descending at this rate, what is their position after 12 minutes?

Mid-Chapter Check

Vocabulary Check

1. Fill in the blank in the sentence below with the correct term. (Lesson 1)

A _____ is a symbol that represents an unknown quantity.

2. Define *arithmetic sequence*. Then provide an example. (Lesson 2)

_____

_____

Skills Check and Problem Solving

Describe the relationship between the terms in each arithmetic sequence. Then write the next three terms in each sequence. (Lesson 2)

3. 5, 8, 11, 14, ...

_____

_____

4. 4, 11, 18, 25, ...

_____

_____

5. 5.8, 10.8, 15.8, 20.8, ...

_____

_____

Use the Distributive Property to rewrite each expression. (Lesson 4)

6. $4(x + 9) =$ _____

7. $2(x + 5) =$ _____

8. $3(-2x + 4) =$ _____

9. **PS Identify Structure** What property is shown by the statement $8x + 0 = 8x$? (Lesson 3)

_____

10. **PS Persevere with Problems** A coach bought some baseball bats and five baseball gloves. Let *b* represent the number of bats. Write an expression that can be used to find the total cost of the bats and gloves. Then find the total cost if he bought three bats. (Lesson 1)

_____

$35

$48

Simplify Algebraic Expressions

Real-World Link

Tools

Music Store Patricia, Hugo, and Sun work at a music store. Each week, Patricia works three more than twice the number of hours that Hugo works. Sun works 2 less hours than Hugo.

1. Let x represent the number of hours that Hugo works each week. The number of hours that Hugo, Patricia, and Sun work can be modeled as shown below. Write an expression that represents each person's number of hours.

Hugo's hours

Patricia's hours

Twice   Three
Hugo   more

Sun's hours

Hugo   Two
         less

Expression: _____   Expression: _____   Expression: _____

2. Model the total number of hours that Patricia and Sun work. Draw the result below. Then write an expression for the drawing.

Expression: _____

3. Like tiles are tiles that have the same shape. Group like tiles together and remove the zero pairs. Draw the result below. Then write an expression for your drawing.

Expression: _____

 Essential Question

HOW can you use numbers and symbols to represent mathematical ideas?

Vocab
 Vocabulary

term
like terms
constant
simplest form

🔵 **Indiana Academic Standards**
7.AF.1, 7.AF.2

PS **Process Standards**
1, 2, 3, 4, 6

Which **PS** Process Standards did you use?
Shade the circle(s) that applies.

① Persevere with Problems

⑤ Use Math Tools

② Reason Abstractly

⑥ Attend to Precision

③ Construct an Argument

⑦ Make Use of Structure

④ Model with Mathematics

⑧ Use Repeated Reasoning

Identify Parts of an Expression

When addition or subtraction signs separate an algebraic expression into parts, each part is called a **term**. Recall that the numerical factor of a term that contains a variable is called the coefficient of the variable.

Like terms contain the same variables to the same powers. For example, $3x^2$ and $-7x^2$ are like terms. So are $8xy^2$ and $12xy^2$. But $10x^2z$ and $22xz^2$ are *not* like terms. A term without a variable is called a **constant**. Constant terms are also like terms.

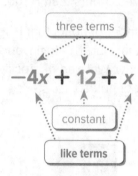

STOP and Reflect

Circle the term below that is a like term with $-4x^3$.

$-4x^2$ x^3 -4

Example

Tutor

1. Identify the terms, like terms, coefficients, and constants in the expression $6n - 7n - 4 + n$.

$6n - 7n - 4 + n = 6n + (-7n) + (-4) + 1n$ Rewrite the expression.

- Terms: $6n, -7n, -4, n$

- Like terms: $6n, -7n, n$ All of these terms have the same variable.

- Coefficients: $6, -7, 1$

- Constants: -4 This is the only term without a variable.

Got It? Do these problems to find out.

Identify the terms, like terms, coefficients, and constants in each expression.

Show your work.

a. $9y - 4 - 11y + 7$

b. $3x + 2 - 10 - 3x$

a. _____

b. _____

Simplify Algebraic Expressions

An algebraic expression is in **simplest form** if it has no like terms and no parentheses. Use the Distributive Property to combine like terms.

Examples

 Tutor

2. Write $4y + y$ in simplest form.

$4y$ and y are like terms.

$4y + y = 4y + 1y$ Identity Property; $y = 1y$

$\qquad = (4 + 1)y$ or $5y$ Distributive Property; Simplify.

---

3. Write $7x - 2 - 7x + 6$ in simplest form.

$7x$ and $-7x$ are like terms. -2 and 6 are also like terms.

$7x - 2 - 7x + 6 = 7x + (-2) + (-7x) + 6$ Definition of subtraction

$\qquad = 7x + (-7x) + (-2) + 6$ Commutative Property

$\qquad = [7 + (-7)]x + (-2) + 6$ Distributive Property

$\qquad = 0x + 4$ Simplify.

$\qquad = 0 + 4$ or 4 Multiplicative Property of zero and Additive Identity Property of zero.

Got It? Do these problems to find out.

c. $4z - z$ **d.** $6 - 3n + 3n$ **e.** $2g - 3 + 11 - 8g$

Equivalent Expressions

To check whether $4y + y$ and $5y$ are equivalent expressions, substitute any value for y and see whether the expressions have the same value.

Show your work.

c. _____

d. _____

e. _____

Real World

Example

 Tutor

4. The cost of a jacket j after a 5% markup can be represented by the expression $j + 0.05j$. Simplify the expression. Then determine the total cost of the jacket after the markup, if the original price is $35.

$j + 0.05j = 1j + 0.05j$ Identity Property; $j = 1j$

$\qquad = (1 + 0.05)j$ Distributive Property

$\qquad = 1.05j$ Simplify.

$1.05j = 1.05(35)$ Replace j with 35 to find the total cost.

$\qquad = 36.75$ Multiply.

So, the cost of the jacket after a 5% markup is $36.75.

Got It? Do this problem to find out.

f. Write an expression in simplest form for the cost of the jacket in Example 4 if the markup is 8%. Then determine the total cost after the markup.

f. _____

Example

Tutor

5. At a concert, you buy some T-shirts for $12.00 each and the same number of CDs for $7.50 each. Write an expression in simplest form that represents the total amount spent.

Let x represent the number of T-shirts and CDs.

$12x + 7.50x$ Write the expression.

$12x + 7.50x = (12 + 7.50)x$ Distributive Property

$= 19.50x$ Simplify.

The expression $19.50x represents the total amount spent.

Got It? Do this problem to find out.

Show your work.

9. _____

g. You have some money. Your friend has $50 less than you. Write an expression in simplest form that represents the total amount of money you and your friend have.

Guided Practice

Check

1. Identify the terms, like terms, coefficients, and constants in $5n - 2n - 3 + n$. (Example 1)

_____

_____

2. Write $4p - 7 + 6p + 10$ in simplest form. (Examples 2 and 3)

_____

_____

3. The cost of a game g with 7% sales tax can be represented by the expression $g + 0.07g$. Simplify the expression. Then determine the total cost of the game after sales tax if the original price is $52. (Example 4)

_____

4. You go to a basketball game and buy 3 waters that cost x dollars each. Your brother buys a bottle of water and a bag of peanuts that costs $4.50. Write an expression in simplest form that represents the total amount of money spent altogether. (Example 5)

_____

5. **Building on the Essential Question** Explain why $2(x - 1) + 3(x - 1) = 5(x - 1)$ is a true statement.

_____

_____

Rate Yourself!

Are you ready to move on? Shade the section that applies.

YES   ?   NO

For more help, go online to access a Personal Tutor.

Tutor

Independent Practice

Go online for Step-by-Step Solutions

eHelp

Identify the terms, like terms, coefficients, and constants in each expression. (Example 1)

1. $2 + 3a + 9a$

_____

_____

_____

2. $7 - 5x + 1$

_____

_____

_____

3. $9 - z + 3 - 2z$

_____

_____

_____

Write each expression in simplest form. (Examples 2 and 3)

4. $n + 5n =$ _____

5. $12c - c =$ _____

6. $-4j - 1 - 4j + 6 =$ _____

7. The cost of a ticket t to a concert with a 3% sales tax can be represented by the expression $t + 0.03t$. Simplify the expression. Then determine the total cost after the sales tax if the original price is $72. (Example 4)

_____

Write an expression in simplest form that represents the total amount in each situation. (Example 5)

8. You rent x pairs of shoes for $2 each. You buy the same number of drinks for $1.50 each. You also pay $9 for a bowling lane.

_____

9. You watch x minutes of television on Monday, the same amount on Wednesday, and 30 minutes on Friday.

_____

10. In a State Legislature, there were 119 more members in the House of Representatives than in the Senate. If there were m members in the Senate, write an expression to represent the total members in the State

Legislature. _____

11. Elian and his friends paid a total of $7 for tickets to the school football game. While at the game, they bought 5 hot dogs at x dollars each, 4 boxes of popcorn at y dollars each, and 2 pretzels at z dollars each.

a. Write an expression to show the total cost of admission and the snacks.

_____

b. Hot dogs cost $4, popcorn cost $3, and pretzels cost $2. What was

the total cost for admission and snacks? _____

PS **Reason Abstractly** Write an expression in simplest form for the perimeter of each figure.

12.

13.

14.

🔥 H.O.T. Problems Higher Order Thinking

15. **PS** **Be Precise** Write an expression that has three terms and simplifies to $4x - 7$. Identify the coefficient(s) and constant(s) in your expression.

_____

_____

16. **PS** **Which One Doesn't Belong?** Identify the expression that is not equivalent to the other three. Explain your reasoning.

$x - 2 + 3x$	$4(x - 2)$	$-2 + 7x - 3x$	$4x - 2$

_____

_____

17. **PS** **Persevere with Problems** Simplify the expression $8x - 2x + 12x - 3$. Show that your answer is true for $x = 2$.

_____

_____

18. **PS** **Justify Conclusions** Determine whether the following statement is *always*, *sometimes*, or *never* true. Explain your reasoning.

When using the Distributive Property, if the term outside the parentheses is negative, then the sign of each term inside the parentheses will change.

_____

_____

_____

_____

Extra Practice

Identify the terms, like terms, coefficients, and constants in each expression.

19. $4 + 5y - 6y + y$

terms: $4, 5y, -6y, y$

like terms: $5y, -6y, y$

coefficients: $5, -6, 1$

constant: 4

20. $n + 4n - 7n - 1$

21. $-3d + 8 - d - 2$

Write each expression in simplest form.

22. $5x + 4 + 9x$

= _____

23. $2 + 3d + d$

= _____

24. $-3r + 7 - 3r - 12$

= _____

Write an expression in simplest form that represents the total amount in each situation.

25. You subscribe to m different magazines. Your friend subscribes to 2 fewer than you.

_____

26. Today is your friend's birthday. She is y years old. Her brother is 5 years younger.

_____

27. You spent m minutes studying on Monday. On Tuesday, you studied 15 more minutes than you did on Monday. Wednesday, you studied 30 minutes less than you did on Tuesday. You studied twice as long on Thursday as you did on Monday. On Friday, you studied 20 minutes less than you did on Thursday. Write an expression in simplest form to represent the number of minutes you studied in all.

_____

28. PS **Reason Abstractly** Write a real-world situation for $7.50y + 9$.

_____

_____

Simplify each expression.

29. $3(4x - 5) + 4(2x + 6)$

= _____

30. $-8(2a - 3b) - 5(6b - 4a)$

= _____

31. $10(5g + 2h - 3) - 4(3g - 4h + 2)$

= _____

32. Vince, Neal, and Patrick collect baseball cards. Neal has 3 fewer cards than twice the number of cards Vince has. Patrick has 5 more baseball cards than Vince. Let x represent the number of baseball cards that Vince has. Use the algebra tiles to represent the number of cards each person has.

	Vince	Neal	Patrick
Model			
Expression			

Write an expression, in simplified form, for the number of baseball cards the three friends have altogether.

33. The table shows the number of tickets needed and the number of times Talia participated in different activities at a carnival. Write an expression, in simplified form, for the total number of tickets that Talia used.

Activity	Tickets	Times Completed
Balloon Pop	3	a
Dunk Tank	4	b
Ring Toss	2	a
Trampoline	5	b

Spiral Review

34. Mica spends $5 for her lunch and $2 for breakfast each day Monday through Friday. Use the Associative Property to find how much money she spends on lunch and breakfast for 4 weeks.

_____

Define a variable. Then write each phrase as an algebraic expression.

35. Anna has volunteered 9 more hours than Tricia

_____

36. the cost of a pair of jeans is 4 times the cost of a book

_____

Evaluate each expression if $x = 2$, $y = 10$, and $z = 4$.

37. $5z - 10$ _____

38. $y \div 2 + x$ _____

39. $x^3 + (y \div x)$ _____

Add Linear Expressions

Homework Luke has 20 math problems and 11 science questions for homework. Cameron has 23 math problems and 10 science questions for homework.

1. The expression below represents the types of exercises that Luke has for homework.

   20 math problems + 11 science questions

   Complete the expression that represents the types of exercises that Cameron has for homework.

   ⬚ math problems + ⬚ science questions

2. Write an expression for the total number of math problems and science questions for both boys.

   ⬚ math problems + ⬚ science questions

3. Suppose Luke has *x* math problems and 5 science questions for homework and Cameron has *x* math problems and 6 science questions. The algebra tiles below represent the total number of math problems and science questions for both boys. Write an expression in simplest form that represents the algebra tiles.

Expression: _____

 Essential Question

HOW can you use numbers and symbols to represent mathematical ideas?

Vocab

Vocabulary

linear expression

🇮 **Indiana Academic Standards**
7.AF.1, 7.AF.2

PS **Process Standards**
1, 2, 3, 4

Which PS Process Standards did you use?
Shade the circle(s) that applies.

① Persevere with Problems

② Reason Abstractly

③ Construct an Argument

④ Model with Mathematics

⑤ Use Math Tools

⑥ Attend to Precision

⑦ Make Use of Structure

⑧ Use Repeated Reasoning

Add Linear Expressions

A **linear expression** is an algebraic expression in which the variable is raised to the first power and variable are not multiplied or divided. The table below gives some examples of expressions that are linear and some examples of expressions that are not linear.

Linear Expressions	Nonlinear Expressions
$5x$	$5mn$
$3x + 2$	$3x^3 + 2$
$x - 7$	$x^4 - 7$

You can add linear expression with or without models. Sometimes you will need to use zero pairs.

Examples

Tutor

Add.

1. $(2x + 3) + (x + 4)$

Model each linear expression.

$2x + 3$ $x + 4$

Combine like tiles and write a linear expression for the combined tiles.

$2x \; + \; x \; + \; 3 \; + \; 4$

So, $(2x + 3) + (x + 4) = 3x + 7$.

2. $(2x - 1) + (x - 5)$

$(2x - 1) + (x - 5) = [2x + (-1)] + [x + (-5)]$ Definition of subtraction

$$\begin{aligned} & 2x + (-1) \\ + \; & x + (-5) \\ \hline & 3x + (-6) \end{aligned}$$ Arrange like terms in columns.

Add.

So, $(2x - 1) + (x - 5) = 3x + (-6)$ or $3x - 6$.

Show your work.

Got It? Do these problems to find out.

a. $(3x + 5) + (2x + 3)$ **b.** $(2x - 4) + (3x - 7)$

a. _____

b. _____

Examples

Tutor

3. Find $(2x - 3) + (-x + 4)$. Use models if needed.

$2x$ + (-3) $-x$ + 4

Model each linear expression.

Combine like tiles. Then remove all zero pairs and write a linear expression for the remaining tiles.

x + 1

So, $(2x - 3) + (-x + 4) = x + 1$.

4. Find $2(x + 3) + (3x + 1)$.

$2(x + 3) + (3x + 1) = (2 \cdot x + 2 \cdot 3) + (3x + 1)$ Use the Distributive Property.

$= (2x + 6) + (3x + 1)$ Simplify.

$2x + 6$
$\underline{+\ 3x + 1}$ Arrange like terms in columns.
$5x + 7$ Add.

So, $2(x + 3) + (3x + 1) = 5x + 7$.

5. Find $5(x - 4) + (2x - 7)$.

$5(x - 4) + (2x - 7) = (5 \cdot x - 5 \cdot 4) + (2x - 7)$ Use the Distributive Property.

$= (5x - 20) + (2x - 7)$ Simplify.

$5x - 20$
$\underline{+\ 2x -\ \ 7}$ Arrange like terms in columns.
$7x - 27$ Add.

So, $5(x - 4) + (2x - 7) = 7x - 27$.

Got It? Do these problems to find out.

Add. Use models if needed.

c. $(x - 1) + (2x + 3)$ **d.** $(x - 4) + (-2x + 1)$

e. $6(x + 7) + (x + 3)$ **f.** $(12x + 19) + 2(x - 10)$

Show your work.

c. _____

d. _____

e. _____

f. _____

Example

Properties
The Commutative Property allows the terms of the expression to be reordered.

6. Write a linear expression in simplest form to represent the perimeter of the triangle. Find the perimeter if the value of *x* is 5 centimeters.

$(3x - 3)$ cm $(2x + 9)$ cm

$(5x)$ cm

Write a linear expression for the perimeter of the triangle.

$(3x - 3) + (2x + 9) + (5x)$ Write each expression.

$(3x + 2x + 5x) + (-3 + 9)$ Rearrange to combine like terms.

$10x + 6$ Add.

Find the perimeter.

$10x + 6 = 10(5) + 6$ or 56   Replace *x* with 5. Simplify.

So, the perimeter of the triangle is 56 centimeters.

Got It? Do this problem to find out.

g. A rectangle has side lengths $(x + 4)$ feet and $(2x - 2)$ feet. Write a linear expression in simplest form to represent the perimeter. Find the perimeter if the value of *x* is 7 feet.

g. _____

Guided Practice

Add. Use models if needed. (Examples 1–5)

1. $(2x + 3) + (x + 1) = $ _____

2. $10(x - 2) + (6x - 6) = $ _____

3. Write a linear expression in simplest form to represent the perimeter of the pentagon. Then find the perimeter if the value of *x* is 3 yards. (Example 6)

$(3x)$ yd $(3x)$ yd

$(2x)$ yd $(2x)$ yd

$(x + 4)$ yd

Rate Yourself!

How confident are you about adding linear expressions? Check the box that applies.

4. **Building on the Essential Question** Explain how adding linear expressions is similar to simplifying expressions.

For more help, go online to access a Personal Tutor.

 FOLDABLES Time to update your Foldable!

Independent Practice

Go online for Step-by-Step Solutions

Add. Use models if needed. (Examples 1–5)

1. $(4x + 8) + (7x + 3) =$ _____

2. $(-3x + 7) + (-6x + 9) =$ _____

3. $(x - 10) + (3x - 6) =$ _____

4. $(-3x - 7) + (4x + 7) =$ _____

5. $2(x + 14) + (2x - 14) =$ _____

6. $(11x - 8) + 7(x - 1) =$ _____

7. Write a linear expression in simplest form to represent the perimeter of the triangle at the right. Then find the perimeter if the value of x is 10 millimeters. (Example 6)

_____

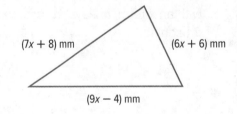

$(7x + 8)$ mm $(6x + 6)$ mm $(9x - 4)$ mm

8. A rectangle has side lengths $(2x - 5)$ meters and $(2x + 6)$ meters. Write a linear expression in simplest form to represent the perimeter. Find the perimeter if the value of x is 12 meters. (Example 6)

_____

9. Find the sum of $(x + 5)$, $(-4x - 2)$, and $(2x - 1)$.

_____

Add.

10. $(-3.5x + 1.7) + (9.1x - 0.3) =$ _____

11. $(0.5x + 15) + (8.2x - 16.6) =$ _____

12. **PS** **Reason Abstractly** The table shows the breakdown of the points scored in last week's basketball game.

	1st Quarter Field Goal Points	2nd Quarter Field Goal Points	3rd Quarter Field Goal Points	4th Quarter Field Goal Points	Total Free Throw Points
Panthers	$2x - 6$	$x + 2$	$2x$	$x - 6$	9

a. Write a linear expression in simplest form to represent the total field goal points scored in the first two quarters.

_____

b. Write a linear expression in simplest form to represent the total points scored in the game.

_____

H.O.T. Problems Higher Order Thinking

13. **PS** **Reason Inductively** Write two linear expressions with a sum of $-5x + 4$.

_____

_____

14. **PS** **Construct an Argument** Will the sum of two linear expressions, each with an x-term, *always, sometimes,* or *never* have an x-term? Explain your reasoning.

_____

_____

_____

15. **PS** **Persevere with Problems** An integer can be represented by x. The next integer can then be represented as $(x + 1)$. Write a linear expression that represents the sum of any two consecutive integers. Show that the sum of any two consecutive integers is always odd.

_____

_____

_____

16. **PS** **Reason Inductively** Explain how algebra tiles represent like terms and zero pairs.

_____

_____

_____

_____

Extra Practice

Add. Use models if needed.

17. $(-x + 10) + (-3x + 6) =$ <u>$-4x + 16$</u>

Homework Help ➡

$-x + 10$

$(+) -3x + 6$

$-4x + 16$

18. $(-4x + 3) + (-2x + 8) =$ _____

19. $(-6x + 5) + (4x - 7) =$ _____

20. $(-4x + 5) + (15x - 3) =$ _____

21. $(-5x + 4) + -1(x - 1) =$ _____

22. $17(2x - 5) + (-x + 4) =$ _____

23. Write a linear expression in simplest form to represent the perimeter of the trapezoid at the right. Then find the perimeter if the value of x is 7 yards. _____

(7x + 3) yd

(6x + 3) yd   (6x + 3) yd

(5x) yd

24. Ⓟ **Reason Abstractly** The table shows the points earned by a contestant in four rounds on a game show.

Round 1	Round 2	Round 3	Round 4
2x + 40	5x + 12	100	6x − 10

Show your work.

a. Write a linear expression in simplest form to represent the total points earned by the contestant in rounds 1 and 2.

_____

b. Write a linear expression in simplest form to represent the total points earned in all four rounds.

_____

c. If the value of x is 8, what is the total points earned in all four rounds?

_____

25. Karina makes *x* dollars per hour working at the grocery store. She makes *y* dollars per hour working at the library. One week she worked 9 hours at the grocery store and 12 hours at the library. Determine if each statement is true or false.

a. The expression 21*x* represents Karina's earnings from the library. ☐ True ☐ False

b. The expression 9*y* represents Karina's earnings from the grocery store. ☐ True ☐ False

c. The expression 9*x* + 12*y* represents Karina's total earnings for the week. ☐ True ☐ False

26. A triangle has the side lengths represented by the expressions shown in the figure. Select the appropriate numbers and expressions to complete the model representing the perimeter of the triangle.

$x - 2$

$4x + 2$

$2x + 3$

☐ + ☐
☐ + ☐
+ ☐ + ☐
+ ☐ + ☐

x	−1
2*x*	1
4*x*	2
5*x*	3
7*x*	7
−2	

Spiral Review

Use the Distributive Property to evaluate each expression.

27. 7(9 − 4) = _____

28. (9 + 2)6 = _____

29. 5(9 + 8) = _____

30. The number of students in each of the seventh grade homerooms that volunteer in the office are shown in the table. Use mental math to find the total number of students who volunteered. Explain.

Office Volunteers	
Homeroom	**Number of Students**
A	6
B	5
C	4
D	8

Subtract Linear Expressions

Real-World Link

Watch ▶

Dog Sledding The Iditarod is a dog sledding race over 1,150 miles across Alaska. The table shows two winning times.

Iditarod				
	Days	**Hours**	**Minutes**	**Seconds**
Race 1	9	11	46	48
Race 2	9	5	8	41

1. What is the difference in hours, minutes, and seconds between the two races?

   ☐ h   ☐ min   ☐ s

2. Explain how you could find the difference in times between any two races, given the days, hours, minutes, and seconds.

   _____

   _____

3. Describe another situation in which finding the difference involves subtracting like units.

   _____

   _____

   _____

   _____

 Essential Question

HOW can you use numbers and symbols to represent mathematical ideas?

ⓘ **Indiana Academic Standards**
7.AF.1, 7.AF.2

PS **Process Standards**
1, 2, 3, 4

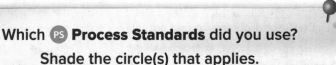

Which PS **Process Standards did you use?**
Shade the circle(s) that applies.

① Persevere with Problems   ⑤ Use Math Tools

② Reason Abstractly   ⑥ Attend to Precision

③ Construct an Argument   ⑦ Make Use of Structure

④ Model with Mathematics   ⑧ Use Repeated Reasoning

Subtract Linear Expressions

When subtracting linear expressions, subtract like terms. Use zero pairs if needed.

Examples

Subtract. Use models if needed.

1. $(6x + 3) - (2x + 2)$

6x + 3

Model the linear expression $6x + 3$.

4x + 1

To subtract $2x + 2$, remove two x-tiles and two 1-tiles. Then write the linear expression for the remaining tiles.

There are four x-tiles and one 1-tile remaining.

So, $(6x + 3) - (2x + 2) = 4x + 1$.

· ·

2. $(2x - 3) - (x - 2)$

2x + (−3)

Model the linear expression $2x - 3$.

x + (−1)

To subtract $x - 2$, remove one x-tile and two −1-tiles. Then write the linear expression for the remaining tiles.

There is one x-tile and one −1-tile remaining.

So, $(2x - 3) - (x - 2) = x - 1$.

Show your work.

Got It? Do these problems to find out.

a. _____

b. _____

a. $(5x - 9) - (2x - 7)$ **b.** $(6x - 10) - (2x - 8)$

Example

3. Find $(-2x - 4) - (2x)$. Use models if needed.

$-2x$ + (-4)

Model the linear expression $-2x - 4$.

zero pairs

Since there are no positive x-tiles to remove, add two zero pairs of x-tiles. Remove two positive x-tiles.

So, $(-2x - 4) - (2x) = -4x - 4$.

Got It? Do these problems to find out.

c. $(3x - 2) - (5x - 4)$

d. $(4x - 4) - (-2x + 2)$

Show your work.

c. _____

d. _____

Use the Additive Inverse to Subtract

When subtracting integers, you add the opposite, or the additive inverse. The same process is used when subtracting linear expressions.

Examples

4. Find $(6x + 5) - (3x + 1)$.

$$
\begin{array}{r}
6x + 5 \\
(+)\ -3x - 1 \\
\hline
3x + 4
\end{array}
$$

Arrange like terms in columns.

The additive inverse of $3x + 1$ is $(-3x - 1)$.

Additive Inverse

The additive inverse is found by multiplying the linear expression by -1.

5. Find $(-4x - 7) - (-5x - 2)$.

$$
\begin{array}{r}
-4x - 7 \\
(+)\ 5x + 2 \\
\hline
x - 5
\end{array}
$$

Arrange like terms in columns.

The additive inverse of $(-5x - 2)$ is $(5x + 2)$.

Got It? Do these problems to find out.

e. $(4x - 3) - (2x + 7)$

f. $(5x - 4) - (2x + 3)$

e. _____

f. _____

Example

 Tutor

6. A hat store tracks the sale of college and professional team hats for *m* months. The number of college hats sold is represented by $(6m + 3)$. The number of professional hats sold is represented by $(5m - 2)$. Write an expression to show how many more college hats were sold than professional hats. Then evaluate the expression if *m* equals 10.

Find $(6m + 3) - (5m - 2)$.

$$\begin{array}{r} 6m + 3 \\ (+)\,-5m + 2 \\ \hline m + 5 \end{array}$$

Arrange like terms in columns.

The additive inverse of $5m - 2$ is $(-5m + 2)$.

Evaluate the expression if $m = 10$.

$m + 5 = \mathbf{10} + 5$ Substitute 10 for *m*.

$ = 15$ Simplify.

So, 15 more college team hats were sold.

Guided Practice

 Check ✓

Subtract. Use models if needed. (Examples 1–5)

1. $(2x + 4) - (-x + 5) = $ _____

2. $(6x + 9) - (7x - 1) = $ _____

 Show your work.

3. The number of runs scored by the home team at a baseball game is represented by $(x + 7)$. The number of runs scored by the visiting team is represented by $(3x - 7)$. Write an expression to find how many more runs the home team scored than the visiting team. Then evaluate the expression if the value of *x* is 6. (Example 6)

_____

4. **Building on the Essential Question** How can you use the additive inverse to help you subtract linear expressions?

_____

_____

_____

Rate Yourself!

How well do you understand subtracting linear expressions? Circle the image that applies.

Clear   Somewhat Clear   Not So Clear

For more help, go online to access a Personal Tutor. Tutor

 FOLDABLES Time to update your Foldable!

Independent Practice

Go online for Step-by-Step Solutions

Subtract. Use models if needed. (Examples 1–5)

1. $(9x + 5) - (4x + 3) =$ _____

2. $(-x + 3) - (x - 5) =$ _____

3. $(3x + 4) - (x + 2) =$ _____

4. $(7x + 5) - (3x + 2) =$ _____

5. $(9x - 8) - (x + 4) =$ _____

6. $(9x - 12) - (5x - 7) =$ _____

7. **PS Reason Abstractly** The number of customers in a store on the first day is represented by $(6x - 3)$. The number of customers on the second day is represented by $(x - 1)$. Write an expression to find how many more customers visited the store on the first day. Then evaluate the expression if x is equal to 50. (Example 6)

_____

8. The perimeter of the garden shown is $(6x + 2)$ units. Find the length of the missing side.

_____

9. The cost for shipping a package that weighs x pounds from Boise to Los Angeles is shown at the right. How much more does Shipping Central charge than Globe Delivery?

_____

Company	Cost ($)
Shipping Central	$3x + 3.50$
Globe Delivery	$2x + 2.99$

10. Find the difference in the given lengths of the polygons. _____

(7x + 2) units

(6x − 5) units

 H.O.T. Problems Higher Order Thinking

11. **PS** **Find the Error** Theresa is finding $(5x + 3) - (2x + 1)$. Find her mistake and correct it.

_____

_____

_____

_____

_____

_____

$$(5x + 3) - (2x + 1)$$
$$= 5x + 3 - 2x + 1$$
$$= 5x - 2x + 3 + 1$$
$$= 3x + 4$$

12. **PS** **Reason Inductively** Name two linear expressions whose difference is $5x - 4$.

_____

_____

13. **PS** **Persevere with Problems** One linear expression is subtracted from a second linear expression and the difference is $x - 5$. What is the difference when the second linear expression is subtracted from

the first? _____

14. **PS** **Persevere with Problems** Suppose A and B represent linear expressions. If $A + B = 2x - 2$ and $A - B = 4x - 8$, find A and B.

_____

15. **PS** **Reason Inductively** Explain how you can apply the rule for subtracting integers to linear expressions.

_____

_____

Extra Practice

Subtract. Use models if needed.

16. $(-3x - 2) - (7x + 9) =$ $\underline{\quad -10x - 11 \quad}$

Homework Help

$$\begin{array}{r} -3x - 2 \\ (+) -7x - 9 \\ \hline -10x - 11 \end{array}$$

17. $(-2x - 1) - (x - 7) =$ _____

18. $(9x + 5) - (6x - 8) =$ _____

19. $(-8x + 1) - (8x - 1) =$ _____

20. $(4x + 10) - (-3x + 5) =$ _____

21. $(-6x - 11) - (-2x - 4) =$ _____

22. **PS** **Reason Abstractly** The number of questions on a math test is represented $(3x + 1)$. The number of questions on a spelling test is represented by $(x + 12)$. Write an expression to find how many more questions were on the math test. Then evaluate the expression if the value of x is 8.

_____

Subtract.

23. $(5.7x - 0.8) - (4.9x - 1.4) =$ _____

24. $\left(-\dfrac{5}{6}x + 5\dfrac{1}{2}\right) - \left(\dfrac{2}{3}x + 4\right) =$ _____

25. $2(x + 1) - 3x =$ _____

26. $5(x - 3) - x =$ _____

27. The costs for a large pizza and each topping for two pizzerias are shown in the table.

Pizzeria	Cost per Pizza ($)	Cost per Topping ($)
Mario's Pizza	10	1.25
Pizza Palace	12	1.50

Select the appropriate values to complete the model to show how much more a pizza with *t* toppings costs at Pizza Palace than at Mario's Pizza.

0.25	2.75	1.25	1.50
2	10	12	22

$$\boxed{} + \boxed{}\ t - (\boxed{} + \boxed{}\ t) = \boxed{} + \boxed{}\ t$$

28. Mei wants to frame a picture. The picture is $(12x + 4)$ units long, and the frame is $(7x + 1)$ units long. Determine if each statement is true or false.

a. The picture is longer than the frame.   ☐ True ☐ False

b. The frame is longer than the picture.   ☐ True ☐ False

c. Mei will have to trim $(5x + 3)$ units from the picture to fit it in the frame.   ☐ True ☐ False

Spiral Review

29. Camilla wants to attach a string of lights to the edges of her patio for a party. She does not want the string to go across the edge with the steps. Write a linear expression that represents the length of string in feet she will need. Then find the length if $x = 3$.

_____

Evaluate each expression if $x = \dfrac{1}{2}$ and $y = \dfrac{3}{4}$.

30. xy _____

31. $x - y$ _____

32. $x + y$ _____

33. x^3 _____

34. $3y + 2x$ _____

35. $x \div y$ _____

Inquiry Lab
Factor Linear Expressions

Indiana Academic Standards
7.AF.1

PS Process Standards
1, 3

 HOW do models help you factor linear expressions?

Max has enough 1 inch square glass tiles to create a rectangular piece of mosaic art that has an area of 24 square inches. Some of the possible dimensions of the rectangle are listed in the table. Write the two missing possible dimensions.

Each of the dimensions listed are factors of 24. Sometimes, you know the product and are asked to find the factors. This process is called *factoring*.

Length (in.)	Width (in.)
24	1
3	8

Hands-On Activity 1

Tools

Use algebra tiles to factor 2x + 6.

Step 1 Model the expression 2x + 6.

Step 2 Arrange the tiles into a rectangle with equal rows and columns. The total area of the tiles represents the product. Its length and width represent the factors.

The rectangle has a width of two 1-tiles and a length of one x-tile and three 1-tiles.

So, 2x + 6 = 2(x + ☐).

Hands-On Activity 2

Use algebra tiles to factor 2x − 8.

Step 1   Model the expression 2x − 8.

Step 2   Arrange the tiles into a rectangle with equal rows and columns.

The rectangle has a width of two 1-tiles and a length of one x-tile and four −1-tiles.

So, 2x − 8 = _____ .

Hands-On Activity 3

Use algebra tiles to factor 3x − 6.

Step 1   Draw the tiles that represent the expression 3x − 6.

Step 2   Redraw the tiles into a rectangle with equal rows and columns.

The rectangle has a width of _____ 1-tiles and a length of one x-tile and _____ −1-tiles.

So, 3x − 6 = _____ .

Investigate

Work with a partner. Factor each expression by arranging the appropriate algebra tiles into equal rows and columns. Draw the finished product.

1. $4x + 6 =$ _____

Show your work.

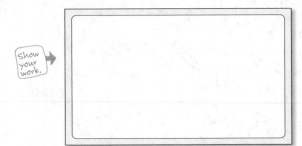

2. $5x + 10 =$ _____

3. $3x + 12 =$ _____

4. $4x - 10 =$ _____

5. $3x - 9 =$ _____

6. $2x - 4 =$ _____

7. $4x + 2 =$ _____

8. $5x - 5 =$ _____

Work with a partner to complete the table. Use algebra tiles if needed.

	Original Expression	Factored Expression	Distributive Property
	$2x + 8$	$2(x + 4)$	$2(x) + 2(4) = 2x + 8$
9.	$4x - 8$	$4(x - \boxed{})$	$4(x) - 4(2) = 4x - 8$
10.	$6x + 2$	$2(\boxed{}x + 1)$	$2(3x) + 2(1) =$
11.	$2x - 10$		$2(x) - 2(5) =$
12.	$8x + 6$		

13. **PS Reason Inductively** How is factoring related to using the Distributive Property?

_____

_____

14. **PS Construct an Argument** Is the expression $2x - 2$ equivalent to the expression $2(x - 2)$? Explain.

_____

_____

Create

On Your Own

15. **PS Justify Conclusions** Explain how you could use algebra tiles to factor $5x + 15$.

_____

_____

_____

16. **Inquiry** HOW do models help you factor linear expressions?

_____

_____

_____

Factor Linear Expressions

 ## Real-World Link

Yard Sale A rectangular yard is being separated into four equal-size sections for different items at a yard sale. The area of the yard is $(8x + 12)$ square meters.

Housewares

Toys

Clothing

Books

1. How can you find the area of each section of the yard sale?

_____

_____

2. What is the area of each section? Explain your answer.

_____

_____

_____

_____

3. The algebra tiles represent the area of the entire yard sale. Fill in the length and width. Write an expression that represents the area in terms of the length and

width of the model. _____

Essential Question

HOW can you use numbers and symbols to represent mathematical ideas?

Vocab **Vocabulary**

monomial
factor
factored form

Indiana Academic Standards
7.AF.1, 7.AF.2

PS Process Standards
1, 2, 3, 4

Which PS Process Standards did you use?
Shade the circle(s) that applies.

① Persevere with Problems

② Reason Abstractly

③ Construct an Argument

④ Model with Mathematics

⑤ Use Math Tools

⑥ Attend to Precision

⑦ Make Use of Structure

⑧ Use Repeated Reasoning

Find the GCF of Monomials

A **monomial** is a number, a variable, or a product of a number and one or more variables.

Monomials	Not Monomials
25, x, 40x	$x + 4$, 40x + 120

To **factor** a number means to write it as a product of its factors. A monomial can be factored using the same method you would use to factor a number.

The greatest common factor (GCF) of two monomials is the greatest monomial that is a factor of both.

Examples

Tutor

Find the GCF of each pair of monomials.

1. 4x, 12x

$4x = 2 \cdot 2 \cdot x$ Write the prime factorization of 4x and 12x.

$12x = 2 \cdot 2 \cdot 3 \cdot x$ Circle the common factors.

The GCF of 4x and 12x is 2 · 2 · x or 4x.

2. 18a, 20ab

$18a = 2 \cdot 3 \cdot 3 \cdot a$ Write the prime factorization of 18a and 20ab.

$20ab = 2 \cdot 2 \cdot 5 \cdot a \cdot b$ Circle the common factors.

The GCF of 18a and 20ab is 2 · a or 2a.

3. 12cd, 36cd

$12cd = 2 \cdot 2 \cdot 3 \cdot c \cdot d$ Write the prime factorization of 12cd and 36cd.

$36cd = 2 \cdot 2 \cdot 3 \cdot 3 \cdot c \cdot d$ Circle the common factors.

The GCF of 12cd and 36cd is 2 · 2 · 3 · c · d or 12cd.

Show your work.

Got It? Do these problems to find out.

Find the GCF of each pair of monomials.

   a. 12, 28c **b.** 25x, 15xy **c.** 42mn, 14mn

a. _____

b. _____

c. _____

Factor Linear Expressions

You can use the Distributive Property and the work backward strategy to express a linear expression as a product of its factors. A linear expression is in **factored form** when it is expressed as the product of its factors.

$$8x + 4y = 4(2x) + 4(y) \qquad \text{The GCF of } 8x \text{ and } 4y \text{ is 4.}$$
$$= 4(2x + y) \qquad \text{Distributive Property}$$

Examples

Tutor

4. Factor $3x + 9$.

> **Method 1** Use a model.

Arrange three x-tiles and nine 1-tiles into equal rows and columns. The rectangle has a width of three 1-tiles, or 3, and *a* length of one x-tile and three 1-tiles, or $x + 3$.

> **Method 2** Use the GCF.

$3x = 3 \cdot x \qquad$ Write the prime factorization of $3x$ and 9.
$9 = 3 \cdot 3 \qquad$ Circle the common factors.

The GCF of $3x$ and 9 is 3. Write each term as a product of the GCF and its remaining factors.

$3x + 9 = 3(x) + 3(3)$
$ = 3(x + 3) \qquad$ Distributive Property

So, $3x + 9 = 3(x + 3)$.

. . . .

5. Factor $12x + 7y$.

Find the GCF of $12x$ and $7y$.

$12x = 2 \cdot 2 \cdot 3 \cdot x$
$7y = 1 \cdot 7 \cdot y$

There are no common factors, so $12x + 7y$ *cannot be factored*.

Got It? Do these problems to find out.

Factor each expression. If the expression cannot be factored, write *cannot be factored*. Use algebra tiles if needed.

d. $4x - 28$ **e.** $3x + 33y$ **f.** $4x + 35$

> **Factoring Expressions**
>
> To check your factored answers, multiply your factors out. You should get your original expression as a result.

Show your work.

d. _____

e. _____

f. _____

Example

6. The drawing of a garden at the right has a total area of $(15x + 18)$ square feet. Find possible dimensions of the garden.

$15x$ 18

Factor $15x + 18$.

$15x = 3 \cdot 5 \cdot x$ Write the prime factorization of $15x$ and 18.

$18 = 2 \cdot 3 \cdot 3$ Circle the common factors.

The GCF of $15x$ and 18 is 3. Write each term as a product of the GCF and its remaining factors.

$15x + 18 = \mathbf{3}(5x) + \mathbf{3}(6)$

$\qquad\qquad = \mathbf{3}(5x + 6)$ Distributive Property

So, the possible dimensions are 3 feet by $(5x + 6)$ feet.

Guided Practice

 Check

Find the GCF of each pair of monomials. (Examples 1–3)

1. $32x, 18$ _____

 Show your work.

2. $27s, 54st$ _____

3. $18cd, 30cd$ _____

Factor each expression. If the expression cannot be factored, write cannot be factored. Use algebra tiles if needed. (Examples 4 and 5)

4. $36x + 24$ _____

5. $4x + 9$ _____

6. $14x - 16y$ _____

7. Mr. Phen's monthly income can be represented by the expression $25x + 120$ where x is the number of hours worked. Factor the expression $25x + 120$. (Example 6)

_____

8. @ **Building on the Essential Question** Explain how the GCF is used to factor an expression. Use the term *Distributive Property* in your response.

_____

_____

_____

Rate Yourself!

Are you ready to move on? Shade the section that applies.

YES   ?   NO

For more help, go online to access a Personal Tutor.   Tutor

FOLDABLES   Time to update your Foldable!

Independent Practice

Go online for Step-by-Step Solutions

Find the GCF of each pair of monomials. (Examples 1–3)

Show your work.

1. 24, 48*m* _____

2. 32*a*, 48*b* _____

3 36*k*, 144*km* _____

Factor each expression. If the expression cannot be *factored*, write *cannot be factored*. Use algebra tiles if needed. (Examples 4 and 5)

4. 3*x* + 6 _____

5. 2*x* − 15 _____

6. 12*x* + 30*y* _____

7 The area of a rectangular dance floor is (4*x* − 8) square units. Factor 4*x* − 8 to find possible dimensions of the dance floor. (Example 6)

_____

8. The area of a rectangular porch is (9*x* + 18) square units. Factor 9*x* + 18 to find possible dimensions of the porch. (Example 6)

_____

9. Six friends visited a museum to see the new holograms exhibit. The group paid for admission to the museum and $12 for parking. The total cost of the visit can be represented by the expression $6*x* + $12. What expression would represent the cost of the visit for one person?

_____

10. The diagram represents a flower border that is 3 feet wide surrounding a rectangular sitting area. Write an expression in factored form that represents the area of the flower border.

PS Reason Abstractly Write an expression in factored form to represent the total area of each rectangle.

11.

5x   20

_____

12.

7   49x

_____

13.

36   20x   40

_____

14.

18

6x

12

_____

H.O.T. Problems Higher Order Thinking

15. **PS Reason Inductively** Write two monomials whose greatest common factor is 4m.

_____

_____

16. **PS Find the Error** Jamar is factoring 90x − 15. Find his mistake and correct it.

_____

_____

_____

_____

_____

$$90x - 15 = 15(6x)$$
$$= 9$$

17. **PS Persevere with Problems** The area of a rectangle is found using the formula $A = \ell w$, where ℓ is the length and w is the width of the rectangle. Write an expression in factored form that represents the area of the shaded region at the right.

6x

2   4

3y

_____

Extra Practice

Find the GCF of each pair of monomials.

18. 63p, 84 _21_

$63p = 3 \cdot 3 \cdot 7 \cdot p$

$84 = 2 \cdot 2 \cdot 3 \cdot 7$

Homework Help ➡ The GCF of 63p and 84
is 3 · 7 or 21.

19. 30rs, 42rs _6rs_

$30rs = 2 \cdot 3 \cdot 5 \cdot r \cdot s$

$42rs = 2 \cdot 3 \cdot 7 \cdot r \cdot s$

The GCF of 30rs and 42rs
is 2 · 3 · r · s or 6rs.

20. 60jk, 45jkm _____

21. 40x, 60x _____

22. 54gh, 72g _____

23. 100xy, 75xyz _____

Factor each expression. If the expression cannot be factored, write *cannot be factored*. Use algebra tiles if needed.

24. 5x + 5 _____

25. 18x + 6 _____

26. 4x − 7 _____

27. 10x − 35 _____

28. 32x + 24y _____

29. 30x − 40 _____

30. James has $120 in his savings account and plans to save $x each month for 6 months. The expression $6x + $120 represents the total amount in the account after 6 months. Factor the expression 6x + 120.

_____

31. A square scrapbooking page has a perimeter of (8x + 20) inches. What is the length of one side of the scrapbooking page?

_____

Copy and Solve Write an expression in factored form that is equivalent to the given expression. Show your work on a separate piece of paper.

32. $\frac{1}{2}x + 4$

33. $\frac{2}{3}x + 6$

34. $\frac{3}{4}x - 24$

35. $\frac{5}{6}x - 30$

36. $\frac{2}{5}x + 16$

37. $\frac{3}{8}x + 18$

38. Select the correct terms to fill in the Venn diagram to show the factors of 12 and 18x.

1	9
2	12
3	18
4	x
6	

Factors of 12   Factors of 18x

What is the GCF of 12 and 18x? Explain how the Venn diagram helped you find the GCF.

39. Which pairs of monomials have a GCF of 4a? Select all that apply.

☐ 8a, 18a   ☐ 16a, 8b   ☐ 16ab, 12a   ☐ 28a, 20a

Spiral Review

Use the Distributive Property to rewrite each expression.

40. $4(x + 1) =$ _____

41. $3(a + 10) =$ _____

42. $7(2b + 5) =$ _____

43. The letters P, E, M, D, A, and S form PEMDAS. This is a mnemonic device that can be used to help you remember the order of operations. Each letter stands for something. Complete the organizer.

P ········▶ Parentheses

E ········▶ _____

M ········▶ Multiplication

D ········▶ _____

A ········▶ _____

S ········▶ _____

21ST CENTURY CAREER
in Animal Conservation

Shark Scientist

Are you fascinated by sharks, especially those that are found around the coasts of the United States? If so, you should consider a career as a shark scientist. Shark scientists use satellite-tracking devices, called tags, to study and track the movements of sharks. By analyzing the data transmitted by the tags, scientists are able to learn more about the biology and ecology of sharks. Their research is helpful in protecting shark populations around the world.

College & Career
READINESS

Is This the Career for You?

Are you interested in a career as a shark scientist? Take some of the following courses in high school.

◆ Algebra
◆ Calculus
◆ Physics
◆ Statistics

Find out how math relates to a career in Animal Conservation.

423

PS Tag, You're It!

The *fork length* of a shark is the length from the tip of the snout to the fork of the tail. Use the information on the note cards to solve each problem.

1. Write an expression to represent the total length of a hammerhead shark that has a fork length of *f* feet. _____

2. Use the expression from Exercise 1 to find the total length of a hammerhead shark that has a fork length of 11.6 feet. _____

3. Write an expression to represent the average fork length of a tiger shark, given the average fork length s of a sandbar shark. _____

4. Use the expression from Exercise 3 to find the average fork length of a tiger shark if the average fork length of a sandbar shark is 129 centimeters. _____

5. Write an expression to find the average fork length of a white shark with a total length of *t* centimeters. _____

6. The total length of a white shark is 204 centimeters. Use the expression in Exercise 5 to find the approximate fork length of the white shark. _____

Tiger Shark

A study found that the average fork length of a tiger shark is 55 centimeters less than twice the average fork length of a sandbar shark.

Hammerhead Shark

The total length of a hammerhead shark is about 1.3 times the fork length.

White Shark

The fork length of a white shark is about 5.74 centimeters less than 0.94 times the total length *t*.

PS Career Project

It's time to update your career portfolio! Describe the skills that would be necessary for a shark scientist to possess. Determine whether this type of career would be a good fit for you.

_____

_____

_____

_____

_____

List several challenges associated with this career.

- _____
- _____
- _____
- _____
- _____

Chapter Review

Vocabulary Check

In the puzzle below, write a vocabulary term for each clue.

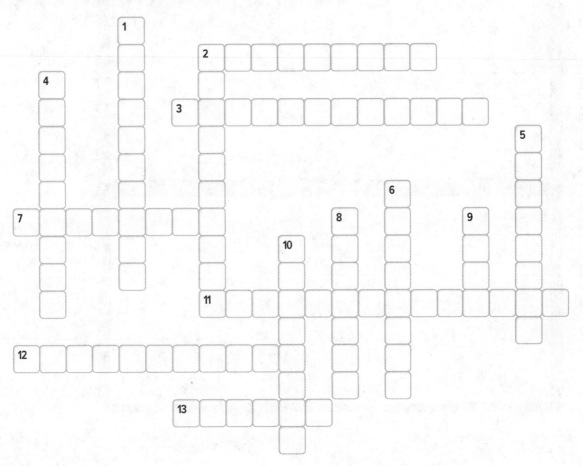

Across

2. a type of expression that contains a variable or variables

3. an algebraic expression that has no like terms and no parentheses is in this form (two words)

7. an ordered list of numbers

11. an example showing a statement is not true

12. the numerical factor of a multiplication expression

13. what is done to a variable to represent an unknown quantity

Down

1. expressions like 4(3 + 2) and 4(3) + 4(2)

2. a sequence in which each term is found by adding the same number

4. terms that include the same variable

5. a letter or symbol

6. a statement that is true for any number or variable

8. a branch of mathematics that uses variables

9. a number in a sequence

10. a term that contains a number only

Use Your FOLDABLES

Use your Foldable to help review the chapter.

Tape here

Linear Expressions

Explanation

Explanation

Got it?

Draw a line to match each expression with its equivalent expression.

1. $3 + 1$

a. $8 - 4x$

2. $4(2 - x)$

b. $5x + 5$

3. $3x - 2 - x + 6$

c. $3(x + 7)$

4. $2(x + 2) + (3x + 1)$

d. $1 + 3$

5. $3x + 21$

e. $2x + 4$

Power Up! Performance Task

Movie Time

The Townsends, a family of five, are going to the local movie theater. The family consists of two adults and three children. Mr. Townsend wants to calculate the cost of the night out. He looks up the admission prices online.

> ### Admission:
> Adults — $10.50
> Children — $6.50
>
> All shows before 6 P.M. $\frac{1}{2}$ price

Before leaving, Mr. Townsend decides that he will get some items at the theater concession stand, a large drink for each person and a large tub of popcorn for everyone to share. He will not know the prices of the items at the concession stand until they arrive.

Write your answers on another piece of paper. Show all of your work to receive full credit.

Part A
Write an expression that represents the cost of the admission prices and the concession stand items based on the available information. Let d represent the cost for a large drink and let p represent the cost of the popcorn. The initial expression must include parentheses. Then simplify the expression by using the Distributive Property and combining like terms.

Part B
Two children from next door join the Townsends. The neighbor children have movie passes and have already eaten, so Mr. Townsend will only need to pay for two more large drinks. At the concession stand, one of the children gives Mr. Townsend a five dollar bill to help pay for the drinks. Write an expression that represents the cost of the drinks for the neighbor children and includes the money given to Mr. Townsend.

Part C
While at the concession stand, Mr. Townsend sees that the large tub of popcorn is $7.50, and large drinks are $6 each. Using your answers from Part A and Part B, write an expression that represents the total cost. Then substitute the values for the popcorn and drinks in your expression. What is the total cost for the evening?

Reflect

Answering the Essential Question

Use what you learned about algebraic expressions to complete the graphic organizer. Then answer the chapter's Essential Question below.

When do you use a variable?

 Essential Question

HOW can you use numbers and symbols to represent mathematical ideas?

How do you know which operation symbol to use?

Answer the Essential Question. HOW can you use numbers and symbols to represent mathematical ideas?

Chapter 6
Equations and Inequalities

Essential Question

WHAT does it mean to say two quantities are equal?

Indiana Academic Standards
7.C.8, 7.AF.2, 7.AF.3

PS Process Standards
1, 2, 3, 4, 5, 7

Math in the Real World

Driving Suppose you live in a state where you must be at least 16 years of age to obtain a driver's license. Circle the statement that represents this age.

DRIVER LICENSE

NAME: Joan Smith
AGE: $a < 16$
       $a = 16$
       $a \geq 16$
ADDRESS:
1234 Anyplace Dr.

FOLDABLES
Study Organizer

1 Cut out the Foldable on page FL5 of this book.

2 Place your Foldable on page 524.

3 Use the Foldable to help you learn about equations and inequalities.

Vocabulary

Addition Property of Equality	equation	solution
Addition Property of Inequality	equivalent equation	Subtraction Property of Equality
coefficient	inequality	Subtraction Property of Inequality
Division Property of Equality	Multiplication Property of Equality	two-step equation
Division Property of Inequality	Multiplication Property of Inequality	two-step inequality

Study Skill: Reading Math

Identify Key Information Have you ever tried to solve a word problem and didn't know where to start. Start by looking for key words in the text and images. Then write the important information in one sentence.

1. Highlight or circle key words in the following real-world problem.

   During a recent Super Bowl, millions of pounds of potato chips and tortilla chips were consumed. The number of pounds of potato chips consumed was 3.1 million pounds more than the number of pounds of tortilla chips. How many pounds of tortilla chips were consumed?

2. Write a sentence that summarizes the information provided. Include information from the text and the image. _____

12.4 million pounds   ? million pounds

Place a checkmark below the face that expresses how much you know about each concept. Then scan the chapter to find a definition or example of it.

😞 I have no clue.   😐 I've heard of it.   😊 I know it!

Equations and Inequalities

Concept	😞	😐	😊	Definition or Example
inequalities				
solving one-step equations				
solving inequalities by addition or subtraction				
solving inequalities by multiplication or division				
solving two-step equations				
solving two-step inequalities				

Here are a few examples of how equations are used in the real world.

Activity 1 Describe a situation when you only had a set amount of money to spend and you needed to buy a certain number of items. Then explain how you determined what you could buy.

_____

_____

Activity 2 Go online at **connectED.mcgraw-hill.com** to read the graphic novel *Movie Night*. How much does each DVD cost? How much money do they need for popcorn? _____

Seth, Marisol, and Jamar in
Movie Night

NEW RELEAS[E]

Hey guys. Help me pick out some movies for movie night at school.

How much money can we spend?

Don't forget the popcorn.

Are You Ready?

Try the Quick Check below.
Or, take the Online Readiness Quiz.

Quick Review

Example 1

Write the phrase as an algebraic expression.

Phrase: five dollars more than Jennifer earned

Variable: Let d represent the number of dollars Jennifer earned.

Expression: $d + 5$

Example 2

Is 3, 4, or 5 the solution of the equation $x + 8 = 12$?

Value of x	$x + 8 = 12$	Are both sides equal?
3	$3 + 8 \stackrel{?}{=} 12$ $11 \neq 12$	no
4	$4 + 8 \stackrel{?}{=} 12$ $12 = 12$	yes ✓
5	$5 + 8 \stackrel{?}{=} 12$ $13 \neq 12$	no

The solution is 4 since replacing x with 4 results in a true sentence.

Quick Check

Words and Symbols Write the phrase as an algebraic expression.

1. 3 more runs than the Pirates scored

_____

2. a number decreased by eight

_____

3. ten dollars more than Grace has

_____

 Show your work.

One-Step Equations Identify the solution of each equation from the list given.

4. $8 + w = 17$; 7, 8, 9 _____

5. $d - 12 = 5$; 16, 17, 18 _____

6. $6 = 3y$; 2, 3, 4 _____

7. $7 \div c = 7$; 0, 1, 2 _____

8. $a + 8 = 23$; 13, 14, 15 _____

9. $10 = 45 - n$; 35, 36, 37 _____

How Did You Do?

Which problems did you answer correctly in the Quick Check?
Shade those exercise numbers below.

① ② ③ ④ ⑤ ⑥ ⑦ ⑧ ⑨

Inquiry Lab
Solve One-Step Addition and Subtraction Equations

 Inquiry HOW can bar diagrams or algebra tiles help you solve an equation?

Indiana Academic Standards
7.AF.2

PS Process Standards
1, 2, 3, 5

In a recent year, 19 of the 50 states had a law banning the use of handheld cell phones while driving a school bus. Determine how many states did *not* have this law.

Hands-On Activity 1

You can represent this situation with an equation.

Step 1 The bar diagram represents the total number of states and the number of states that have passed a cell phone law. Fill in the missing information.

	⬚ states	
states with a law	**states that do not have a law**	
⬚ states	?	

Step 2 Write an equation from the bar diagram. Let *x* represent the states that do not have a cell phone law for school bus drivers.

$$19 + x = 50$$

Step 3 Use the *work backward* strategy to solve the equation. Since $19 + x = 50$, $x = 50 - 19$. So, $x = \boxed{}$.

Check $19 + \boxed{} = 50$ ✓

So, $\boxed{}$ states did *not* have a law banning the use of cell phones by bus drivers.

Inquiry Lab Solve One-Step Addition and Subtraction Equations **433**

Work with a partner to solve each problem.

1. Draw a bar diagram and write an addition equation to represent the following situation. Then solve the equation.

   The sum of a number and four is equal to 18.

   Equation: _____   Solution: $x =$ _____

2. **PS Use Math Tools** Jack collects postage stamps. He sold 7 of his stamps and had 29 stamps left. Complete the bar diagram below. Then write and solve a subtraction equation to find the number of stamps Jack had at the beginning.

   Equation: _____   Solution: $n =$ _____

   So, Jack had ☐ stamps at the beginning.

 Analyze and Reflect

Collaborate

3. Suppose Jack sold 15 stamps and had 21 stamps left. How would the bar diagram change?

   _____

   _____

4. **PS Reason Abstractly** Suppose Jack had 40 stamps in the beginning and sold 7 of them. How would the bar diagram change? What equation could you write to represent the situation?

   _____

   _____

Hands-On Activity 2

Solve $x - 3 = -2$ using algebra tiles.

Remember a 1-tile and −1 tile combine to make a *zero pair*. You can add or subtract zero pairs from either side of an equation without changing its value.

Step 1 Model the equation.

$$x - 3 \qquad = \qquad -2$$

Step 2 Add three 1-tiles to the left side of the mat and _____ 1-tiles to the right side of the mat to form zero pairs on each side of the mat.

$$x - 3 + 3 \qquad = \qquad -2 + 3$$

Step 3 Remove all of the zero pairs from each side. There is _____ 1-tile on the right side of the mat.

$$x \qquad = \qquad 1$$

Therefore, $x = \boxed{}$.

Check $\boxed{} - 3 = -2$ ✔

Investigate

PS Use Math Tools Work with a partner to solve each equation. Use algebra tiles. Show your work using drawings.

5. $x + 4 = 4$ $x = $ _____

Show your work.

6. $-2 = x + 1$ $x = $ _____

7. $x - 1 = -3$ $x = $ _____

8. $4 = x - 2$ $x = $ _____

Analyze and Reflect

Work with a partner to complete the table. The first one is done for you.

	Equation	Related Equation
	$x + 3 = 4$	$x = 4 - 3$
9.	$6 + x = 10$	
10.	$x + 3 = -1$	
11.	$6 + x = -7$	

Create

On Your Own

12. **PS Construct an Argument** Write a rule that you can use to solve addition equations without using models or a drawing.

_____

_____

13. **Inquiry** HOW can bar diagrams or algebra tiles help you solve an equation?

_____

_____

Solve One-Step Addition and Subtraction Equations

Vocabulary Start-Up

An **equation** is a sentence stating that two quantities are equal. The value of a variable that makes an equation true is called the **solution** of the equation.

$$x + 2 = 6$$
$$\underline{-2 = -2}$$
$$x = 4$$

The equations $x + 2 = 6$ and $x = 4$ are **equivalent equations** because they have the same solution, 4.

Circle the equations below that are equivalent to $x = 3$. Use algebra tiles if needed.

$x + 3 = 6$	$x + 1 = 6$	$x + 6 = 8$
$x + 3 = 3$	$x + 1 = 4$	$x + 2 = 5$

Real-World Link

Video Games Robyn had some video games, and then she bought 4 more games. Now she has 10 games. This scenario can be described using the equation $x + 4 = 10$.

1. What does x represent in the equation?

_____

2. Write two different equations that are equivalent to $x + 4 = 10$.

_____

Which PS **Process Standards** did you use?
Shade the circle(s) that applies.

① Persevere with Problems   ⑤ Use Math Tools

② Reason Abstractly   ⑥ Attend to Precision

③ Construct an Argument   ⑦ Make Use of Structure

④ Model with Mathematics   ⑧ Use Repeated Reasoning

Essential Question

WHAT does it mean to say two quantities are equal?

Vocabulary

equation
solution
equivalent equation
subtraction property of equality
addition property of equality

Indiana Academic Standards
7.AF.2

PS **Process Standards**
1, 2, 3, 4, 5

Key Concept

Subtraction Property of Equality

Words   The **Subtraction Property of Equality** states that the two sides of an equation remain equal when you subtract the same number from each side.

Symbols   If $a = b$, then $a - c = b - c$.

You can use bar diagrams and the *work backward* problem-solving strategy to solve equations arithmetically. Or, you can use the properties of equality to solve equations algebraically.

Examples

1. Solve $x + 6 = 4$. Check your solution.

$$\begin{aligned} x + 6 &= 4 & &\text{Write the equation.} \\ -6 &= -6 & &\text{Subtraction Property of Equality} \\ \hline x &= -2 & &\text{Simplify.} \end{aligned}$$

Check $x + 6 = 4$ Write the original equation.

$-2 + 6 \stackrel{?}{=} 4$ Replace x with -2.

$4 = 4$ ✓   The sentence is true.

So, the solution is -2.

> **Solutions**
> Notice that your new equation, $x = -2$, has the same solution as the original equation, $x + 6 = 4$.

2. Solve $-5 = b + 8$. Check your solution.

$$\begin{aligned} -5 &= b + 8 & &\text{Write the equation.} \\ -8 &= -8 & &\text{Subtraction Property of Equality} \\ \hline -13 &= b & &\text{Simplify.} \end{aligned}$$

Check $-5 = b + 8$ Write the original equation.

$-5 \stackrel{?}{=} -13 + 8$ Replace b with -13.

$-5 = -5$ ✓   The sentence is true.

So, the solution is -13.

Got it? Do these problems to find out.

Solve each equation. Check your solution.

   a. $y + 6 = 9$ **b.** $x + 3 = 1$ **c.** $-3 = a + 4$

Show your work.

a. _____

b. _____

c. _____

Work Zone

Example

3. An angelfish can grow to be 12 inches long. If an angelfish is 8.5 inches longer than a clown fish, how long is a clown fish?

Words	An angelfish is 8.5 inches longer than a clown fish.
Variable	Let c represent the length of the clown fish.
Equation	12 $\quad = \quad c \quad + \quad$ 8.5

$$12 = c + 8.5 \quad \text{Write the equation.}$$
$$\underline{-8.5 = \quad -8.5} \quad \text{Subtraction Property of Equality}$$
$$3.5 = c \quad \text{Simplify.}$$

A clown fish is 3.5 inches long.

Solve Arithmetically

You can use a bar diagram to solve an equation arithmetically.

⊢– angelfish, 12 inches –⊣
clown fish	
⊢–c–⊣⊢– 8.5 inches –⊣

Work backward to solve for c.

$c = 12 - 8.5 = 3.5$

Got it? Do this problem to find out.

d. The highest recorded temperature in Warsaw, Missouri, is 118°F. This is 158° greater than the city's lowest recorded temperature. Find the lowest recorded temperature.

Show your work.

d. _____

Addition Property of Equality   **Key Concept**

Words	The **Addition Property of Equality** states that the two sides of an equation remain equal when you add the same number to each side.
Symbols	If $a = b$, then $a + c = b + c$.

Example

4. Solve $x - 2 = 1$. Check your solution.

$$x - 2 = 1 \quad \text{Write the equation.}$$
$$\underline{+2 = +2} \quad \text{Addition Property of Equality}$$
$$x = 3 \quad \text{Simplify.}$$

The solution is 3.   **Check** $3 - 2 = 1$ ✓

Show your work.

e. _____

f. _____

Got it? Do these problems to find out.

e. $y - 3 = 4$ **f.** $r - 4 = -2$ **g.** $q - 8 = -9$

g. _____

Models

A bar diagram can be used to represent this situation.

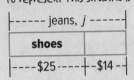

------ jeans, *j* ------	
shoes	
----$25----	-$14--

$j = 25 + 14 = 39$

Example

5. A pair of shoes costs **$25. This is $14 less than the cost of a pair of jeans. Find the cost of the jeans.**

Shoes are $14 less than jeans. Let *j* represent the cost of jeans.

$$25 = j - 14 \qquad \text{Write the equation.}$$
$$\underline{+14 = +14} \qquad \text{Addition Property of Equality}$$
$$39 = j \qquad \text{Simplify.}$$

The jeans cost $39.

 Show your work.

Got it? Do this problem to find out.

h. The average lifespan of a tiger is 17 years. This is 3 years less than the average lifespan of a lion. Write and solve an equation to find the average lifespan of a lion.

h. _____

Guided Practice

 Check

Solve each equation. Check your solution. (Examples 1, 2, and 4)

1. $n + 6 = 8$

2. $7 = y + 2$

3. $-7 = c - 6$

 Show your work.

4. Orville and Wilbur Wright made the first airplane flights in 1903. Wilbur's flight was 364 feet. This was 120 feet longer than Orville's flight. Write an equation to represent the flights. Use a bar diagram if needed. Then solve to find the length of Orville's flight. (Examples 3 and 5)

_____

5. **Building on the Essential Question** What are two methods for solving a real-world problem that can be represented by an equation?

_____

_____

_____

Rate Yourself!

☐ I understand how to solve one-step addition and subtraction equations.

▶▶ Great! You're ready to move on!

☐ I still have some questions about solving equations.

📖 No Problem! Go online to access a Personal Tutor.

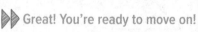

Independent Practice

Go online for Step-by-Step Solutions

Solve each equation. Check your solution. (Examples 1, 2, and 4)

1. $a + 3 = 10$

2. $y + 5 = -11$

3 $s - 8 = 9$

4. $5 = x + 8$

5. $-2 = p - 1$

6. $14 = s + 7$

Use a bar diagram to solve arithmetically. Then use an equation to solve algebraically. (Examples 3 and 5)

7 Last week Tiffany practiced her bassoon a total of 7 hours. This was 2 hours more than she practiced the previous week. How many hours did Tiffany practice the previous week?

8. In a recent presidential election, Ohio had 18 electoral votes. This is 20 votes less than Texas had. How many electoral votes did Texas have?

9. **PS** **Multiple Representations** Use the table to solve.

a. **Symbols** The difference in speeds of El Toro and T Express is 5 miles per hour. If El Toro has the greater speed, write and solve a subtraction equation to find its speed.

Tallest Wooden Roller Coasters	Height (feet)	Drop (feet)	Speed (mph)
Colossos	h	159	68
T Express	184	151	65
El Toro	181	176	s
Voyage	163	d	67

b. **Diagram** Voyage has a drop that is 22 feet less than El Toro. Draw a bar diagram to the right and write an equation to find the **drop** of Voyage.

c. **Words** Let h represent the height of the Colossos roller coaster. Explain why $h - 13 = 184$ and $h - 34 = 163$ are equivalent equations. Then explain the meaning of the solution.

10. The sum of the measures of the angles of a triangle is 180°. Write and solve an equation to find the missing measure.

11. The sum of the measures of a quadrilateral is 360°. Write and solve an equation to find the missing measure.

H.O.T. Problems Higher Order Thinking

12. (PS) **Reason Inductively** Write an addition equation and a subtraction equation that have 10 as a solution.

13. (PS) **Find the Error** Aisha is finding $b + 5 = -8$. Find her mistake and correct it.

14. (PS) **Reason Abstractly** Suppose $x + y = 11$ and the value of x increases by 2. If their sum remains the same, what must happen to the value of y? Justify your response

15. (PS) **Which One Doesn't Belong?** Identify the equation that does not belong with the other three. Explain your reasoning.

| $x + 4 = -2$ | $x + 5 = -1$ | $x + 2 = 8$ | $3 - x = 9$ |

16. (PS) **Reason Inductively** In the equation $x + y = 5$, the value for x is a whole number greater than 2 but less than 6. Find the possible solutions for y.

Extra Practice

Solve each equation. Check your solution.

17. $r + 6 = -3$

Homework Help →
$$r + 6 = -3$$
$$\underline{ - 6 = -6}$$
$$r = -9$$

18. $w - 7 = 11$

19. $k + 3 = -9$

20. $-1 = q - 8$

21. $9 = r + 2$

22. $y + 15 = 11$

PS **Use Math Tools** Use a bar diagram to solve arthimetically. Then use an equation to solve algebraically.

23. The Miami Heat scored 79 points. This was 13 points less than the Chicago Bulls. How many points did the Chicago Bulls score?

24. Zach is $15\frac{1}{2}$ years old. This is 3 years younger than his brother Lou. How old is Lou?

25. The table shows a golfer's scores for four rounds of a recent U.S. Women's Open. Her total score was even with par. What was her score for the third round?

Round	Score
First	−1
Second	−3
Third	s
Fourth	+2

Copy and Solve Solve each equation. Check your solution. Show your work on a separate piece of paper.

26. $a - 3.5 = 14.9$

27. $b + 2.25 = 1$

28. $-\dfrac{1}{3} = r - \dfrac{3}{4}$

29. $x - 2.8 = 9.5$

30. $r - 8.5 = -2.1$

31. $z - 9.4 = -3.6$

32. $m + \dfrac{5}{6} = \dfrac{11}{12}$

33. $-\dfrac{5}{6} + c = -\dfrac{11}{12}$

34. $s - \dfrac{1}{9} = \dfrac{5}{18}$

35. The model represents the equation
$x - 2 = 5$. Determine if each statement
is true or false.

a. To solve the equation, add 2 positive
counters to each side of the equation mat. ☐ True ☐ False

b. To solve the equation, add 5 negative
to each side of the equation mat. ☐ True ☐ False

c. The value of x is 7. ☐ True ☐ False

36. Britney practiced the piano a total of 7 hours this week. This is 3 hours
less than she practiced last week. Select the correct labels to complete
the bar diagram that is used to find the number of hours w Britney
practiced last week.

this week
last week, w
3 hours
4 hours
7 hours
10 hours

How many hours did Britney practice the piano last week? ☐

Spiral Review

Multiply or divide.

37. $5(-4) =$ _____

38. $\dfrac{36}{-9} =$ _____

39. $(-10)(-6) =$ _____

40. $\dfrac{-42}{-7} =$ _____

41. $(-3)(12) =$ _____

42. $\dfrac{-54}{2} =$ _____

43. While playing a round of golf, Tina had a
score of three under par after the first three
holes. Write and solve an equation to find
Tina's average score per hole h after three

holes. _____

44. On Friday morning, the temperature dropped
2 degrees per hour for four hours. Write and
solve an equation to find the total number
of degrees d the temperature dropped on

Friday morning. _____

Inquiry Lab

Multiplication Equations with Bar Diagrams

 HOW do you know which operation to use when solving an equation?

Indiana Academic Standards
7.AF.2

PS **Process Standards**
1, 2, 3

Sakiya tutors students to earn money to buy a new Blu-ray™ player that costs $63. She is able to tutor seven hours in a week. How much should she charge per hour to have enough money by the end of the week?

What do you know? _____

_____

What do you need to find? _____

_____

Hands-On Activity

Step 1 Draw a bar diagram that represents the money Sakiya needs to earn and the number of hours she is available to tutor that week.

hour 1	hour 2	hour 3	hour 4			

$\vdash$--- ? ---$\dashv$

$\vdash$-------------------$ \$ \boxed{}$-------------------$\dashv$

Step 2 Write an equation from the bar diagram. Let x represent the amount she should charge each hour.

$$7x = 63$$

Step 3 Use the *work backward* strategy to solve the equation. Since

$7x = 63$, $x = 63 \div 7$. So, $x = \boxed{}$.

Check $7 \times \boxed{} = 63$ ✓

So, Sakiya should charge $\boxed{}$ per hour.

Work with a partner to solve.

1. The screen on Lin's cell phone allows for 8 lines of text per message. The maximum number of characters for each message is 160. How many characters can each line hold? Complete the bar diagram below and write an equation. Then solve the equation.

Work with a partner to answer the following question.

2. **PS Make a Conjecture** Refer to Exercise 1. Suppose Lin's cell phone allows 4 lines of text and a maximum of 80 characters for each text message. How would the bar diagram and equation change?

3. **PS Reason Abstractly** Keyani spent $70 for 4 hours of dance classes. How much did she spend per hour of dance class? Draw a bar diagram below and write an equation. Then solve the equation.

4. **Inquiry** HOW do you know which operation to use when solving an equation?

Multiplication and Division Equations

Vocabulary Start-Up

The expression 3x means *3 times the value of x*. The numerical factor of a multiplication expression like 3x is called a **coefficient**. So, 3 is the coefficient of x.

The figure below illustrates the multiplication equation $3x = 6$.

Since there are 3 *x*s, each *x* is matched with 2.

$$3x = 6 \qquad x = 2$$

The solution of $3x = 6$ is 2.

Write an equation that represents each of the models below. Identify the coefficient in your equation. Then solve.

1.

Equation: _____

Coefficient: ☐

Solution: ☐

2.

Equation: _____

Coefficient: ☐

Solution: ☐

Essential Question

WHAT does it mean to say two quantities are equal?

Vocabulary

coefficient
division property of equality
multiplication property of equality

🅙 **Indiana Academic Standards**
7.AF.2

PS Process Standards
1, 2, 3, 4, 7

Which **PS** **Process Standards** did you use?
Shade the circle(s) that applies.

① Persevere with Problems
② Reason Abstractly
③ Construct an Argument
④ Model with Mathematics
⑤ Use Math Tools
⑥ Attend to Precision
⑦ Make Use of Structure
⑧ Use Repeated Reasoning

Division Property of Equality

Words   The **Division Property of Equality** states that the two sides of an equation remain equal when you divide each side by the same nonzero number.

Symbols   If $a = b$ and $c \neq 0$, then $\frac{a}{c} = \frac{b}{c}$.

Work Zone

You can use the Division Property of Equality to solve multiplication equations.

Examples

Tutor

1. Solve $20 = 4x$. Check your solution.

$20 = 4x$ Write the equation.

$\dfrac{20}{4} = \dfrac{4x}{4}$ Division Property of Equality

$5 = x$ Simplify.

Check $20 = 4x$ Write the original equation.

$20 \overset{?}{=} 4(5)$ Replace x with 5.

$20 = 20$ ✓   This sentence is true.

So, the solution is 5.

- -

2. Solve $-8y = 24$. Check your solution.

$-8y = 24$ Write the equation.

$\dfrac{-8y}{-8} = \dfrac{24}{-8}$ Division Property of Equality

$y = -3$ Simplify.

Check $-8y = 24$ Write the original equation.

$-8(-3) \overset{?}{=} 24$ Replace y with -3.

$24 = 24$ ✓   This sentence is true.

So, the solution is -3.

Show your work.

a. _____

b. _____

c. _____

Got it? Do these problems to find out.

Solve each equation. Check your solution.

    a. $30 = 6x$ **b.** $-6a = 36$ **c.** $-9d = -72$

Example Tutor

3. Lelah sent 574 text messages last week. On average, how many messages did she send each day?

Let m represent the number of messages Lelah sent.

$574 = 7m$ Write the equation. There are 7 days in one week.

$\dfrac{574}{7} = \dfrac{7m}{7}$ Division Property of Equality

$82 = m$ Simplify.

Lelah sent 82 messages on average each day.

Got it? Do this problem to find out.

d. Mrs. Acosta's car can travel an average of 24 miles on each gallon of gasoline. Write and solve an equation to find how many gallons of gasoline she will need for a trip of 348 miles.

Solve Arithmetically

You can use a bar diagram to solve an equation arithmetically.

| text messages in 1 week, 574 |

| m | m | m | m | m | m | m |

⊢ – ⊣
text messages in 1 day

Work backward to solve for m.

$m = 574 \div 7 = 82$

Show your work.

d. _____

Multiplication Property of Equality Key Concept

Words   The **Multiplication Property of Equality** states that the two sides of an equation remain equal if you multiply each side by the same number.

Symbols   If $a = b$, then $ac = bc$.

You can use the Multiplication Property of Equality to solve division equations.

Example Tutor

4. Solve $\dfrac{a}{-4} = -9$.

$\dfrac{a}{-4} = -9$ Write the equation.

$\dfrac{a}{-4}(-4) = -9(-4)$ Multiplication Property of Equality

$a = 36$ Simplify.

Got it? Do these problems to find out.

e. $\dfrac{y}{-3} = -8$ **f.** $\dfrac{m}{5} = -7$ **g.** $30 = \dfrac{b}{-6}$

e. _____

f. _____

g. _____

Example

5. The distance *d* Tina travels in her car while driving 60 miles per hour for 3 hours is given by the equation $\frac{d}{3} = 60$. How far did she travel?

$$\frac{d}{3} = 60 \qquad \text{Write the equation.}$$

$$\frac{d}{3}(3) = 60(3) \qquad \text{Multiplication Property of Equality}$$

$$d = 180 \qquad \text{Simplify.}$$

Tina traveled 180 miles.

Distance Formula

The distance formula, distance = rate × time, can be written as $d = rt$, $r = \frac{d}{t}$, or $t = \frac{d}{r}$.

Guided Practice

Solve each equation. Check your solution. (Examples 1, 2, and 4)

1. $6c = 18$

2. $24 = -8x$

3. $7m = -28$

4. $\frac{p}{9} = 9$

5. $\frac{a}{12} = -3$

6. $\frac{n}{-10} = -4$

7. Antonia earns $6 per hour helping her grandmother. Write and solve an equation to find how many hours she needs to work to earn $48. (Example 3) _____

8. A shark can swim at an average speed of 25 miles per hour. At this rate, how far can a shark swim in 2.4 hours? Use $r = \frac{d}{t}$. (Example 5) _____

9. **Building on the Essential Question** How is the process for solving multiplication and division one-step equations like solving one-step addition and subtraction equations?

_____

_____

_____

Rate Yourself!

How confident are you about solving one-step multiplication and division equations? Check the box that applies.

□ □ □ □ □

For more help, go online to access a Personal Tutor.

Independent Practice

Go online for Step-by-Step Solutions

Solve each equation. Check your solution. (Examples 1, 2, and 4)

1. $7a = 49$

 Show your work.

2. $-6 = 2x$

3. $-32 = -4b$

4. $\dfrac{u}{6} = 9$

5. $-8 = \dfrac{c}{-10}$

6. $54 = -9d$

7 $-12y = 60$

8. $\dfrac{r}{20} = -2$

9. $\dfrac{g}{10} = -9$

10. Brandy wants to buy a digital camera that costs $300. Suppose she saves $15 each week. In how many weeks will she have enough money for the camera? Use a bar diagram to solve arithmetically. Then use an equation to solve algebraically. (Example 3) _____

 Show your work.

11 A race car can travel at a rate of 205 miles per hour. At this rate, how far would it travel in 3 hours? Use $r = \dfrac{d}{t}$. Write an equation and then solve.
(Example 5)

12. A certain hurricane travels at 20.88 kilometers per hour. The distance from Cuba to Key West is 145 kilometers. Write and solve a multiplication equation to find about how long it would take the hurricane to travel from Cuba to Key West.

13. **PS Multiple Representations** Kennedy saves $5.50 for each hour she works. She needs to save an additional $44 to buy an E-reader. How many more hours does Kennedy need to work to pay for the E-reader?

a. **Diagram** Draw a bar diagram that represents the situation.

Show your work.

b. **Algebra** Write an equation that represents the situation.

c. **Words** Describe the process you would use to solve your equation. Then solve.

H.O.T. Problems Higher Order Thinking

14. **PS Reason Abstractly** Describe a real-world situation in which you would use a division equation to solve a problem. Write your equation and then solve your problem.

Situation: _____

Equation: _____ Solution: _____

15. **PS Identify Structure** *True* or *false*. To solve the equation $5x = 20$ you can use the Multiplication Property of Equality. Explain your reasoning.

16. **PS Persevere with Problems** Solve $3|x| = 12$. Explain your reasoning.

17. **PS Persevere with Problems** Explain how you would solve $\frac{-30}{x} = 6$. Then solve the equation.

Extra Practice

Solve each equation. Check your solution.

18. $-4j = 36$

$-4j = 36$

$\dfrac{-4j}{-4} = \dfrac{36}{-4}$

$j = -9$

19. $-4s = -16$

20. $63 = -9d$

21. $\dfrac{m}{10} = 7$

$\dfrac{m}{10} = 7$

$\dfrac{m}{10}(10) = 7(10)$

$m = 70$

22. $\dfrac{h}{-3} = 12$

23. $\dfrac{g}{12} = -10$

24. The width of a computer monitor is 1.25 times its height. Find the height of the computer monitor at the right. Use a bar diagram to solve arithmetically. Then use an equation to solve algebraically. _____

25. A dragonfly, the fastest insect, can fly a distance of 50 feet at a speed of 25 feet per second. Find the time in seconds. Write the equation in the form $d = rt$, then solve.

_____

26. **PS Find the Error** Raul is solving $-6x = 72$. Find his mistake and correct it.

_____

_____

_____

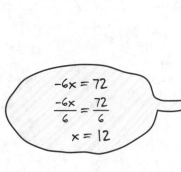

$-6x = 72$

$\dfrac{-6x}{6} = \dfrac{72}{6}$

$x = 12$

Power Up! Test Practice

27. The formula $A = bh$ can be used to find the area A of a parallelogram with base b and height h. The parallelogram shown has an area of 56 square inches.

7 in.

b

What is the length of the base? ◻

28. The table shows the prices of different satellite radio plans. Mrs. Freedman paid $99 for m months of satellite radio under Plan A. Fill in each box to write a multiplication equation to represent the situation.

◻ × ◻ = ◻

m	16.50
11.99	99
14.35	

How many months of service did Mrs. Freedman purchase? ◻

Satellite Radio Plans

Plan	Cost per Month ($)
A	16.50
B	14.35
C	11.99

Spiral Review

Write each improper fraction as a mixed number and each mixed number as an improper fraction.

29. $\dfrac{10}{3} =$ _____

30. $\dfrac{40}{7} =$ _____

31. $\dfrac{101}{100} =$ _____

32. $2\dfrac{2}{7} =$ _____

33. $3\dfrac{1}{4} =$ _____

34. $10\dfrac{5}{9} =$ _____

Divide.

35. $6 \div 1.5 =$ _____

36. $3.6 \div 0.4 =$ _____

37. $2.73 \div 1.3 =$ _____

Multiply. Write in simplest form.

38. $\dfrac{2}{9} \times \dfrac{7}{5} =$ _____

39. $\dfrac{3}{4} \times 7 =$ _____

40. $\dfrac{5}{8} \times \dfrac{4}{15} =$ _____

Inquiry Lab
Solve Equations with Rational Coefficients

 Inquiry HOW can you use bar diagrams to solve equations with rational coefficients?

Indiana Academic Standards
7.AF.2

PS Process Standards
1, 3

Two thirds of Chen's homeroom class plan to participate in the school talent show. If 16 students from the class plan to participate, how many students are in the homeroom class?

What do you know? _____

_____

What do you need to find? _____

_____

Hands-On Activity

You can represent the situation above with an equation.

Step 1 Draw a bar diagram that represents the total number of students in the class and how many plan to participate.

number of students in class

number of students
who plan to participate

Step 2 Write an equation from the bar diagram. Let c represent the total number of students in the class. _____

Step 3 Find the number of students represented by the sections of the bar. Write that number in each section of the bar in Step 1.

Since each section represents 8 students, there are 8 × 3 or ☐ students in the class.

Check $\frac{2}{3} \times 24 = \frac{2}{3} \times \frac{24}{1}$

$= \frac{48}{3}$ or 16 ✓

Investigate

Work with a partner to solve the following problem.

1. Eliana is spending $\frac{3}{5}$ of her monthly allowance on a costume for the talent show. She plans to spend $24. Draw a bar diagram to represent the situation. Then write and solve an equation to find the amount of Eliana's monthly allowance.

Equation: _____   Solution: _____

Analyze and Reflect

Work with a partner to answer the following question.

2. **PS Make a Conjecture** Suppose Eliana planned on spending $\frac{3}{4}$ of her monthly allowance on a costume. How would the diagram and equation be different?

_____

_____

Create

3. **PS Model with Mathematics** Write a real-world problem that could be represented by the equation $\frac{2}{3}x = 12$. Then solve the equation.

_____

_____

_____

4. **Inquiry** HOW can you use bar diagrams to solve equations with rational coefficients?

_____

_____

_____

Solve Equations with Rational Coefficients

 Real-World Link

Social Networks Three-fourths of the students in Aaliyah's class belong to a social network. There are 15 students in her class that belong to a social network.

Essential Question

WHAT does it mean to say two quantities are equal?

Indiana Academic Standards
7.AF.2

PS Process Standards
1, 2, 3, 4

1. Create a bar diagram and shade $\frac{3}{4}$, or 0.75, of it.

Label 15 along the bottom to show the amount of the bar that represents 15 students.

2. Based on the diagram, circle the equation that can be used to find c, the number of students in Aaliyah's class.

$$15c = \frac{3}{4} \qquad 0.75c = 15 \qquad 4c = 15$$

3. Based on what you know about solving equations, explain how you could solve the equation you circled in Exercise 2.

_____

4. How many students are in Aaliyah's class?

_____

Which PS Process Standards did you use?
Shade the circle(s) that applies.

① Persevere with Problems   ⑤ Use Math Tools

② Reason Abstractly   ⑥ Attend to Precision

③ Construct an Argument   ⑦ Make Use of Structure

④ Model with Mathematics   ⑧ Use Repeated Reasoning

Work Zone

Division with Decimals

```
        64.
0.25) 16.00
    − 150
      100
    − 100
        0
```

a. _____

b. _____

c. _____

d. _____

Decimal Coefficients

If the coefficient is a decimal, divide each side by the coefficient.

Example

Tutor

1. Solve $16 = 0.25n$. Check your solution.

$16 = 0.25n$ Write the equation.

$\dfrac{16}{0.25} = \dfrac{0.25n}{0.25}$ Division Property of Equality

$64 = n$ Simplify.

Check $16 = 0.25n$ Write the original equation.

$16 \stackrel{?}{=} 0.25 \cdot 64$ Replace n with 64.

$16 = 16$ ✓   This sentence is true.

The solution is 64.

Show your work.

Got it? Do these problems to find out.

a. $6.4 = 0.8m$ b. $-2.8p = 4.2$ c. $-4.7k = -10.81$

Real World Example

Tutor

2. Jaya's coach agreed to buy ice cream for all of the team members. Ice cream cones are $2.40 each. Write and solve an equation to find how many cones the coach can buy with $30.

Let n represent the number of cones the coach can buy.

$2.4n = 30$ Write the equation; $2.40 = 2.4$.

$\dfrac{2.4n}{2.4} = \dfrac{30}{2.4}$ Division Property of Equality

$n = 12.5$ Simplify.

Since the number of ice cream cones must be a whole number, there is enough money for 12 ice cream cones.

Got it? Do this problem to find out.

d. Suppose the ice cream cones cost $2.80 each. How many ice cream cones could the coach buy with $42?

Fraction Coefficients

Recall that two numbers with a product of 1 are called multiplicative inverses, or reciprocals. If the coefficient in a multiplication equation is a fraction, multiply each side by the reciprocal of the coefficient.

Examples

 Tutor

3. Solve $\frac{3}{4}x = \frac{12}{20}$.

$$\frac{3}{4}x = \frac{12}{20}$$ Write the equation.

$$\left(\frac{4}{3}\right) \cdot \frac{3}{4}x = \left(\frac{4}{3}\right) \cdot \frac{12}{20}$$ Multiply each side by the reciprocal of $\frac{3}{4}$, $\frac{4}{3}$.

$$\overset{1}{\underset{1}{\frac{\cancel{4}}{3}}} \cdot \overset{1}{\underset{1}{\frac{\cancel{3}}{\cancel{4}}}}x = \overset{1}{\underset{1}{\frac{\cancel{4}}{3}}} \cdot \overset{4}{\underset{5}{\frac{\cancel{12}}{\cancel{20}}}}$$ Divide by common factors.

$$x = \frac{4}{5}$$ Simplify. Check the solution.

4. Solve $-\frac{7}{9}d = 5$. **Check your solution.**

$$-\frac{7}{9}d = 5$$ Write the equation.

$$\left(-\frac{9}{7}\right) \cdot \left(-\frac{7}{9}\right)d = \left(-\frac{9}{7}\right) \cdot 5$$ Multiply each side by the reciprocal of $-\frac{7}{9}$, $-\frac{9}{7}$.

$$\left(-\frac{9}{7}\right) \cdot \left(-\frac{7}{9}\right)d = \left(-\frac{9}{7}\right) \cdot \frac{5}{1}$$ Write 5 as $\frac{5}{1}$.

$$\left(-\frac{\cancel{9}}{7}\right) \cdot \left(-\frac{7}{\cancel{9}}\right)d = \left(-\frac{9}{7}\right) \cdot \frac{5}{1}$$ Divide by common factors.

$$d = -\frac{45}{7} \text{ or } -6\frac{3}{7}$$ Simplify.

Check $-\frac{7}{9}d = 5$ Write the original equation.

$$-\frac{7}{9}\left(-\frac{45}{7}\right) \overset{?}{=} 5$$ Replace d with $-\frac{45}{7}$.

$$\frac{315}{63} \overset{?}{=} 5$$ Simplify.

$$5 = 5 \checkmark$$ This sentence is true.

Got it? Do these problems to find out.

e. $\frac{1}{2}x = 8$ **f.** $-\frac{3}{4}x = 9$ **g.** $-\frac{7}{8}x = -\frac{21}{64}$

> **Fractions as Coefficients**
>
> The expression $\frac{3}{4}x$ can be read as $\frac{3}{4}$ of x, $\frac{3}{4}$ multiplied by x, $3x$ divided by 4, or $\frac{x}{4}$ multiplied by 3.

 Show your work.

e. _____

f. _____

g. _____

Example

5. Valerie needs $\frac{2}{3}$ yard of fabric to make each hat for the school play. Write and solve an equation to find how many hats she can make with 6 yards of fabric.

Write and solve a multiplication equation. Let n represent the number of hats.

$\frac{2}{3}n = 6$ Write the equation.

$\left(\frac{3}{2}\right) \cdot \frac{2}{3}n = \left(\frac{3}{2}\right) \cdot 6$ Multiply each side by $\frac{3}{2}$.

$n = 9$ Simplify.

So, Valerie can make 9 hats.

Bar Diagrams

A bar diagram can be used to represent this situation.

$n = 6 \div \frac{2}{3} = \frac{6}{1} \times \frac{3}{2} = 9$

Guided Practice

Solve each equation. Check your solution. (Examples 1, 3, and 4)

1. $1.6k = 3.2$

2. $-2.5b = 20.5$

3. $-\frac{1}{2} = -\frac{5}{18}h$

Write and solve an equation. (Examples 2 and 5)

4. The average growth of human hair is 0.5 inch per month. Find how long it takes a human to grow 3 inches of hair.

Equation: _____   Solution: _____

5. Three fourths of the fruit in a refrigerator are apples. There are 24 apples in the refrigerator. How many pieces of fruit are in the refrigerator?

Equation: _____   Solution: _____

6. **Building on the Essential Question** What is the process for solving a multiplication equation with a rational coefficient? _____

_____

_____

_____

Rate Yourself!

Are you ready to move on? Shade the section that applies.

YES   ?   NO

For more help, go online to access a Personal Tutor.

Independent Practice

Go online for Step-by-Step Solutions

Solve each equation. Check your solution. (Examples 1, 3, and 4)

1. $1.2x = 6$

show your work.

2. $14.4 = -2.4b$

3 $-3.6h = -10.8$

4. $\frac{2}{5}t = \frac{12}{25}$

5. $-3\frac{1}{3} = -\frac{1}{2}g$

6. $-\frac{7}{9}m = \frac{11}{6}$

7 **Financial Literacy** Dillon deposited $\frac{3}{4}$ of his paycheck into the bank. The deposit slip shows how much he deposited. Write and solve an equation to find the amount of his paycheck. (Example 2)

Equation: _____   Solution: _____

DEPOSIT
CHECKS   4 6 . 5 0
Name: Dillon Gates
Date: 9/22
Great Savings Bank
Transaction #
•54334589D•3221•8755P   DEPOSIT $ 4 6 . 5 0

8. Twenty-four students brought their permission slips to attend the class field trip to the local art museum. If this represented eight tenths of the class, how many students are in the class? Use a bar diagram to solve arithmetically. Then use an equation to solve algebraically. (Example 5)

Equation: _____   Solution: _____

9. **PS** **Justify Conclusions** Seventy-five percent, or 15, of the students in Emily's homeroom class are going on a field trip. Two thirds, or 12, of the students in Santiago's homeroom class are going on the field trip. Which class has more students? Justify your answer. _____

_____

_____

10. **(PS) Reason Abstractly** Nora and Ryan are making stuffed animals for a toy drive. The table shows the fabric purchases they made. Who purchased the more expensive fabric?

Explain your reasoning. _____

Purchaser	Amount Purchased (yd)	Amount Paid ($)
Nora	$\frac{2}{3}$	4
Ryan	0.8	6

_____

_____

_____

🔥 H.O.T. Problems Higher Order Thinking

11. **(PS) Reason Inductively** Complete the statement: If $8 = \frac{m}{4}$, then

$m - 12 = \blacksquare$. Explain. _____

_____

12. **(PS) Which One Doesn't Belong?** Identify the pair of numbers that does

not belong with the other three. Explain. _____

_____

| $\frac{9}{6}, \frac{6}{9}$ | $4, \frac{1}{4}$ | $\frac{3}{5}, 5$ | $\frac{2}{7}, \frac{7}{2}$ |

13. **(PS) Persevere with Problems** The formula for the area of a trapezoid is $A = \frac{1}{2}h(b_1 + b_2)$, where b_1 and b_2 are both bases and h is the height. Find the value of h in terms of A, b_1, and b_2. Justify your answer.

_____

_____

_____

14. **(PS) Model with Mathematics** Write a real-world problem that can be represented by the equation $224 = 3.5r$. Then solve the problem and explain the solution.

_____

_____

_____

Extra Practice

Solve each equation. Check your solution.

15. $0.4d = 2.8$

Homework
Help

$0.4d = 2.8$

$\dfrac{0.4d}{0.4} = \dfrac{2.8d}{0.4}$

$d = 7$

16. $-5w = -24.5$

17. $-22.8 = 6n$

18. $\dfrac{7}{8}k = \dfrac{5}{6}$

$\dfrac{7}{8}k = \dfrac{5}{6}$

$\left(\dfrac{8}{7}\right) \cdot \dfrac{7}{8}k = \left(\dfrac{8}{7}\right) \cdot \dfrac{5}{6}$

$k = \dfrac{40}{42}$ or $\dfrac{20}{21}$

19. $-6\dfrac{1}{4} = \dfrac{3}{5}c$

20. $-\dfrac{4}{7}v = -8\dfrac{2}{3}$

21. The Mammoth Cave Discovery Tour includes an elevation change of 140 feet. This is $\dfrac{7}{15}$ of the elevation change on the Wild Cave Tour. What is the elevation change on the Wild Cave Tour? Use a bar diagram to solve arithmetically. Then use an equation to solve algebraically.

Equation: _____   Solution: _____

22. 🅟🅢 **Model with Mathematics** Refer to the graphic novel frame below. Write and solve an equation to find how many movies they have time to show.

Equation: _____   Solution: _____

23. Which of the following high speed trains are traveling at a rate of 150 miles per hour? Select all that apply.

☐ a train that travels 100 miles in $\frac{2}{3}$ hour   ☐ a train that travels 160 miles in $\frac{5}{6}$ hour

☐ a train that travels 125 miles in $\frac{4}{5}$ hour   ☐ a train that travels 90 miles in $\frac{3}{5}$ hour

24. The table shows the results of a survey. Of those surveyed, 275 students said they prefer pop music.

Write an equation that could be used to find the total number of students s who were surveyed. ⬚

How many students were surveyed? ⬚

Music Preference	
Type	Fraction of Students
Jazz	$\frac{1}{8}$
Pop	$\frac{5}{8}$
Rap	$\frac{1}{4}$

Spiral Review

Use the order of operations to evaluate each expression.

25. $6 \times 4 - 2 = $ _____

26. $70 - 5 \times 4 = $ _____

27. $18 \div 2 - 7 = $ _____

28. Write *add, divide, multiply,* and *subtract* in the correct order to complete the following sentence.
When using the order of operations to evaluate an expression,

always _____ and _____ before you _____

and _____ .

Write and evaluate an expression for each situation.

29. Used paperback books are $0.25, and hardback books are $0.50. If you buy 3 paperback books and 5 hardback books, how much money do you spend?

Expression: _____   Solution: _____

30. Suppose you order 2 pizzas, 2 garlic breads, and 1 order of BBQ wings. How much change would you receive from $30?

Expression: _____   Solution: _____

Item	Cost
14" pizza	$8
garlic bread	$2
BBQ wings	$4

Inquiry Lab
Solve Two-Step Equations

 Inquiry HOW can a bar diagram or algebra tiles help you solve a real-world problem?

Indiana Academic Standards
7.AF.2

PS **Process Standards**
1, 2, 3, 4

Latoya plays basketball and tennis. She has two basketballs and three tennis balls that weigh a total of 48 ounces. Each tennis ball weighs 2 ounces. What is the weight of a basketball?

Hands-On Activity 1

You can use a bar diagram to represent the situation.

Step 1 Draw a bar diagram that represents the total weight.

48 oz				
basketball		tennis	tennis	
?-----------	?-----------	2 oz	2 oz	☐

Step 2 Write an equation that is modeled by the bar diagram. Let x represent the weight of a basketball.

total weight
$$2x + 6 = 48$$
2 basketballs   3 tennis balls

Step 3 Use the bar diagram to solve the equation. Subtract the weight of the tennis balls, ☐ ounces, from the total weight, ☐ ounces.

The two basketballs together weigh ☐ − ☐, or ☐ ounces.

Divide the weight by ☐ to find the weight of one basketball.

So, $x =$ ☐. The weight of one basketball is ☐ ÷ ☐, or ☐ ounces.

Check $2 \cdot$ ☐ $+ 6 = 48$ ✓

The weight of one basketball is ☐ ounces.

Hands-On Activity 2

You can use algebra tiles to model and solve the equation $4x - 2 = 10$.

Step 1 Model the equation.

$4x - 2 = 10$

Step 2 Add ☐ 1-tiles to each side of the mat to form zero pairs on the left side.

$4x - 2 + 2 = 10 + 2$

Step 3 Remove both zero pairs from the left side so that the variable is by itself.

$4x = 12$

Step 4 Divide the remaining tiles into ☐ equal groups.

$$\frac{4x}{4} = \frac{12}{4}$$

So, $x = $ ☐.

Check $4 \cdot$ ☐ $- 2 = 10$ ✓

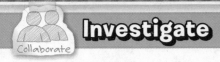

Investigate

Work with a partner to solve the following problem.

1. **PS Reason Abstractly** Ryan is saving money to buy a skateboard that costs $85. He has already saved $40. He plans to save the same amount each week for three weeks. Draw a bar diagram. Then write an equation. How much should Ryan save each week?

Work with a partner to solve each equation. Use algebra tiles. Show your work using drawings.

2. $2x + 1 = 5$ $x =$ _____

3. $3x + 2 = 11$ $x =$ _____

4. $4x + 3 = -5$ $x =$ _____

5. $2x - 1 = 7$ $x =$ _____

6. $5x - 2 = -7$ $x =$ _____

7. $3x - 4 = 5$ $x =$ _____

Analyze and Reflect

8. **PS Reason Inductively** Work with a partner. Read the steps to model and solve an equation using algebra tiles. Then circle each correct equation.

Steps to Solve	Choices of Equation		
• Add three 1-tiles to each side of the mat. • Divide tiles into two equal groups.	$2x + 3 = 15$	$3x + 2 = 15$	$2x - 3 = 15$
• Add four 1-tiles to each side of the mat. • Divide tiles into three equal groups.	$3x - 4 = 11$	$3x + 4 = 11$	$4x - 3 = 11$
• Remove seven 1-tiles from each side of the mat. • Divide tiles into three equal groups.	$7x + 3 = 10$	$3x + 7 = 10$	$3x - 7 = 10$
• Add two −1-tiles to each side of the mat. • Remove two zero pairs from the left side of the mat. • Divide tiles into five equal groups.	$5x - 2 = -8$	$5x + 2 = -8$	$2x + 5 = -8$

9. **PS Construct an Argument** What did you observe while choosing the correct equations in the table above?

_____

_____

Create

10. **PS Model with Mathematics** Write a real-world problem and an equation that the bar diagram below could represent. Then solve your problem.

```
|------------------- 540 -------------------|
|           |           |           |
|--------200--------+----?----+----?----|
```

_____

_____

_____

_____

11. **Inquiry** HOW can a bar diagram or algebra tiles help you solve a real-world problem?

_____

_____

Solve Two-Step Equations

Balloons A company charges $2 for each balloon in an arrangement and a $3 delivery fee. You have $9 to spend. The equation $2x + 3 = 9$, where x is the number of balloons, represents the situation. Work backward to solve for x.

Start with the amount of money you have to spend. ☐ → Subtract the $3 delivery fee. ☐ → Since each balloon is $2, divide by two. ☐

So, you can purchase ☐ balloons.

Check your work by substituting your solution into the equation.

$$2\left(\boxed{}\right) + 3 \stackrel{?}{=} 9.$$

$$\boxed{} + 3 \stackrel{?}{=} 9$$

$$\boxed{} = 9$$

Essential Question

WHAT does it mean to say two quantities are equal?

Vocab
Vocabulary

two-step equation

Indiana Academic Standards
7.AF.2

PS **Process Standards**
1, 2, 3, 4

1. How many balloons could you have purchased if there was a $1 delivery charge?

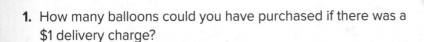

Start with the amount of money you have to spend. ☐ → Subtract the $1 delivery fee. ☐ → Since each balloon is $2, divide by two. ☐

Which **PS** **Process Standards** did you use?
Shade the circle(s) that applies.

① Persevere with Problems

② Reason Abstractly

③ Construct an Argument

④ Model with Mathematics

⑤ Use Math Tools

⑥ Attend to Precision

⑦ Make Use of Structure

⑧ Use Repeated Reasoning

Solve Two-Step Equations

Recall that the *order of operations* ensures that numerical expressions, such as 2 · 5 + 3, have only one value. To reverse the operations, undo them in reverse order.

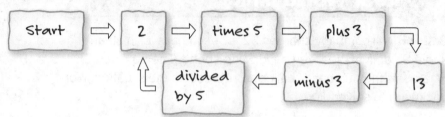

Start ⟹ 2 ⟹ times 5 ⟹ plus 3 ⟹

divided by 5 ⟸ minus 3 ⟸ 13

A **two-step equation**, such as $2x + 3 = 9$, has two different operations, multiplication and addition. To solve a two-step equation, undo the operations in reverse order of the order of operations.

> This equation is written as $px + q = r$, where p, q, and r are rational numbers.

Step 1 Undo the addition or subtraction first.

Step 2 Undo the multiplication or division.

Examples

Tutor

1. Solve $2x + 3 = 9$. Check your solution.

$$2x + 3 = 9$$ Write the equation.

$$\underline{-3 = -3}$$ Undo the addition first by subtracting 3 from each side.

$$2x = 6$$

$$\frac{2x}{2} = \frac{6}{2}$$ Next, undo the multiplication by dividing each side by 2.

$$x = 3$$ Simplify.

Check $\quad 2x + 3 = 9$ Write the original equation.

$\quad\quad\quad 2(3) + 3 \stackrel{?}{=} 9$ Replace x with 3.

$\quad\quad\quad\quad\quad 9 = 9 \checkmark$ The sentence is true.

The solution is 3.

> **STOP and Reflect**
>
> What are the two operations you would perform to solve $3x - 4 = 8$? Write your answer below.

2. Solve $3x + 2 = 23$. **Check your solution.**

$3x + 2 =\ 23$ Write the equation.

$\underline{\quad -2 = -2\quad}$ Undo the addition first by subtracting 2 from each side.

$3x\ \ \ \ =\ 21$

$\dfrac{3x}{3} = \dfrac{21}{3}$ Division Property of Equality

$x = 7$ Simplify.

Check $3x + 2 = 23$ Write the original equation.

$3(7) + 2 \overset{?}{=} 23$ Replace x with 7.

$23 = 23$ ✓   The sentence is true.

The solution is 7.

- -

3. Solve $-2y - 7 = 3$. **Check your solution.**

$-2y - 7 =\ \ 3$ Write the equation.

$\underline{\quad +7 = +7\quad}$ Undo the subtraction first by adding 7 to each side.

$-2y =\ 10$

$\dfrac{-2y}{-2} = \dfrac{10}{-2}$ Division Property of Equality

$y = -5$ Simplify.

The solution is -5.   Check the solution.

- -

Equations

Remember, solutions of the new equation are also solutions of the original equation.

4. Solve $4 + \dfrac{1}{5}r = -1$. **Check your solution.**

$4 + \dfrac{1}{5}r =\ \ -1$ Write the equation.

$\underline{-4\quad\ \ \ \ = -4}$ Undo the addition first by subtracting 4 from each side.

$\dfrac{1}{5}r =\ -5$

$5 \cdot \dfrac{1}{5}r = 5 \cdot (-5)$ Multiplication Property of Equality

$r = -25$ Simplify.

The solution is -25.   Check the solution.

Got it? **Do these problems to find out.**

Solve each equation. Check your solution.

a. $2x + 4 = 10$ **b.** $3x + 5 = 14$ **c.** $5 = 2 + 3x$

d. $4x + 5 = 13$ **e.** $-5s + 8 = -2$ **f.** $-2 + \dfrac{2}{3}w = 10$

Show your work.

a. _____

b. _____

c. _____

d. _____

e. _____

f. _____

Tutor

5. Toya had her birthday party at the movies. It cost $27 for pizza and $8.50 per friend for the movie tickets. How many friends did Toya have at her party if she spent $78?

Words	Cost of pizza	plus	Cost of 1 friend	times	number of friends	equals	$78.
Variable			Let n represent the number of friends.				
Equation	27	+	8.50	·	n	=	78

Solve Arithmetically

You can use a bar diagram to solve an equation arithmetically.

```
|-------- $78 --------|
| pizza  |   tickets  |
|-$27-|---$8.50n----|
```

Subtract 27 from 78. Then divide by 8.5.

$78 - 27 = 51; 51 ÷ 8.5 = 6$

$$27 + 8.50n = 78 \quad \text{Write the equation.}$$
$$\underline{-27 \qquad\qquad = -27} \quad \text{Subtract 27 from each side.}$$
$$8.50n = 51$$
$$\frac{8.50n}{8.50} = \frac{51}{8.50} \quad \text{Division Property of Equality}$$
$$n = 6 \quad \text{Simplify.}$$

Toya can have 6 friends at her party.

Guided Practice

Check ✓

Solve each equation. Check your solution. (Examples 1–4)

1. $13 = 1 + 4s$

2. $-3y - 5 = 10$

3. $-7 = 1 + \frac{2}{3}n$

Show your work.

4. Syreeta wants to buy some CDs that each cost $14, and a DVD that costs $23. She has $65. Write and solve an equation to find how many CDs she can buy. (Example 5)

Equation: _____

Solution: _____

5. **Building on the Essential Question** When solving an equation, explain why it is important to perform identical operations on each side of the equals sign.

_____

_____

_____

Rate Yourself!

How well do you understand solving two-step equations? Circle the image that applies.

Clear   Somewhat Clear   Not So Clear

For more help, go online to access a Personal Tutor.

Tutor

 Time to update your Foldable!

Independent Practice

Go online for Step-by-Step Solutions eHelp

Solve each equation. Check your solution. (Examples 1–4)

1. $3x + 1 = 10$

 Show your work.

2. $-3 + 8n = -5$

3. $4h - 6 = 22$

4. $-8s + 1 = 33$

5. $-4w - 4 = 8$

6. $5 + \frac{1}{7}b = -2$

7. **PS Reason Abstractly** Cristiano is saving money to buy a bike that costs $189. He has saved $99 so far. He plans on saving $10 each week. In how many weeks will he have enough money to buy the bike? Use a bar diagram to solve arithmetically. Then use an equation to solve algebraically. (Example 5)

 Show your work.

Solve each equation. Check your solution.

8. $2r - 3.1 = 1.7$

9. $4t + 3.5 = 12.5$

10. $8m - 5.5 = 10.1$

11 Temperature is usually measured on the Fahrenheit scale (°F) or the Celsius scale (°C). Use the formula $F = 1.8C + 32$ to convert from one scale to the other.

a. Convert the temperature for Alaska's record low in July to Celsius. Round to the nearest degree.

b. Hawaii's record low temperature is −11°C. Find the difference in degrees Fahrenheit between Hawaii's record low temperature and the record low temperature for Alaska in January.

Alaska Record Low Temperatures (°F) by Month	
January	−80
April	−50
July	16
October	−48

12. **⒫ₛ Model with Mathematics** Refer to the graphic novel frame below. Jamar figured that they will spend $39 for popcorn. Each movie cost $19. Write and solve an equation to find how many movies they can purchase.

_____

_____

 H.O.T. Problems Higher Order Thinking

13. **⒫ₛ Reason Inductively** Refer to Exercise 11. Is there a temperature in the table at which the number of degrees Celsius is the same as the number of degrees Fahrenheit? If so, find it. If not, explain why not.

_____

_____

14. **⒫ₛ Persevere with Problems** Suppose your school is selling magazine subscriptions. Each subscription costs $20. The company pays the school half of the total sales in dollars. The school must also pay a one-time fee of $18. Write and solve an equation to determine the fewest number of subscriptions that can be sold to earn a profit of $200.

_____

15. **⒫ₛ Model with Mathematics** Write a real-world problem that can be represented by the equation $\dfrac{(12 + 14) \times h}{2} = 52$. Then solve the problem.

_____

_____

_____

Inquiry Lab
More Two-Step Equations

 Inquiry HOW are equations in $p(x + q) = r$ form different from $px + q = r$ equations?

Indiana Academic Standards
7.AF.2

PS **Process Standards**
1, 3, 4

Mark has two summer jobs. He babysits and helps with the gardening. He works at each job three days a week and earns a total of $240. The table shows his earnings each day. How much does he earn each day babysitting?

Job	Daily Earnings ($)
Babysitting	x
Gardening	30

What do you know? _____

_____

What do you need to find? _____

_____

Hands-On Activity 1

Step 1 Draw a bar diagram that represents the situation.

$x + $30	$x + $30	$x + $30
--- earnings each day ---	--- earnings each day ---	--- earnings each day ---

Step 2 Write an equation that is modeled by the bar diagram.

$3(\$x + \$30) = $ ☐

From the diagram, you can see that one third of Mark's total earnings is equal to $x + $30. So, $\$x + \$30 = \dfrac{\$240}{3}$ or ☐ .

Mark earns ☐ − $30, or ☐ each day babysitting.

Vijay and his brother bought two hamburgers and two lemonades.
The hamburgers cost $6 each. They spent a total of $16. How much did
each lemonade cost?

Hands-On Activity 2

Tools

Use algebra tiles to model the situation described above.

Step 1 Model $2(x + 6) = 16$ using algebra tiles. Use ☐ groups of $(x + 6)$ tiles.

$$2(x + 6) \quad = \quad 16$$

Step 2 Divide the tiles into ☐ equal groups on each side of the mat.

Remove ☐ group from each side.

$$x + 6 \quad = \quad 8$$

Step 3 Remove the same number of 1-tiles from each side.

$$x \quad = \quad 2$$

So, $x =$ ☐. Each lemonade costs ☐.

Investigate

Collaborate

Work with a partner to model and solve each equation. Use a bar diagram for Exercises 1 and 2. Use algebra tiles for Exercises 3–6.

1. $3(x + 5) = 21$ $x =$ _____

2. $2(x - 3) = 10$ $x =$ _____

3. $4(x + 1) = 8$ $x =$ _____

4. $3(x + 2) = -12$ $x =$ _____

5. $2(x - 1) = 6$ $x =$ _____

6. $3(x - 4) = -3$ $x =$ _____

Analyze and Reflect

Work with a partner to write and solve an equation that represents each problem.

7. Refer to Activity 1. If Mark worked four days a week and made $360, how much did he earn babysitting each day?

_____

8. Refer to Activity 2. If Vijay and his brother spent a total of $15, how much did each lemonade cost?

_____

9. **PS Reason Inductively** After modeling an equation using algebra tiles, Angelina used the steps shown below to solve the equation. Write two different equations in $p(x + q) = r$ form that Angelina could have solved.

Step 1   Divide the tiles into three equal groups on both sides of the mat.

Step 2   Remove two groups from each side.

Step 3   Add four 1-tiles to each side.

Equation 1: _____   Equation 2: _____

Create

On Your Own

10. **PS Model with Mathematics** Write a real-world problem that can be represented by the equation $4(x + 15) = 140$. Then solve the problem.

_____

_____

_____

_____

11. **Inquiry** HOW are equations in $p(x + q) = r$ form different from $px + q = r$ equations?

_____

_____

_____

More Two-Step Equations

Museums A new exhibit about dinosaurs is being constructed. The exhibit is a rectangle that is 36 feet long. It has a perimeter of 114 feet. Follow the steps to write an equation that can be used to find the width of the museum exhibit.

 Essential Question

WHAT does it mean to say two quantities are equal?

J **Indiana Academic Standards**
7.AF.2

PS Process Standards
1, 2, 3, 4

Step 1 Draw a diagram to help visualize the exhibit.

Label the length and width. Let *w* represent the width.

$w = 2|w|$

Step 2 Write an expression that represents the sum of the length and width of the exhibit. $w + 3l$

Step 3 Write an expression that represents twice the sum of the length and width. $2(w + 3l)$

Step 4 Write an equation that represents the perimeter of the exhibit. $2(w + 3l) = 114$

Which PS Process Standards did you use?
Shade the circle(s) that applies.

① Persevere with Problems
② Reason Abstractly
③ Construct an Argument
④ Model with Mathematics

⑤ Use Math Tools
⑥ Attend to Precision
⑦ Make Use of Structure
⑧ Use Repeated Reasoning

Solve Two-Step Equations

An equation like $2(w + 36) = 114$ is in the form $p(x + q) = r$. It contains two factors, p and $(x + q)$, and is considered a two-step equation. Solve these equations using the properties of equality.

Examples

Tutor

1. Solve $3(x + 5) = 45$.

Method 1 Solve arithmetically.

	45	
x + 5	x + 5	x + 5

---- ? ----|

Draw a bar diagram. From the diagram, you can see that $x + 5 = 45 \div 3$ or 15.
So, $x = 15 - 5$ or 10.

a+b = a+ (handwritten)

Method 2 Solve algebraically.

$3(x + 5) = 45$ Write the equation.

$\dfrac{3(x + 5)}{3} = \dfrac{45}{3}$ Division Property of Equality

$x + 5 = 15$ Simplify.

$\underline{-5 = -5}$ Subtraction Property of Equality

$x = 10$ Simplify.

2. Solve $5(n - 2) = -30$.

$5(n - 2) = -30$ Write the equation.

$\dfrac{5(n - 2)}{5} = \dfrac{-30}{5}$ Division Property of Equality

$n - 2 = -6$ Simplify.

$\underline{+2 = +2}$ Addition Property of Equality

$n = -4$ Simplify. Check the solution.

Check Your Work
Remember to plug your solution back into the original equation to see if it makes a true statement.

Show your work.

Got it? Do these problems to find out.

a. $2(x + 4) = 20$ **b.** $3(b - 6) = 12$ **c.** $-7(6 + d) = 49$

(handwritten work)
2 2   3   3   →7 -7
-4 10   +6 4   C-   -7
  -4   +6   -6

a. _____ $x = 6$

b. _____ $b = 10$

c. _____ $d = -13$

Equations with Rational Coefficients

Sometimes the factor p, in $p(x + q)$, will be a fraction or decimal.

Examples

3. Solve $\frac{2}{3}(n + 6) = 10$. **Check your solution.**

$$\frac{2}{3}(n + 6) = 10 \qquad \text{Write the equation.}$$

$$\frac{3}{2} \cdot \frac{2}{3}(n + 6) = \frac{3}{2} \cdot 10 \qquad \text{Multiplication Property of Equality}$$

$$(n + 6) = \frac{3}{2} \cdot \left(\frac{\overset{5}{\cancel{10}}}{1}\right) \qquad \frac{2}{3} \cdot \frac{3}{2} = 1; \text{ write 10 as } \frac{10}{1}.$$

$$n + 6 = 15 \qquad \text{Simplify.}$$

$$\underline{-6 = -6} \qquad \text{Subtraction Property of Equality}$$

$$n = 9 \qquad \text{Simplify.}$$

Check
$$\frac{2}{3}(n + 6) = 10 \qquad \text{Write the original equation.}$$

$$\frac{2}{3}(9 + 6) \overset{?}{=} 10 \qquad \text{Replace } n \text{ with 9. Is this sentence true?}$$

$$10 = 10 \checkmark \qquad \text{The sentence is true.}$$

> **Reciprocals**
> The product of a number and its reciprocal is 1.

4. Solve $0.2(c - 3) = -10$. **Check your solution.**

$$0.2(c - 3) = -10 \qquad \text{Write the equation.}$$

$$\frac{0.2(c - 3)}{0.2} = -\frac{10}{0.2} \qquad \text{Division Property of Equality}$$

$$c - 3 = -50 \qquad \text{Simplify.}$$

$$\underline{+3 = +3} \qquad \text{Addition Property of Equality}$$

$$c = -47 \qquad \text{Simplify.}$$

Check $0.2(c - 3) = -10 \qquad$ Write the original equation.

$$0.2(-47 - 3) \overset{?}{=} -10 \qquad \text{Replace } c \text{ with } -47. \text{ Is this sentence true?}$$

$$-10 = -10 \checkmark \qquad \text{The sentence is true.}$$

Got it? Do these problems to find out.

d. $\frac{1}{4}(d - 3) = -15$

e. $0.75(6 + d) = 12$

f. $(t + 3)\frac{5}{9} = 40$

d. $d = (-57)$

e. $d = 10$

f. $t = 69$

5. Jamal and two cousins received the same amount of money to go to a movie. Each boy spent $15. Afterward, the boys had $30 altogether. Write and solve an equation to find the amount of money each boy received.

Let m represent the amount of money each boy received.

$3(m - 15) = 30$	Write the equation.
$\dfrac{3(m - 15)}{3} = \dfrac{30}{3}$	Division Property of Equality
$m - 15 = 10$	Simplify.
$+15 = +15$	Addition Property of Equality
$m = 25$	Simplify.

So, each boy received $25.

Guided Practice

Check ✓

Solve each equation. Check your solution. (Examples 1–4)

1. $2(p + 7) = 18$ $p = 2$

2. $(4 + g)(-11) = 121$ $g = (-15)$

3. $(v + 5)\left(-\dfrac{1}{9}\right) = 6$ $v = (-59)$

4. $0.8(m - 5) = 10$ $m = 17.5$

5. Mr. Singh had three sheets of stickers. He gave 20 stickers from each sheet to his students and has 12 total stickers left. Write and solve an equation to find how many stickers were originally on each sheet. (Example 5)

Equation: $3(s - 20) = 12$

Solution: $s = 24$

6. **Building on the Essential Question** What is the difference between $px + q = r$ and $p(x + q) = r$?

_____

_____

_____

_____

Independent Practice

Go online for Step-by-Step Solutions

eHelp

Solve each equation. Check your solution. (Examples 1–4)

1. $8(s + 3) = 72$ $s = 6$

$\dfrac{8}{8}$ $\dfrac{8}{8}$

9

2. $-7(z - 6) = -70$ $z = 16$

$\dfrac{}{-7}$ $\dfrac{}{-7}$

10

3. $(t + 8)(-2) = 12$ $t = (-14)$

$\dfrac{}{-2}$ $\dfrac{}{-2}$

-6

4. $\dfrac{8}{11}(n - 10) = 64$ $\dfrac{8}{11}$ 88

$\dfrac{11}{8}$ $\dfrac{}{1}$ $\dfrac{}{1}$

$n = 98$

5. $-0.6(r + 0.2) = 1.8$

$\dfrac{}{-0.6}$ $\dfrac{-0.6}{-3}$

$r = (-3.2)$

6. $\left(w - \dfrac{4}{9}\right)\left(-\dfrac{2}{3}\right) = -\dfrac{4}{5}$

$w = \dfrac{29}{45}$

$-\dfrac{54}{45} + \dfrac{20}{45}$

$-\dfrac{24}{45}$

7. The length of each side of an equilateral triangle is increased by 5 inches, so the perimeter is now 60 inches. Write and solve an equation to find the original length of each side of the equilateral triangle. (Example 5)

Equation: $\dfrac{3(s + 5)}{3} = \dfrac{60}{3}$ Solution: $s = 15$ inches

8. PS **Multiple Representations** Miguel and three of his friends went to the movies. They originally had a total of $40. Each boy had the same amount of money and spent $7.50 on a ticket. How much money did each boy have left after buying his ticket?

a. Model Draw a bar diagram that represents the situation.

$40

| m | 7.50 | 7.50 | 7.50 | 7.50 |

b. Algebra Write and solve an equation that represents the situation.

$4(7.50 + m) = 40$. $m = 2.50.

c. Words Explain how you solved your equation.

Divide each side of the equation by 4 to get $7.50 + m$ alone. $40/4 = 10$. Next subtract 7.50 from each side to get m alone. $10 - 7.50 = 2.50$. $m = 2.50

d. Words Compare the arithmetic solution and the algebraic solution.

They are each the same.

9. Mrs. Sorenstam bought one ruler, one compass, and one mechanical pencil at the prices shown in the table for each of her 12 students.

Item	Price ($)
compass	1.49
mechanical pencil	0.59
ruler	0.49

   a. Suppose Mrs. Sorenstam had 36 cents left after buying the school supplies. Write an equation to find the amount of money Mrs. Sorenstam initially had to spend on each student.

   _____

   b. Describe a two-step process you could use to solve your equation. Then solve the equation.

   _____

   _____

 ## H.O.T. Problems   Higher Order Thinking

10. (PS) **Model with Mathematics** Write a real-world situation that can be represented by the equation $2(n + 20) = 110$.

   _____

   _____

   _____

11. (PS) **Find the Error** Marisol is solving the equation $6(x + 3) = 21$. Find her mistake and correct it.

   _____

   _____

   _____

   _____

$$6(x + 3) = 21$$
$$\underline{-3 = -3}$$
$$6x = 18$$
$$x = 3$$

12. (PS) **Persevere with Problems** Solve $p(x + q) = r$ for x.

   _____

13. (PS) **Use Math Tools** Write an equation to represent the bar diagram at the right. Then write a real-world problem that can be represented by the equation and the diagram.

12		
$x - 8$	$x - 8$	$x - 8$

   _____

   _____

   _____

   _____

Extra Practice

Solve each equation. Check your solution.

14. $0.25(3 + a) = 0.5$

Homework Help

$$0.25(3 + a) = 0.5$$
$$\frac{0.25(3 + a)}{0.25} = \frac{0.5}{0.25}$$
$$3 + a = 2$$
$$a = -1$$

15. $12(x - 20) = -48$

16. $-28 = 7(n + 3)$

17. $(t + 9)20 = 140$

18. $\frac{5}{9}(8 + c) = -20$

19. $(d - 3)\frac{2}{5} = 30$

20. **PS** **Reason Abstractly** Anne bought a necklace for each of her three sisters. She paid $7 for each necklace. Suppose she had $9 left. Write and solve an equation to find how much money Anne had initially to spend on each sister.

Equation: _____

Solution: _____

Solve each equation. Check your solution.

21. $1\frac{3}{5}(t - 6) = -0.4$ _____

22. $\left(x + 5\frac{1}{2}\right)0.75 = \frac{5}{8}$ _____

23. Mr. Gomez bought fruit to make fruit salad. He bought $2\frac{1}{2}$ pounds of apples and spent $4.50 on apples and oranges. Write and solve an equation to determine the number of pounds of oranges Mr. Gomez bought.

_____

Fruit	Price per Pound ($)
apples	1.20
bananas	0.50
grapes	1.50
oranges	1.20

24. A rectangular classroom is 32 feet long and has a perimeter of 120 feet. Label the drawing with the correct values to represent the situation. Let w represent the width of the classroom.

☐ ft

☐ ft $P =$ ☐ ft ☐ ft

Write an expression that represents the sum of the length and width.

☐

☐ ft

Write an expression that represents twice the sum of the length and width.

☐

Write an equation you could use to find the perimeter of the classroom.

☐

What is the width of the classroom?

☐

25. Which of the following are operations that you should use to solve the equation $p(x - q) = r$ for x? Select all that apply.

☐ Subtract q from both sides.

☐ Divide both sides by p.

☐ Multiply both sides by p.

☐ Add q to both sides.

Spiral Review

Solve each equation.

26. $x + 3 = 5$

27. $x - 2 = -6$

28. $4x = 12$

29. $-6x = -24$

30. $\frac{x}{2} = -1$

31. $\frac{x}{-3} = 1$

Write the number or numbers from the set {−3, −2, −1, 0, 1, 2, 3} that make each statement true.

32. $4m = 12$ _____

33. $y - 1 = 1$ _____

34. $v > 0$ _____

35. $r \leq 0$ _____

PS Problem-Solving Investigation
Work Backward

Indiana Academic Standards
7.C.8

PS **Process Standards**
1, 3, 4

Case #1 Yard Work

Mike earned extra money by doing yard work for his neighbor. Then he spent $5.50 at the convenience store and four times that amount at the bookstore. Now he has $7.75 left.

How much money did Mike have before he went to the convenience store and the bookstore?

 Understand *What are the facts?*

You know Mike has $7.75 left. You need to find the amount before his purchases.

 Plan *What is your strategy to solve this problem?*

Start with the end result and work backward.

 Solve *How can you apply the strategy?*

He has $7.75 left.
Undo the four times $5.50 spent at the bookstore. Since $5.50 × 4 is $22, add $7.75 and $22.

	$7.75
	+ $22.00
	$29.75

Undo the $5.50 spent at the convenience store.   + $5.50

Add $5.50 and [   ]. $35.25

So, Mike's starting amount was [   ].

 Check *Does the answer make sense?*

Assume Mike started with $35.25. He spent $5.50 and $22. He had

$35 − $5.50 − $22 or [   ] left. So, $35.25 is correct. ✓

Analyze the Strategy

PS **Construct an Argument** Describe how to solve a problem by working

backward. _____

_____

_____

Case #2 Money

Marisa spent $8 on a movie ticket. Then she spent $5 on popcorn and one half of what was left on a drink. She had $2 left.

How much did she have initially?

1 Understand

Read the problem. What are you being asked to find?

I need to find _____.

Underline key words and values. What information do you know?

I know Marisa has ☐ left and that she spent ☐, ☐, and

_____.

Is there any information that you do *not* need to know?

I do not need to know _____.

2 Plan

Choose a problem-solving strategy.

I will use the _____ strategy.

3 Solve

Use your problem-solving strategy to solve the problem.
Marisa has $2 left.

Undo the half-of-what-was-left   _____
amount. Multiply by 2.

Undo the spent $5. Add $5.   _____

Undo the spent $8. Add $8.   _____

So, Marisa had ☐ initially.

4 Check

Use information from the problem to check your answer.

Marisa's initial amount: _____

Amount after spending $8:   _____

Amount after spending $5:   _____

Amount after spending half of what was left: _____

Work with a small group to solve the following cases.
Show your work on a separate piece of paper.

Collaborate

Case #3 Waterfalls

Angel Falls in Venezuela is 3,212 feet high. It is 29 yards higher than 2.5 times the architectural height of the Empire State Building.

Find the architectural height, in feet, of the Empire State Building.

_____

Case #4 Number Theory

Travis works at a kite factory. He checks all the kites before they are packaged. Travis discovered that of the 28 kites that he inspected, 7 kites did not pass: 4 kites did not have tails, and 3 kites had the wrong colors.

Of the 476 kites Travis examined, how many did not have tails and how many had the wrong colors?

Case #5 Time

Timothy's morning schedule is shown.

At what time does Timothy wake up if he arrives at school at 7:35 A.M.?

Timothy's Schedule	
Activity	**Time**
Wake up	■
Get ready for school $-\frac{3}{4}$ h	■
Walk to school $-\frac{5}{12}$ h	7:35 A.M.

Use any strategy!

Case #6 Money

Antonio has saved $28 to spend at the arcade.

If he has 5 bills, how many of each kind of bill does he have?

_____

Mid-Chapter Check

Vocabulary Check

1. Define *equation*. Give an example of two equivalent equations. (Lesson 1)

_____

_____

2. Fill in the blank with the correct term. (Lesson 2)

A _____ is the numerical factor of a multiplication expression like 3*x*.

Skills Check and Problem Solving

Solve each equation. Check your solution. (Lessons 1–5)

3. $21 + m = 33$

4. $a - 5 = -12$

5. $5f = -75$

6. $15 = \dfrac{b}{15}$

7. $19 = 4p + 5$

8. $3(n - 7) = -30$

9. Cameron has 11 adult Fantail goldfish. This is 7 fewer Fantail goldfish than his friend Julia has. Write and solve a subtraction equation to determine the number of Fantail goldfish *g* that Julia has. (Lesson 1)

Equation: _____   Solution: _____

10. **PS Persevere with Problems** The pentagon shown is a regular pentagon, so each side has the same length. The perimeter of the pentagon is 22.5 centimeters. What is the value of *x*? _____

(x − 1.5) cm

Inquiry Lab
Solve Inequalities

Indiana Academic Standards
7.AF.3

PS Process Standards
1, 2, 3, 4

 Inquiry HOW is an inequality like an equation? How is it different?

Mr. Numkena volunteered to drive Hinto and his friends to the school dance. The car can carry up to 5 people, including the driver. How many friends can ride in the car with Hinto?

What do you know? _____

_____

What do you need to find? _____

_____

Hands-On Activity 1

Tools

The real-world situation described above can be represented by the inequality $x + 2 \leq 5$. Let x represent the friends that can ride with Hinto.

$$x + 2 \leq 5$$

Mr. Numkena, Hinto, and friends

Maximum number of people

You can use a balance to model and solve the inequality $x + 2 \leq 5$.

Step 1 On one side of a balance, place a paper bag and ☐ cubes to model $x + 2$.

Step 2 On the other side of a balance, place ☐ cubes.

Add one cube to the bag at a time. Then complete the table.

Number of Friends, x	$x + 2$	Less than or equal to 5?
1	3	yes
2		
3		
4		

$x + 2 \quad \leq \quad 5$

So, up to ☐ friends can ride with Hinto to the school dance.

An *inequality* is a mathematical sentence that compares quantities. The table shows two examples of inequalities.

Words	Symbols
x is less than two	*x* < 2
x is greater than or equal to four	*x* ≥ 4

To solve an inequality means to find values for the variable that make the sentence true. You can use bar diagrams to solve inequalities.

Hands-On Activity 2

An airline charges for checked luggage that weighs more than 50 pounds. Mia's suitcase currently weighs 35 pounds and she still needs to pack her shoes. Find the maximum amount her shoes can weigh so Mia will not be charged a fee.

Step 1   In the bar diagram, write the maximum weight Mia's luggage can be without a fee. Label the weight of Mia's luggage without her shoes.

Step 2   In the bar diagram, write an *x* beside the bar that represents the weight of Mia's luggage.

The weight of Mia's suitcase plus the weight of her shoes must be less than or equal to the maximum luggage weight.

This can be written as $35 + x \le 50$.

Using the bar diagram, Mia's shoes cannot weigh more than $50 - 35$ or ☐ pounds.

Investigate

Collaborate

Work with a partner to solve the following problems.

PS Reason Inductively For Exercises 1–3, assume the paper bag is weightless. Write the inequality represented by each balance. Then write the different possible numbers of cubes in the paper bag if the sides of each balance remain unlevel.

1.

Show your work.

Inequality: _____

Number of Cubes: _____

2.

Inequality: _____

Number of Cubes: _____

3.

Inequality: _____

Number of Cubes: _____

4. **PS Reason Abstractly** At an amusement park, roller coaster riders are required to be at least 48 inches tall. Last year, Myron was 42 inches tall. Complete the bar diagram to determine the number of inches x Myron needed to grow this year to be able to ride the roller coaster. Then write an inequality to represent the situation.

Myron's Height Last Year

Minimum Height of Roller Coaster Rider

0 5 10 15 20 25 30 35 40 45 50 55

So, Myron needed to grow at least _____ inches.

Inequality: _____

Analyze and Reflect

Work with a partner to circle the correct inequality for each situation. The first one is done for you.

Real-World Situation	Inequalities
Yolanda wants to score at least 84% on the next history test.	$x \le 84$ $\boxed{x \ge 84}$
5. To see a certain movie, you must be at least 13 years old.	$n \le 13$ $n \ge 13$
6. Kai has $4.99 left on a music download gift card. She has a download costing $1.99 in her online shopping cart. How much money does Kai have left to spend?	$x + 1.99 \le 4.99$ $x + 1.99 > 4.99$
7. In some states, teens must be at least 16 years old to obtain a driver's license.	$x < 16$ $x > 16$ $x \le 16$ $x \ge 16$
8. The Walter family budgets a maximum amount of $125 per week for groceries. Mr. Walter already spent $40. How much more can the Walter family spend on groceries?	$x + 40 < 125$ $x + 40 > 125$ $x + 40 \le 125$ $x + 40 \ge 125$
9. Miles pays $30 for a ticket to an amusement park. He cannot spend more than $50. How much more money can Miles spend at the amusement park?	$x + 30 < 50$ $x + 30 > 50$ $x + 30 \le 50$ $x + 30 \ge 50$

On Your Own

Create

10. **PS Model with Mathematics** Write a real-world situation that could be represented by $x + 20 \ge 50$.

11. **Inquiry** HOW is an inequality like an equation? How is it different?

Solve Inequalities by Addition or Subtraction

 Real-World Link

Mail A first class stamp can be used for letters and packages weighing thirteen ounces or less. Fisher is mailing pictures to his grandmother, and only has a first class stamp. His envelope weighs 2 ounces. Follow the steps to determine how much the pictures can weigh so that Fisher can use the stamp.

Step 1 Let x represent the weight of the pictures. Write and solve an equation to find the maximum weight of the pictures.

weight of the envelope		weight of the pictures		maximum weight of the package
☐	**+**	**x**	**=**	☐

Solve for x.

So, the maximum weight of the pictures is ☐ ounces.

Step 2 Replace the equals sign in your equation with the less than or equal to symbol, $\leq$.

$2 + x$ ☐ 13

Refer to Step 2. Name three possible values of x that will result in a true sentence.

 Essential Question

WHAT does it mean to say two quantities are equal?

 Vocabulary

subtraction property of inequality
addition property of inequality
inequality

🔵 **Indiana Academic Standards**
7.AF.3

PS **Process Standards**
1, 2, 3, 4

Which **PS** **Process Standards did you use?**
Shade the circle(s) that applies.

① Persevere with Problems   ⑤ Use Math Tools
② Reason Abstractly   ⑥ Attend to Precision
③ Construct an Argument   ⑦ Make Use of Structure
④ Model with Mathematics   ⑧ Use Repeated Reasoning

Solve Inequalities

Work Zone

Words   You can solve inequalities by using the **Addition Property of Inequalities** and the **Subtraction Property of Inequalities**. When you add or subtract the same number from each side of an inequality, the inequality remains true.

Symbols   For all numbers a, b, and c,

    1. if $a > b$, then $a + c > b + c$ and $a - c > b - c$.

    2. if $a < b$, then $a + c < b + c$ and $a - c < b - c$.

Examples

$$
\begin{array}{r}
2 < 4 \\
+3 \quad +3 \\
\hline
5 < 7
\end{array}
\qquad
\begin{array}{r}
6 > 3 \\
-4 \quad -4 \\
\hline
2 > -1
\end{array}
$$

An **inequality** is a mathematical sentence that compares quantities. Solving an inequality means finding values for the variable that make the inequality true.

The table below gives some examples of the words you might use when describing different inequalities.

	Inequalities			
Words	• is less than • is fewer than	• is greater than • is more than • exceeds	• is less than or equal to • is no more than • is at most	• is greater than or equal to • is no less than • is at least
Symbols	$<$	$>$	$\leq$	$\geq$

Examples

Tutor

1. **Solve $x + 3 > 10$.**

$$
\begin{array}{ll}
x + 3 > 10 & \text{Write the inequality.} \\
\underline{-3 \quad -3} & \text{Subtract 3 from each side.} \\
 x > 7 & \text{Simplify.}
\end{array}
$$

Therefore, the solution is $x > 7$.

You can check this solution by substituting a number greater than 7 into the original inequality. Try using 8.

$$
\begin{array}{lll}
\text{Check} & x + 3 > 10 & \text{Write the inequality.} \\
& 8 + 3 \stackrel{?}{>} 10 & \text{Replace } x \text{ with 8. Is this sentence true?} \\
& 11 > 10 & \text{This is a true statement. } \checkmark
\end{array}
$$

2. Solve $-6 \geq n - 5$.

$-6 \geq n - 5$ Write the inequality.

$\underline{+5 \qquad +5}$ Add 5 to each side.

$-1 \geq n$ Simplify.

The solution is $-1 \geq n$ or $n \leq -1$.

You can check this solution by substituting -1 or a number less than -1 into the original inequality.

Got it? Do these problems to find out.

Show your work.

Solve each inequality.

a. $a - 3 < 8$ **b.** $0.4 + y \geq 7$

a. _____

b. _____

Example

3. Solve $a + \dfrac{1}{2} < 2$. Graph the solution set on a number line.

$a + \dfrac{1}{2} < 2$ Write the inequality.

$\underline{-\dfrac{1}{2} \quad -\dfrac{1}{2}}$ Subtract $\dfrac{1}{2}$ from each side.

$a < 1\dfrac{1}{2}$ Simplify.

The solution is $a < 1\dfrac{1}{2}$.   Check your solution.

Graph the solution.

> Place an open dot at $1\dfrac{1}{2}$. Draw a line and an arrow to the left.

Open and Closed Dots

When graphing inequalities, an open dot is used when the value should not be included in the solution, as with $>$ and $<$ inequalities. A closed dot indicates the value is included in the solution, as with $\leq$ and $\geq$ inequalities.

Got it? Do these problems to find out.

Solve each inequality. Graph the solution set on the number line provided.

c. $h + 4 > 4$ **d.** $x - 6 \leq 4$

c. _____

d. _____

Write Inequalities

Inequalities can be used to represent real-world situations. You will want to first identify a variable to represent the unknown value.

 Example Tutor

4. Dylan has $18 to ride go-karts and play games at the state fair. Suppose the go-karts cost $5.50. Write and solve an inequality to find the most he can spend on games.

	Cost of go-kart	plus	cost of games	must be less than or equal to	total amount.
Words					
Symbols	Let x = the cost of the games.				
Inequality	5.5	+	x	≤	18

$5.5 + x \leq 18$ Write the inequality. (5.50 = 5.5)

$\underline{-5.5 \qquad -5.5}$ Subtract 5.5 from each side.

$x \leq 12.5$ Simplify.

So, the most Dylan can spend on games is $12.50.

 Check ✓

Guided Practice

Solve each inequality. Graph the solution set on a number line. (Examples 1–3)

1. $6 + h \geq 12$ _____

2. $14 + t > 5$ _____

 Show your work.

3. An elevator can hold 2,800 pounds or less. Write and solve an inequality that describes how much more weight the elevator can hold if it is currently holding 2,375 pounds. Interpret the solution. (Example 4)

_____

_____

4. ⓔ **Building on the Essential Question** Explain when you would use addition and when you would use subtraction to solve an inequality. _____

_____

_____

Rate Yourself!

Are you ready to move on?
Shade the section that applies.

YES   ?   NO

For more help, go online to access a Personal Tutor.   Tutor

eHelp
Go online for Step-by-Step Solutions

Independent Practice

Solve each inequality. (Examples 1 and 2)

1. $h - 16 \leq -24$ _____

2. $y + 6 \geq -13$ _____

3 $-3 < n - 8$ _____

 Show your work.

4. $3 \leq m + 1.4$ _____

5. $x + 0.7 > -0.3$ _____

6. $w - 8 \geq 5.6$ _____

Solve each inequality. Graph the solution set on a number line. (Example 3)

7. $m + 5 \geq -1$ _____

⟵————————————⟶

8. $-11 > t + 7$ _____

⟵————————————⟶

PS Reason Abstractly Write an inequality and solve each problem. For Exercises 11 and 12, interpret the solution. (Example 4)

9 Four more than a number is more than 13.

Inequality: _____

Solution: _____

10. The sum of a number and 19 is at least 8.2.

Inequality: _____

Solution: _____

11. The high school soccer team can have no more than 26 players. Write and solve an inequality to determine how many more players can make the team if the coach has already chosen 17 players.

Inequality: _____   Solution: _____

Interpretation: _____

12. Lalo has 1,500 minutes per month on his cell phone plan. How many more minutes can he use if he has already talked for 785 minutes?

Inequality: _____   Solution: _____

Interpretation: _____

13. Refer to the diagram below.

Types of Storms

Depression   Tropical Storm   Hurricane

39   74

Wind Speed of Storm (mph)

a. A hurricane has winds that are at least 74 miles per hour. Suppose a tropical storm has winds that are 42 miles per hour. Write and solve an inequality to find how much the winds must increase before the storm becomes a hurricane.

Inequality: _____   Solution: _____

b. A *major storm* has wind speeds that are at least 110 miles per hour. Write and solve an inequality that describes how much greater these wind speeds are than the slowest hurricane.

Inequality: _____   Solution: _____

 H.O.T. Problems Higher Order Thinking

14. (PS) **Reason Inductively** Compare and contrast the solutions of

$a - 3 = 15$ and $a - 3 \geq 15$. _____

_____

_____

15. (PS) **Model with Mathematics** Write an addition inequality for the solution set graphed below.

16   18   20   22   24

16. (PS) **Persevere with Problems** Solve $x + b > c$ for x.

_____

17. (PS) **Reason Inductively** Does the graph shown at the right show the solution set of the inequality $x + 3 \geq 2$? If not, explain how you

−2   −1   0   1   2

would change the graph to show the actual solution set. _____

_____

_____

Extra Practice

Solve each inequality.

18. $10 < b - 8$ ___$18 < b$___

$$10 < b - 8$$
$$\underline{+8 \qquad +8}$$
$$18 < b$$

19. $1.2 + m \le 5.5$ _____

20. $c - 1\frac{1}{4} > -2\frac{1}{2}$ _____

PS Model with Mathematics Solve each inequality. Graph the solution set on a number line.

21. $-21 < a - 16$ _____

⟵――――――――――――――⟶

22. $t - 6.2 < 4$ _____

⟵――――――――――――――⟶

Write an inequality and solve each problem.

23. Eight less than a number is less than 10.

Inequality: _____

Solution: _____

24. The difference between a number and $21\frac{1}{2}$ is no more than $14\frac{1}{4}$.

Inequality: _____

Solution: _____

25. There were a total of 125 cars at a car dealership. A salesperson sold 68 of the cars in one month. Write and solve an inequality that describes how many more cars, at most, the salesman has left to sell. Interpret the solution.

Inequality: _____

Solution: _____

Interpretation: _____

Copy and Solve Solve each inequality. Graph the solution set on a number line. Show your work on a separate sheet of paper.

26. $n - \frac{1}{5} \le \frac{3}{10}$

27. $6 > x + 3\frac{1}{3}$

28. $c + 1\frac{1}{4} < 5$

29. $9 \le m - 2\frac{1}{5}$

30. $\frac{3}{4} + d > 4\frac{1}{2}$

31. $-\frac{7}{8} \le n + 3\frac{5}{16}$

32. Joaquin can send up to 250 text messages each month. So far this month, he has sent 141 text messages. Let *t* represent the number of text messages Joaquin can send during the rest of the month.

Write an inequality to model the situation

Solve the inequality for *t*.

Graph the solution on the number line.

Interpret the solution to the inequality. Explain your reasoning.

33. Which inequality has the solution set shown in the number line below? Select all that apply.

−5 −4 −3 −2 −1 0 1 2 3 4 5

☐ $x + 4 \leq 7$ ☐ $12 > x + 9$ ☐ $x + 1 \leq 2$ ☐ $-7 \geq x - 10$

Spiral Review

Solve each equation. Then graph each solution on the number line below.

34. $x + 2 = 1$

35. $x - 1 = -5$

36. $2x = 10$

37. $-2x = 4$

38. $\frac{x}{2} = 1$

39. $\frac{x}{-2} = 3$

Solve Inequalities by Multiplication or Division

Real-World Link

Science An astronaut in a space suit weighs about 300 pounds on Earth, but only 50 pounds on the Moon.

weight on Earth   weight on Moon

300 lb   >   50 lb

1. If the astronaut and space suit each weighed half as much, would the inequality still be true?

$$\frac{300}{2} > \frac{50}{2}$$ Divide each side by 2.

$$\boxed{} > \boxed{}$$

Is the inequality still true? (Circle) yes or no.

Yes   No

2. Is the weight of one astronaut greater on Pluto or Earth? Would the weight of 5 astronauts be greater on Pluto or on Earth? Explain by using an inequality.

_____

_____

Location	Weight of Astronaut (lb)
Earth	300
Moon	50
Pluto	67
Jupiter	796

3. Is the weight of one astronaut greater on Jupiter or on Earth? Would the weight of 5 astronauts be greater on Jupiter or on Earth? Explain by using an inequality.

_____

Vocabulary

multiplication property of inequality

division property of inequality

Indiana Academic Standards
7.AF.3

PS Process Standards
1, 2, 3, 4, 7

Which **PS Process Standards** did you use?
Shade the circle(s) that applies.

1. Persevere with Problems
2. Reason Abstractly
3. Construct an Argument
4. Model with Mathematics

5. Use Math Tools
6. Attend to Precision
7. Make Use of Structure
8. Use Repeated Reasoning

Multiplication and Division Properties of Inequality, Positive Number

Words The **Multiplication Property of Inequality** and the **Division Property of Inequality** state that an inequality remains true when you multiply or divide each side of an inequality by a positive number.

Symbols For all numbers a, b, and c, where $c > 0$,

1. if $a > b$, then $ac > bc$ and $\frac{a}{c} > \frac{b}{c}$.
2. if $a < b$, then $ac < bc$ and $\frac{a}{c} < \frac{b}{c}$.

These properties are also true for $a \geq b$ and $a \leq b$.

Work Zone

STOP and Reflect

What does the inequality $c > 0$ mean? Explain below.

You can solve inequalities by using the Multiplication Property of Inequality and the Division Property of Inequality.

Examples

1. Solve $8x \leq 40$.

$8x \leq 40$ Write the inequality.

$\frac{8x}{8} \leq \frac{40}{8}$ Divide each side by 8.

$x \leq 5$ Simplify.

The solution is $x \leq 5$. You can check this solution by substituting 5 or a number less than 5 into the inequality.

2. Solve $\frac{d}{2} > 7$.

$\frac{d}{2} > 7$ Write the inequality.

$2\left(\frac{d}{2}\right) > 2(7)$ Multiply each side by 2.

$d > 14$ Simplify.

The solution is $d > 14$. You can check this solution by substituting a number greater than 14 into the inequality.

Got it? Do these problems to find out.

a. $4x < 40$

b. $6 \geq \frac{x}{7}$

a. _____

b. _____

Show your work.

Multiplication and Division Properties of Inequality, Negative Number

Words When you multiply or divide each side of an inequality by a negative number, the inequality symbol must be reversed for the inequality to remain true.

Symbols For all numbers a, b, and c, where $c < 0$,

1. if $a > b$, then $ac < bc$ and $\frac{a}{c} < \frac{b}{c}$.

2. if $a < b$, then $ac > bc$ and $\frac{a}{c} > \frac{b}{c}$.

Examples

$7 > 1$

$-2(7) < -2(1)$ Reverse the symbols.

$-14 < -2$

$-4 < 16$

$\frac{-4}{-4} > \frac{16}{-4}$

$1 > -4$

These properties are also true for $a \geq b$ and $a \leq b$.

> **STOP and Reflect**
>
> What does the inequality $c < 0$ mean? Expain below.

Examples

Tutor

3. Solve $-2g < 10$. Graph the solution set on a number line.

$-2g < 10$ Write the inequality.

$\dfrac{-2g}{-2} > \dfrac{10}{-2}$ Divide each side by -2 and reverse the symbol.

$g > -5$ Simplify.

4. Solve $\dfrac{x}{-3} \leq 4$. Graph the solution set on a number line.

$\dfrac{x}{-3} \leq 4$ Write the inequality.

$-3\left(\dfrac{x}{-3}\right) \geq -3(4)$ Multiply each side by -3 and reverse the symbol.

$x \geq -12$ Simplify.

Got it? Do these problems to find out.

c. $\dfrac{k}{-2} < 9$

c. _____

Example

Tutor

5. Ling earns $8 per hour working at the zoo. Write and solve an inequality that can be used to find how many hours she must work in a week to earn at least $120. Interpret the solution.

Words	Amount earned times per hour	number of hours	is at least	amount earned each week.
Variable	Let x represent the number of hours.			
Inequality	8 •	x	$\geq$	120

$8x \geq 120$ Write the inequality.

$\dfrac{8x}{8} \geq \dfrac{120}{8}$ Divide each side by 8.

$x \geq 15$ Simplify.

So, Ling must work at least 15 hours.

Guided Practice

Check ✓

Solve each inequality. Graph the solution set on a number line. (Examples 1–4)

1. $-3n \leq -22$ _____

2. $\dfrac{t}{-4} < -11$ _____

3. At a baseball game you can get a single hot dog for $2. You have $10 to spend. Write and solve an inequality to find the number of hot dogs you can buy. Interpret the

solution. (Example 5) _____

_____

Rate Yourself!

How confident are you about solving multiplication and division inequalities? Check the box that applies.

4. **Building on the Essential Question** Explain when you should reverse the inequality symbol when solving

an inequality. _____

_____

_____

☹   😐   😊

☐ ☐ ☐ ☐ ☐

For more help, go online to access a Personal Tutor.

Tutor

Independent Practice

Go online for Step-by-Step Solutions

Solve each inequality. (Examples 1 and 2)

1. $6y < 18$ _____

2. $-3s \geq 33$ _____

3. $60 \leq \dfrac{m}{3}$ _____

4. $\dfrac{t}{-2} < 6$ _____

5. $\dfrac{m}{-14} \leq -4$ _____

6. $-56 \leq -8x$ _____

7. $12n \leq 54$ _____

8. $\dfrac{h}{9} > \dfrac{1}{4}$ _____

9. $\dfrac{w}{-5} \geq 9$ _____

Solve each inequality. Graph the solution set on a number line. (Examples 3 and 4)

10. $4x \geq 36$ _____

11. $20 < 5t$ _____

12. $\dfrac{s}{-6} > -16$ _____

13. $\dfrac{x}{-4} \geq 8$ _____

14. A pool charges $4 each visit, or you can buy a membership. Write and solve an inequality to find how many times a person should use the pool so that a membership is less expensive than paying each time. Interpret the solution. (Example 5)

Inequality: _____ Solution: _____

Interpretation: _____

_____

15. **PS** **Reason Inductively** Cross out the inequality that does not belong in the organizer shown at the right. Then explain your reasoning.

_____

_____

_____

$-2x > 12$ $\quad$ $-2 < x + 4$

$\frac{x}{2} < -3$ $\quad$ $-7 > x - 1$

Write an inequality for each sentence. Then solve the inequality.

16. Sixteen is less than eight times a number.

Inequality: _____

Solution: _____

17. The product of a number and five is at the most 30.

Inequality: _____

Solution: _____

H.O.T. Problems Higher Order Thinking

18. **PS** **Identify Structure** Write two different inequalities that have the solution $y > 6$. One inequality should be solved using multiplication properties, and the other should be solved using division properties.

_____

19. **PS** **Persevere with Problems** You score 15, 16, 17, 14, and 19 points out of 20 possible points on five tests. What must you score on the sixth test to have an average of at least 16 points?

_____

20. **PS** **Reason Inductively** The inequalities $3x > 2$ and $9x > 6$ are equivalent inequalities. Write another inequality that is equivalent to $3x > 2$ and $9x > 6$.

_____

21. **PS** **Persevere with Problems** Consider the inequalities $b \geq 4$ and $b \leq 13$.

a. Graph each inequality on the number line.

b. Do the solution sets of the two inequalities overlap? If so, what does this overlapping area represent?

_____

c. A compound inequality is an inequality that combines two inequalities. Write a compound inequality for the situation.

_____

d. Look back at the graph of the solutions for both inequalities. Make another graph that shows only the solution of the compound inequality.

Extra Practice

Solve each inequality.

22. $-10n > -20$ $n < 2$

$$-10n > -20$$

 $$\frac{-10n}{-10} < \frac{-20}{-10}$$

$$n < 2$$

23. $-7y < 35$ _____

24. $15 < 3r$ _____

25. $12p \geq -72$ _____

26. $\dfrac{t}{-7} > 10$ _____

27. $-8 < \dfrac{y}{5}$ _____

Solve each inequality. Graph the solution set on a number line.

28. $\dfrac{h}{5} \leq -12$ _____

29. $-3w < -39$ _____

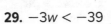

30. $15 < 4x$ _____

31. $10 \leq \dfrac{t}{-2}$ _____

32. (PS) **Reason Abstractly** Each game at a carnival costs $0.50, or you can pay $15 and play an unlimited amount of games. Write and solve an inequality to find how many times you should play a game so that the unlimited game play is less expensive than paying each time. Interpret the solution.

Inequality: _____   Solution: _____

Interpretation: _____

Write an inequality for each sentence. Then solve the inequality.

33. The product of a number and 4 is at least −12.

Inequality: _____

Solution: _____

34. Five times a number is less than −45.

Inequality: _____

Solution: _____

35. Caitlin earns $7 per hour babysitting. She wants to earn at least $105 for a camping trip. Determine if each statement is true or false.

a. The inequality $\frac{h}{7} \geq 105$ models how many hours Caitlin must babysit to earn at least $105.　　☐ True　☐ False

b. The inequality $7h \geq 105$ models how many hours Caitlin must babysit to earn at least $105.　　☐ True　☐ False

c. Caitlin must babysit up to 15 hours in order to earn at least $105.　　☐ True　☐ False

36. Soccer balls cost $24 each at Sports Emporium. Coach Neville can spend at most $120 on equipment for the soccer team. Let b represent the number of soccer balls Coach Neville can buy.

Write an inequality to model the situation. ⬚

Solve the inequality for b. ⬚

Graph the solution on the number line.

How many soccer balls can Coach Neville buy? List all of the possible answers.

⬚

Spiral Review

Solve each equation. Check your solution.

37. $5k + 6 = 16$

38. $-14 = 2x - 8$

39. $-4n + 3 = 13$

40. $25 = 7m + 4$

41. $10.5 + h = 22.5$

42. $14n - 32 = 22$

Solve Two-Step Inequalities

 Real-World Link

Newspapers Kaitlyn is placing an ad in the local newspaper for a pottery class. The cost of placing an ad is shown in the table.

Service	Cost ($)
10-day ad with 3 lines	38.00
each additional line	9.00

1. Complete the equation to find the total cost c of an ad with 4 or more lines. Use x as the variable.

cost of a 10-day add with only 3 lines	cost of each additional line	total cost

$$\boxed{} \quad + \quad \boxed{}\,x \quad = \quad \boxed{}$$

2. How much will it cost to place the ad if it is 5 lines long?

_____

3. Suppose Kaitlyn can spend only $50 on the ad. Does she have enough money to place the ad? Circle yes or no.

       yes   no

If the answer is no, how much more money will Kaitlyn

need? Explain. _____

_____

Essential Question

WHAT does it mean to say two quantities are equal?

Vocabulary

two-step inequality

Indiana Academic Standards
7.AF.3

PS Process Standards
1, 2, 3, 4, 5

Which PS Process Standards did you use?
Shade the circle(s) that applies.

① Persevere with Problems
② Reason Abstractly
③ Construct an Argument
④ Model with Mathematics

⑤ Use Math Tools
⑥ Attend to Precision
⑦ Make Use of Structure
⑧ Use Repeated Reasoning

Solve a Two-Step Inequality

A **two-step inequality** is an inequality that contains two operations. To solve a two-step inequality, use inverse operations to undo each operation in reverse order of the order of operations.

Examples

Tutor

1. Solve $3x + 4 \geq 16$. Graph the solution set on a number line.

$3x + 4 \geq 16$	Write the inequality.
$\underline{\;\;\; -4 \quad -4 \;\;\;}$	Subtract 4 from each side
$3x \quad\;\; \geq 12$	Simplify.
$\dfrac{3x}{3} \geq \dfrac{12}{3}$	Divide each side by 3.
$x \geq 4$	Simplify.

Graph the solution set.

Draw a closed dot at 4 with an arrow to the right.

2. Solve $5 + 4x < 33$. Graph the solution set on a number line.

$5 + 4x < 33$	Write the inequality.
$\underline{-5 \qquad\quad -5}$	Subtract 5 from each side.
$4x < 28$	Simplify.
$\dfrac{4x}{4} < \dfrac{28}{4}$	Divide each side by 4.
$x < 7$	Simplify.

Graph the solution set.

Draw an open dot at 7 with an arrow to the left.

Show your work.

Got it? Do this problem to find out.

a. _____

a. Solve $2x + 8 > 24$. Graph the solution on the number line provided.

Examples

3. Solve $7 - 2x > 11$. Graph the solution set on a number line.

$7 - 2x > 11$	Write the inequality.
$\underline{-7 \qquad -7}$	Subtract 7 from each side.
$-2x > 4$	Simplify.
$\dfrac{-2x}{-2} < \dfrac{4}{-2}$	Divide each side by −2. Reverse inequality symbol.
$x < -2$	Simplify. Check your solution.

Graph the solution set.

Draw an open dot at −2 with an arrow to the left.

You can check the solution by substituting a number less than −2 into the original inequality. Try using −3.

Check	$7 - 2x > 11$	Write the inequality.
	$7 - 2(-3) \overset{?}{>} 11$	Replace x with −3. Is the sentence true?
	$13 > 11$	This is a true statement. ✔

> **Solving Inequalities**
> Remember that if multiplying or dividing by a negative number when solving inequalities, reverse the direction of the inequality symbol.

4. Solve $\dfrac{x}{2} - 5 < -8$. Graph the solution set on a number line.

$\dfrac{x}{2} - 5 < -8$	Write the inequality.
$\underline{+5 \quad +5}$	Add 5 to each side.
$\dfrac{x}{2} < -3$	Simplify.
$\dfrac{x}{2}(2) < -3(2)$	Multiply each side by 2.
$x < -6$	Simplify. Check your solution.

Graph the solution set.

Draw an open dot at −6 with an arrow to the left.

Got it? Do these problems to find out.

Solve each inequality. Graph the solution set on the number line provided.

b. $\dfrac{x}{2} + 9 \geq 5$

b. _____

c. $8 - \dfrac{x}{3} \leq 7$

c. _____

show your work.

5. Halfway through the bowling league season, Stewart has 34 strikes. He averages 2 strikes per game. Write and solve an inequality to find how many more games it will take for Stewart to have at least 61 strikes, the league record. Interpret the solution.

The number of strikes plus two strikes per game is at least 61. Let g represent the number of games he needs to bowl.

$$34 + 2g \geq 61 \qquad \text{Write the inequality.}$$
$$\underline{-34 \qquad\quad -34} \qquad \text{Subtract 34 from each side.}$$
$$2g \geq 27 \qquad \text{Simplify.}$$
$$\frac{2g}{2} \geq \frac{27}{2} \qquad \text{Divide each side by 2.}$$
$$g \geq 13.5 \qquad \text{Simplify.}$$

Stewart should have at least 61 strikes after 14 more games.

Guided Practice

Solve each inequality. Graph the solution set on a number line. (Examples 1–4)

1. $5x - 7 \geq 43 =$ _____

<!-- number line -->

2. $11 \leq 7 + \dfrac{x}{5}$ _____

<!-- number line -->

3. **Financial Literacy** A rental car company charges $45 plus $0.20 per mile to rent a car. Mr. Lawrence does not want to spend more than $100 for his rental car. Write and solve an inequality to find how many miles he can drive and not spend more than $100. Interpret the solution. (Example 5)

_____

_____

4. **Building on the Essential Question** Compare $2x + 8 > 18$ and $2x + 8 \leq 18$.

_____

_____

_____

_____

Rate Yourself!

How well do you understand solving two-step inequalities? Circle the image that applies.

Clear   Somewhat   Not So
                Clear   Clear

For more help, go online to access a Personal Tutor.

Independent Practice

Go online for Step-by-Step Solutions

Solve each inequality. Graph the solution set on a number line. (Examples 1–4)

1. $6x + 14 \geq 20$ _____

 Show your work.

←———————————————→

2. $4x - 13 < 11$ _____

←———————————————→

3. $-20 > -2x + 4$ _____

←———————————————→

4. $\frac{x}{13} + 3 \geq 4$ _____

←———————————————→

5. Tyler needs at least $205 for a new video game system. He has already saved $30. He earns $7 an hour at his job. Write and solve an inequality to find how many hours he will need to work to buy the system. Interpret the solution. (Example 5)

Inequality: _____

Solution: _____

Interpretation: _____

PS Reason Abstractly Write and solve an inequality for each sentence.

6. Three times a number increased by four is less than −62.

_____

7. The quotient of a number and −5 increased by one is at most 7.

_____

8. The quotient of a number and 3 minus two is at least −12.

_____

9. The product of −2 and a number minus six is greater than −18.

_____

Write a two-step inequality that could be represented by each number line.

10.

11.

12.

13.

 H.O.T. Problems Higher Order Thinking

14. (PS) **Model with Mathematics** Write a real-world example that could be solved by using the inequality $4x + 8 \geq 32$. Then solve the inequality.

15. (PS) **Persevere with Problems** In five games, you score 16, 12, 15, 13, and 17 points. Write and solve an inequality to determine how many points you must score in the sixth game to have an average of at least 15 points.

16. (PS) **Use Math Tools** Solve $-x + 6 > -(2x + 4)$. Then graph the solution set on the number line.

Solution: _____

17. (PS) **Model with Mathematics** Write and solve a real-world problem that can be represented by the inequality $4(x - 2.8) \leq 45$.

Extra Practice

Solve each inequality. Graph the solution set on a number line.

18. $4x - 15 \leq 5$ $\underline{x \leq 5}$

$$4x - 15 \leq 5$$
$$\underline{+\ 15 + 15}$$
$$4x \leq 20$$
$$x \leq 5$$

Homework Help ➡

19. $-73 \geq 15 + 11x$ _____

20. $\frac{x}{5} - 2 > 1$ _____

21. $9 \leq \frac{x}{14} + 6$ _____

22. Catie is starting a babysitting business. She spent $26 to make signs to advertise. She charges an initial fee of $5 and then $3 for each hour of service. Write and solve an inequality to find the number of hours she will have to babysit to make a profit. Interpret the solution.

Inequality: _____   Solution: _____

Interpretation: _____

23. **PS** **Reason Abstractly** As a salesperson, Audrey earns $75 per week plus $5 per sale. This week, she wants her pay to be at least $125. Write and solve an inequality for the number of sales Audrey needs to make. Interpret the solution.

Inequality: _____   Solution: _____

Interpretation: _____

24. Elijah and his sister went to the movies. They had $34 altogether and spent $9.50 per ticket. Elijah and his sister bought the same snacks. Write and solve an inequality for the amount that each person spent on snacks. Interpret the solution.

Inequality: _____   Solution: _____

Interpretation: _____

25. Which of the following are operations that you should use to solve $-2x - 5 < 7$ for x? Select all that apply.

☐ Subtract 7 from both sides.　　　　☐ Add 5 to both sides.

☐ Divide both sides by -2.　　　　☐ Reverse the inequality symbol.

26. The table shows the cost of renting a jet ski.

Rental Period	Cost ($)
First hour	$55
Each additional 15-minutes	$10

Jeremy can spend no more than $105 on a jet ski rental. Let x represent the number of additional 15-minute increments. Fill in each box to write an inequality to represent the situation.

☐☐☐☐ + ☐☐☐☐ ≤ ☐☐☐☐

$10x$	10
$55x$	55
$105x$	105
<	≤
>	≥

What is the greatest length of time Jeremy can rent the jet ski?

☐☐☐☐☐☐☐☐☐

Spiral Review

Solve and graph each inequality.

27. $n + 1 > -2$

⟵————————————⟶

Solution: _____

28. $-2y > 12$

⟵————————————⟶

Solution: _____

29. $\dfrac{t}{-1} > -2$

⟵————————————⟶

Solution: _____

Solve each equation. Check your solution.

30. $5y + 6 = 46$ _____　　**31.** $-4k - 1 = 47$ _____　　**32.** $5 = 8m + 1$ _____

33. Michael's dad is 30 years of age. He is 2 years more than four times Michael's age m. Write and solve a two-step equation to determine Michael's age.

Equation: _____　　Solution: _____

21ST CENTURY CAREER
in Veterinary Medicine

Veterinary Technician

If you love being around animals, enjoy working with your hands, and are good at analyzing problems, a challenging career in veterinary medicine might be a perfect fit for you. Veterinary technicians help veterinarians by helping to diagnose and treat medical conditions. They may work in private clinics, animal hospitals, zoos, aquariums, or wildlife rehabilitation centers.

College & Career
READINESS

Is This the Career for You?

Are you interested in a career as a veterinary technician? Take some of the following courses in high school.

◆ Algebra
◆ Animal Science
◆ Biology
◆ Chemistry
◆ Veterinary Assisting

Find out how math relates to a career in Veterinary Medicine.

PS Vet Techs Don't Monkey Around

**For each problem, use the information in the tables to write an equation.
Then solve the equation.**

1. The minimum tail length of an emperor tamarin is 1.6 inches greater than that of a golden lion tamarin. What is the minimum tail length of a golden lion tamarin?

_____

2. The minimum body length of a golden lion tamarin is 5.3 inches less than the maximum body length. What is the maximum body length? _____

3. Tamarins live an average of 15 years. This is 13 years less than the years that one tamarin in captivity lived. How long did the tamarin in captivity live? _____

4. The maximum weight of a golden lion tamarin is about 1.97 times the maximum weight of an emperor tamarin. What is the maximum weight of an emperor tamarin? Round to the nearest tenth.

_____

5. For an emperor tamarin, the maximum total length, including the body and tail, is 27 inches. What is the maximum body length of an emperor tamarin?

_____

Emperor Tamarin Monkeys		
Measure	Minimum	Maximum
Body length	9.2 in.	b
Tail length	14 in.	16.6 in.
Weight	10.7 oz	w

Golden Lion Tamarin Monkeys		
Measure	Minimum	Maximum
Body length	7.9 in.	ℓ
Tail length	t	15.7 in.
Weight	12.7 oz	28 oz

PS Career Project

It's time to update your career portfolio! Go to the Occupational Outlook Handbook online and research a career as a veterinary technician. Include brief descriptions of the work environment, education and training requirements, and the job outlook.

_____

_____

_____

_____

_____

Do you think you would enjoy a career as a veterinary technician? Why or why not?

- _____
- _____
- _____
- _____
- _____

Chapter Review

Vocabulary Check

Unscramble each of the clue words.

TOW-SETP

☐ ☐ ☐ — ☐ ☐ ☐ ☐
7

PYORERPT

☐ ☐ ☐ ☐ ☐ ☐ ☐
            8

DODTIINA

☐ ☐ ☐ ☐ ☐ ☐ ☐
   6

NIIOSDIV

☐ ☐ ☐ ☐ ☐ ☐ ☐

LABVIERA

☐ ☐ ☐ ☐ ☐ ☐ ☐
     5

AILEYQUITN

☐ ☐ ☐ ☐ ☐ ☐ ☐ ☐ ☐
 2

BISTAUTORNC

☐ ☐ ☐ ☐ ☐ ☐ ☐ ☐ ☐ ☐
 3

NUATIEQO

☐ ☐ ☐ ☐ ☐ ☐ ☐
1

TIULINTICPOLMA

☐ ☐ ☐ ☐ ☐ ☐ ☐ ☐ ☐ ☐ ☐ ☐
      4

Use the numbered letters to find another vocabulary term from this chapter.

☐ ☐ ☐ ☐ ☐ ☐ ☐ ☐
1 2 3 4 5 6 7 8

Use your Foldable to help review the chapter.

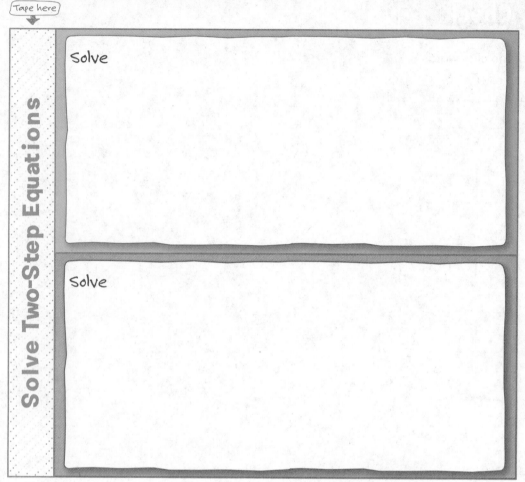

Tape here

Solve Two-Step Equations

Solve

Solve

Got it?

Match each phrase with the correct term.

1. the value of a variable that makes an equation true

2. the numerical factor in a multiplication expression

3. equations that have the same solution

4. a sentence stating that two quantities are equal

a. equivalent equations

b. equation

c. Addition Property of Equality

d. coefficient

e. formula

f. solution

Power Up! Performance Task

Fall Reading

Gordon's English teacher assigned a book to be read by October 31st. The students may select a book from the table, and Gordon chose *City Streets*.

Book	Number of Pages
City Streets	387
Life and Time	411
Myopia	435

Write your answers on another piece of paper. Show all of your work to receive full credit.

Part A

By October 19th, Gordon had read 35 pages. Starting on October 20th, he decides to read the same number of pages each day until he finishes the book on October 30th. Write and solve an equation to represent the situation. Let p represent the number of pages read per day. How many pages does Gordon read per day?

Part B

Gordon's friend, Kendrick, selected *Myopia*. He read eight pages in class on October 19th and begins reading again on October 23rd. He needs to read at least 350 pages by the end of the day on October 28th. Write and solve an inequality to represent this situation and graph the solution on a number line. Let p represent the number of pages read per day. How many pages must Kendrick read per day to accomplish his goal?

Reflect

 Answering the Essential Question

Use what you learned about equations and inequalities to complete the graphic organizer.

When do you use an equals sign?

Essential Question

WHAT does it mean to say two quantities are equal?

When do you use an inequality symbol?

Answer the Essential Question. WHAT does it mean to say two quantities are equal?

UNIT PROJECT

Stand Up and Be Counted The U.S. Census is used to determine the number of U.S. House of Representative members that each state is assigned. In this project you will:

- **Collaborate** with your classmates as you research Census data and the U.S. House of Representatives.
- **Share** the results of your research in a creative way.
- **Reflect** on how you can communicate mathematical ideas effectively.

Collaborate

Go Online Work with your group to research and complete each activity. You will use your results in the Share section on the following page.

1. Explore the official U.S. Census web site to find the 2010 state populations. There will be interactive maps that display this information. Write down a few facts you find interesting.

2. Create a table that displays the population and the number of U.S. Representatives for your state and three other states. Then create a line plot for the number of U.S. Representatives.

3. Write an equation that uses any state's population x and its number of U.S. Representative members y to describes the number of people per U.S. Representative z.

4. Use your equation from Exercise 3 to determine the approximate number of people per U.S. Representative for the four states you chose. Interpret the results.

5. Look at the 2000 and 2010 census. How did the population of your state and states in your region change? Did the population change affect the number of U.S. Representatives assigned?

6. States can be categorized by population size and density. Write at least two inequalities that compare the states using these categories.

With your group, decide on a way to share what you have learned about the U.S. House of Representatives and state populations. Some suggestions are listed below, but you can also think of other creative ways to present your information. Remember to show how you used mathematics to complete each of the activities in this project!

- Act as a Census representative and create a presentation to encourage people to participate in the census and explain why it is important.
- Write a letter or email to your Representative about what you learned in this project and how it can be used to improve your community.

Check out the note on the right to connect this project with other subjects.

connect with **Social Studies**

Civic Literacy Research the Electoral College. Some questions to consider are:

- Why was it established?
- What is the relationship between the United States House of Representatives and the Electoral College?

 Reflect

On Your Own

7. ℯ **Answer the Essential Question** How can you communicate mathematical ideas effectively?

a. How did you use what you learned about expressions to help you communicate mathematical ideas effectively in this project?

_____

_____

_____

b. How did you use what you learned about equations and inequalities to help you communicate mathematical ideas effectively in this project?

_____

_____

_____

UNIT 4
Geometry

Essential Question

HOW can you use different measurements to solve real-life problems?

Chapter 7
Geometric Figures

Geometric shapes can be drawn freehand, with a ruler and protractor, or using technology. In this chapter, you will draw two- and three-dimensional figures. You will also solve problems involving scale drawings of geometric figures.

Chapter 8
Measure Figures

Real-life problems involving area, surface area, and volume can be solved by using formulas. In this chapter, you will use formulas to find the area and circumference of a circle and to find the surface area and volume of prisms and pyramids.

Unit Project Preview

Turn Over a New Leaf Leaves serve an important purpose for plants and trees, and there are scientific reasons why they are flat.

Make a sketch of a leaf. Estimate the area of the leaf in square units.

At the end of Chapter 8, you'll complete a project to investigate the relationship between the volume and surface area of a leaf. So, put on your hiking shoes, and don't forget to bring along your measuring tools. You're about to go on a nature hike!

Chapter 7
Geometric Figures

Indiana Academic Standards
7.GM.1, 7.GM.2, 7.GM.3, 7.GM.4
PS Process Standards
1, 2, 3, 4, 5, 6, 7, 8

Essential Question

HOW does geometry help us describe real-world objects?

Math in the Real World

Robots that could be programmed and digitally operated were invented by George Devol in 1954.

The actual length of the robot's arm is 15 inches. A drawing of the robot is $\frac{1}{5}$ the size of the actual robot. Fill in the blank below with the correct measurement for the robot's arm.

Study Organizer

Cut out the Foldable on page FL7 of this book.

Place your Foldable on page 604.

Use the Foldable throughout this chapter to help you learn about geometric figures.

Vocabulary

acute angle	diagonal	right triangle
acute triangle	edge	scale
adjacent angles	equilateral triangle	scale drawing
base	face	scale factor
complementary angles	isosceles triangle	scale model
cone	obtuse angle	scalene triangle
congruent	obtuse triangle	skew line
congruent segments	plane	straight angle
coplanar	polyhedron	supplementary angles
cross section	prism	triangle
cylinder	pyramid	vertex
	right angle	vertical angles

Study Skill: Reading Math

The Language of Mathematics Many of the words you use in math and science are also used in everyday language, such as the leg of a person and the leg of a right triangle.

Usage	Example
Some words are used in science and in mathematics, but the meanings are different.	$x + 4 = -2$ $x = -6$ solution
Some words are used only in mathematics.	hypotenuse

Explain how the everyday meaning of *face* is different than its mathematical meaning.

Everyday meaning: _____

_____

Mathematical meaning: _____

Read each statement. Decide whether you agree (A) or disagree (D). Place a checkmark in the appropriate column and then justify your reasoning.

Geometric Figures			
Statement	A	D	Why?
The common endpoint shared by the two sides of an angle is called the origin.			
A pair of adjacent supplementary angles forms a right angle.			
The sum of the measures of the angles in any triangle is 180°.			
A scale drawing/model represents an object that is too large or too small to be drawn at actual size.			
An isosceles triangle has three congruent sides.			
A cylinder has two parallel congruent circular bases.			

When Will You Use This?

Here are a few examples of how scale drawings are used in the real world.

Activity 1 Use the Internet to find a map of the area where you live. Find the map distance, in inches, between your school and your home. Describe a method you could use to find the actual distance once you know the map distance.

Raul, Caitlyn, and Jamar in

Campfire Song

Activity 2 Go online at **connectED.mcgraw-hill.com** to read the graphic novel *Campfire Song*. On the map, how many units long is the line connecting the cabin to the lake?

Are You Ready?

Try the Quick Check below.
Or, take the Online Readiness Quiz.

Quick Review

Example 1

Use a protractor to measure angle *ABC*.

Align the center of the protractor with the vertex of the angle.

Make sure one ray of the angle passes through zero on the protractor.

Read the measure on the protractor where the other ray crosses the protractor.

The angle measures 65°.

Example 2

Find the area of the triangle.

9 ft

8 ft

$A = \frac{1}{2}bh$ — Area of a triangle

$A = \frac{1}{2}(8 \cdot 9)$ — Replace *b* with 8 and *h* with 9.

$A = 36$ — Simplify.

The area of the triangle is 36 square feet.

Quick Check

Angle Measures Use a protractor to measure each angle.

1.

Show your work.

2.

3.

Area Find the area of each triangle.

4.

4 cm

5 cm

5. base: 3.2 yd
   height: 4.2 yd

How Did You Do?

Which problems did you answer correctly in the Quick Check?
Shade those exercise numbers below.

1 2 3 4 5

Classify Angles

Vocabulary Start-Up

An angle is formed by two rays that share a common endpoint. The **vertex** is the point where the two rays meet.

Complete the table by drawing the hands of a clock to represent each angle.

Type of Angle			
Right	**Acute**	**Obtuse**	**Straight**
exactly 90°	*less than 90°*	*greater than 90°*	*exactly 180°*
clock	clock	clock	clock

🌎 Real-World Link

The angle formed by a bike ramp is shown.

1. What type of angle is formed?

_____

2. Estimate the measure of the angle.

_____

> **Which PS Process Standards did you use?**
> **Shade the circle(s) that applies.**
>
> ① Persevere with Problems   ⑤ Use Math Tools
> ② Reason Abstractly   ⑥ Attend to Precision
> ③ Construct an Argument   ⑦ Make Use of Structure
> ④ Model with Mathematics   ⑧ Use Repeated Reasoning

❓ Essential Question

HOW does geometry help us describe real-world objects?

Vocabulary

vertex
right angle
acute angle
obtuse angle
straight angle
vertical angles
congruent
adjacent angles

Math Symbols
∠
≅

🔵 **Indiana Academic Standards**
7.GM.4

PS Process Standards
1, 3, 4, 7

Key Concept — Name and Identify Angles

Work Zone

Words	Models	Symbols
Two angles are **vertical** if they are opposite angles formed by the intersection of two lines. Vertical angles are **congruent** or have the same measure.	∠1 and ∠3, ∠2 and ∠4	∠1 ≅ ∠3 ∠2 ≅ ∠4
Two angles are **adjacent** if they share a common vertex, a common side, and do not overlap.		Adjacent angle pairs are ∠1 and ∠2, ∠2 and ∠3, ∠3 and ∠4, and ∠4 and ∠1.

You can name an angle by its vertex and by its points.

Example

1. **Name the angle shown at the right. Then classify it as *acute, right, obtuse,* or *straight*.**

- Use the vertex as the middle letter and a point from each side, ∠XYZ or ∠ZYX.
- Use the vertex only, ∠Y.
- Use a number, ∠1.

Since the angle is less than 90°, it is an acute angle.

Symbols

The symbol for angle is ∠.

The symbol ≅ means is congruent to.

 Show your work.

Got it? Do these problems to find out.

Name each angle in four ways. Then classify each angle as *acute, right, obtuse,* or *straight*.

a.

b.

c.

a. _____

b. _____

c. _____

Example

2. Identify a pair of vertical angles and adjacent angles in the diagram at the right. Justify your response.

Since ∠2 and ∠4 are opposite angles formed by the intersection of two lines, they are vertical angles.

Since ∠1 and ∠2 share a common side and vertex, and they do not overlap, they are adjacent angles.

Got it? Do this problem to find out.

d. Refer to the diagram in Example 2. Identify different pairs of vertical and adjacent angles. Justify your response.

Show your work.

d. _____

Find a Missing Measure

You can use what you learned about vertical and adjacent angles to find the value of a missing measure.

Example

3. What is the value of x in the figure?

The angle labeled (2x + 2)° and the angle labeled 130° are vertical angles.

(2x + 2)°
(3y − 10)°   50°
130°

Since vertical angles are congruent, (2x + 2)° equals 130°.

$2x + 2 = 130$ Write the equation.

$\underline{-2 = -2}$ Subtract 2 from each side.

$\dfrac{2x}{2} = \dfrac{128}{2}$ Divide each side by 2.

$x = 64$

So, the value of x is 64.

Got it? Do this problem to find out.

e. What is the value of y in the figure in Example 2?

e. _____

Example

4. What is the value of *x* shown in the sidewalk?

The angle labeled 115° and the angle labeled 5*x* are adjacent angles. Together they form a straight angle or 180°.

$$115 + 5x = 180 \quad \text{Write the equation.}$$
$$\underline{-115 \qquad = -115} \quad \begin{array}{l}\text{Subtract 115} \\ \text{from each side.}\end{array}$$
$$\frac{5x}{5} = \frac{65}{5} \quad \text{Divide each side by 5.}$$
$$x = 13$$

So, the value of *x* is 13.

Guided Practice

1. Name the angle below in four ways. Then classify it as *acute, right, obtuse,* or *straight.* (Example 1)

_____

2. Find the value of *x* in the figure. (Examples 3–4)

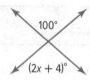

_____

3. Identify a pair of vertical angles and adjacent angles on the railroad crossing sign. Justify your response. (Example 2)

Show your work. ➜ _____

_____

_____

_____

4. **Building on the Essential Question** Describe the differences between vertical and adjacent angles.

_____

_____

_____

_____

_____

_____

Rate Yourself!

How confident are you about classifying angles? Check the box that applies.

😞 😐 😊

For more help, go online to access a Personal Tutor. Tutor

FOLDABLES Time to update your Foldable!

Independent Practice

Go online for Step-by-Step Solutions

Name each angle in four ways. Then classify the angle as *acute,* *right,*
obtuse, **or** *straight.* (Example 1)

1.

_____

_____

2.

_____

_____

3.

_____

_____

PS Identify Structure Refer to the diagram at the right. Identify
each angle pair as *adjacent,* *vertical,* or *neither.* (Example 2)

4. ∠2 and ∠5 _____

5. ∠4 and ∠6 _____

6. ∠3 and ∠4 _____

7. ∠5 and ∠6 _____

8. ∠1 and ∠3 _____

9. ∠1 and ∠4 _____

10. What is the value of *x* in the figure at the right? (Examples 3 and 4) _____

11. What is the value of *x* in the figure at the right? (Examples 3 and 4) _____

12. Angles *ABC* and *DBE* are vertical angles. If the measure of ∠*ABC* is 40°, what is the measure of ∠*ABD*?

 H.O.T. Problems Higher Order Thinking

13. **Model with Mathematics** Draw examples of angles that represent real-world objects. Be sure to include at least three of the following angles: acute, right, obtuse, straight, vertical, and adjacent. Verify by measuring the angles.

---

14. **Reason Inductively** Explain how you can use a protractor to measure the angle shown. Find the measure of the angle.

 Persevere with Problems Determine whether each statement is *true* or *false*. If the statement is true, provide a diagram to support it. If the statement is false, explain why.

15. A pair of obtuse angles can also be vertical angles.

16. A pair of straight angles can also be adjacent angles.

Show your work.

Show your work.

17. **Reason Inductively** Lines ℓ and *k* shown at the right are parallel and are intersected by line *j*. Explain how you can write and solve equations to find the measure of each angle. Then find the measure of each angle.

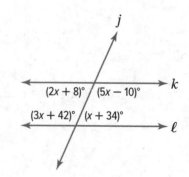

$(2x + 8)°$ / $(5x − 10)°$ *k*

$(3x + 42)°$ / $(x + 34)°$ ℓ

j

Extra Practice

Name each angle in four ways. Then classify the angle as *acute*, *right*, *obtuse*, or *straight*.

18.

∠MNP, ∠PNM, ∠N, ∠7;

straight

19.

_____

_____

20.

_____

_____

21. The corner where the states of Utah, Arizona, New Mexico, and Colorado meet is called the Four Corners.

  a. Identify a pair of vertical angles. Justify your response.

  _____

  _____

  _____

  b. Identify a pair of adjacent angles. Justify your response.

  _____

  _____

  _____

22. What is the value of *x* in the figure at the right?

_____

23. What is the value of *x* in the figure at the right?

_____

$(12x - 3)°$

$105°$

24. PS Identify Structure The John Hancock Center in Chicago is shown at the right. Classify each pair of angles.

  a. ∠1 and ∠2 _____

  b. ∠2 and ∠4 _____

  c. ∠3 and ∠4 _____

  d. ∠1 and ∠3 _____

  e. If the measure of ∠2 is 66°, what are the measures of

  the other angles? _____

  _____

25. Refer to the figure at the right.

Fill in each box to make a true statement.

a. ∠1 and ∠4 are [   ] angles.

b. ∠3 and ∠4 are [   ] angles.

c. ∠2 and ∠4 are [   ] angles.

d. ∠2 and ∠3 are [   ] angles.

26. In the figure below, ∠OLN and ∠PLR are vertical angles.

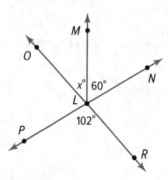

Select values to complete the equation to find the measure of ∠MLO.

[   ] + [   ] = [   ]

x°	30°	60°
90°	102°	180°

What is the measure of ∠MLO? [   ]

Spiral Review

Use a protractor to find the measure of each angle.

27.

_____

28.

_____

29.

_____

30. Name the line segment at the right in two ways.

_____

31. What is the name for a quadrilateral with all right angles and opposite sides that are parallel and congruent?

_____

Complementary and Supplementary Angles

 Real-World Link

Watch ▶

Bridges Engineers use angles to construct bridges. The Golden Gate Bridge is created by combining angles as shown.

1. What types of angles make up the two angles marked in the drawing of the bridge? _____

2. What is the sum of the two angles marked in the drawing of the bridge? _____

3. In the space below, draw a figure that contains two angles that have a sum of 90°.

 Show your work.

 Essential Question

HOW does geometry help us describe real-world objects?

Vocab
Vocabulary

complementary angles
supplementary angles

Math Symbols
$m\angle 1$

Indiana Academic Standards
7.GM.4

PS **Process Standards**
1, 3, 4, 7

Which PS **Process Standards** did you use?
Shade the circle(s) that applies.

① Persevere with Problems
② Reason Abstractly
③ Construct an Argument
④ Model with Mathematics

⑤ Use Math Tools
⑥ Attend to Precision
⑦ Make Use of Structure
⑧ Use Repeated Reasoning

Pairs of Angles

Work Zone

Words	Models	Symbols
Two angles are **complementary** if the sum of their measures is 90°.		$m\angle1 + m\angle2 = 90°$
Two angles are **supplementary** if the sum of their measures is 180°.		$m\angle3 + m\angle4 = 180°$

A special relationship exists between two angles with a sum of 90°. A special relationship also exists between two angles with a sum of 180°. The symbol $m\angle1$ means *the measure of angle 1*.

Examples

Tutor

Identify each pair of angles as *complementary, supplementary,* or *neither*.

1.

$\angle1$ and $\angle2$ form a straight angle. So, the angles are supplementary.

Adjacent

As shown in Example 2, angles do not need to be adjacent to be complementary or supplementary angles.

2.

$60° + 30° = 90°$ The angles are complementary.

Show your work.

Got it? Do these problems to find out.

a. _____

b. _____

a.

b.

Find a Missing Measure

You can use angle relationships to find missing measures.

Examples

Watch ▶ | Tutor 💬

3. Find the value of *x*.

Since the two angles form a right angle, they are complementary.

Words	The sum of the measures of ∠ABC and ∠CBD	is	90°.
Variable	Let 2*x* represent the measure of ∠CBD.		
Equation	28 + 2*x*	=	90

$28 + 2x = 90$ Write the equation.

$-28 \quad = -28$ Subtract 28 from each side.

$\dfrac{2x}{2} = \dfrac{62}{2}$ Divide each side by 2.

$x = 31$

So, the value of *x* is 31.

- - - - - - - - - -

4. The angles shown are supplementary. Find the value of *x*.

$123 + 3x = 180$ Write the equation.

$-123 \quad = -123$ Subtract 123 from each side.

$\dfrac{3x}{3} = \dfrac{57}{3}$ Divide each side by 3.

$x = 19$

So, the value of *x* is 19.

Got it? Do this problem to find out.

c. Find the value of *x*.

c. _____

Example

5. The picture shows a support brace for a gate. Find the value of x.

The angle labeled 80° and the angle labeled 10x are supplementary angles.

$80 + 10x = 180$ Write the equation.

$\underline{-80 \qquad = -80}$ Subtract 80 from each side.

$\dfrac{10x}{10} = \dfrac{100}{10}$ Divide each side by 10.

$x = 10$

So, the value of x is 10.

Got it? Do this problem to find out.

 Show your work.

d. _____

d. A pair of scissors forms the angles shown. What is the value of x?

Guided Practice

Identify each pair of angles as *complementary*, *supplementary*, or *neither*. (Examples 1 and 2)

1.
135° 45°

2. 23° 67°

3. Find the value of x. (Examples 3–5)

_____

G (3x)° 45° H J K

4. **Building on the Essential Question** How are vertical, adjacent, complementary, and supplementary angles related? _____

_____

_____

_____

Rate Yourself!

Are you ready to move on? Shade the section that applies.

I have a few questions. / I'm ready to move on. / I have a lot of questions.

For more help, go online to access a Personal Tutor.

Tutor

Independent Practice

eHelp

Go online for Step-by-Step Solutions

Identify each pair of angles as *complementary*, *supplementary*, or *neither*.
(Examples 1 and 2)

1.

43°

2.

61° 119°

3.

2

1

_____ _____

Find the measure of *x* in each figure. (Examples 3 and 4)

4.

40°

(2x)°

5.

(6x)° 60°

_____ _____

6. ∠A and ∠B are complementary angles. The measure of ∠B is (4x)°, and the measure of ∠A is 50°. What is the value of x? (Example 5)

_____

7. A skateboard ramp forms a 42° angle as shown.

Find the value of x. (Example 5)

_____

42°

(6x)°

Use the figure at the right to name the following.

8. a pair of supplementary angles

_____

9. a pair of complementary angles

_____

10. a pair of vertical angles

_____

B C

A K

J G D

I

H F E

11. Use the figure at the right.

 a. Are ∠1 and ∠2 vertical angles, adjacent angles, or neither? ∠2 and ∠3? ∠1 and ∠3?

_____

 b. Write an equation representing the sum of $m\angle 1$ and $m\angle 2$. Then write an equation representing the sum of $m\angle 2$ and $m\angle 3$.

_____

 c. Solve the equations you wrote in part **b** for $m\angle 1$ and $m\angle 3$, respectively. What do you notice?

_____

 d. **Make a Conjecture** Use your answer from part **c** to make a conjecture as to the relationship between vertical angles.

_____

_____

H.O.T. Problems Higher Order Thinking

12. PS **Reason Inductively** When a basketball hits a hard, level surface, it bounces off at the same angle at which it hits. Use the figure to find the angle at which the ball hit the floor.

_____

13. PS **Persevere with Problems** Find the measure of each angle in the given situation.

 a. complementary angles E and F, where $m\angle E = (x - 10)°$ and $m\angle F = (x + 2)°$

_____

 b. supplementary angles B and C, where $m\angle B = (2x - 40)°$ and $m\angle C = (2x + 20)°$

_____

14. PS **Persevere with Problems** In the figure shown, the sum of the measures of ∠YXZ and ∠WXV is 75°. What is the measure of ∠ZXW?

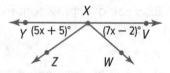

_____

15. PS **Reason Inductively** Is the statement below *always*, *sometimes*, or *never* true? Explain.

 If two angles are right angles, they must be supplementary.

_____

_____

_____

Extra Practice

Identify each pair of angles as *complementary*, *supplementary*, or *neither*.

16.

Homework Help

∠1 and ∠2 form a
straight angle. So, the
angles are supplementary.

17.

_____

18.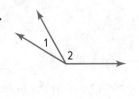

_____

19. ∠J and ∠K are supplementary. The measure of ∠J is $(9x)°$ and the measure of ∠K is 45°. What is the value of x?

_____

20. ∠C and ∠D are complementary. The measure of ∠C is $(4x)°$ and the measure of ∠D is 26°. What is the value of x?

_____

PS **Identify Structure** Determine whether each statement is *always*, *sometimes*, or *never* true. Explain your reasoning.

21. Two obtuse angles are supplementary.

_____

_____

_____

_____

22. Two vertical angles are complementary.

_____

_____

_____

_____

23. **PS** **Multiple Representations** Line *a* passes through (1, 4) and (−4, −1). Line *b* passes through (−3, 4) and (2, −1).

a. **Graphs** Graph each line on the same coordinate plane.

b. **Words** Describe the lines.

_____

c. **Numbers** What is the slope of each line?

_____

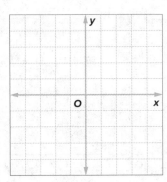

24. Which angle pairs below are supplementary? Select all that apply.

☐ ☐ ☐ ☐

25. The angle at which the light ray hits the water is equal to the angle at which the light ray is reflected from the water.

Select values to complete the equation below to find the value of *x*.

$$2 \times \boxed{} + \boxed{} = \boxed{}$$

x°
45°
60°
90°
180°

What is the measure of the angle at which the light ray hits the water?

What is the measure of the angle at which the light ray is reflected from the water?

$\boxed{}$

Spiral Review

Graph each figure with the given vertices on the coordinate plane. Then classify each figure.

26. (1, 3), (1, 6), (5, 5), and (5, 3)

27. (1, 2), (5, 2), (5, 6), and (1, 6)

Similar Triangles and Indirect Measurement

Vocabulary Start-Up

Indirect measurement allows you to use properties of similar polygons to find distances or lengths that are difficult to measure directly.

Complete the graphic organizer. List three real-world examples in the Venn diagram for each method of measurement.

Direct
Measurement
your arm

Indirect
Measurement
Statue of
Liberty's arm

Write the name of an object that could be measured by either

method. _____

 ### 🌎 Real-World Link

Shadows Legend says that Thales, the first Greek mathematician, was the first to determine the height of the pyramids by examining the shadows made by the Sun.

1. What appears to be true about the corresponding

   angles in the two triangles? _____

2. If the corresponding sides are proportional, what could you

   conclude about the triangles? _____

Which ⓅⓈ **Process Standards** did you use?
Shade the circle(s) that applies.

① Persevere with Problems
② Reason Abstractly
③ Construct an Argument
④ Model with Mathematics

⑤ Use Math Tools
⑥ Attend to Precision
⑦ Make Use of Structure
⑧ Use Repeated Reasoning

 Essential Question

HOW can you determine congruence and similarity?

Vocabulary

indirect measurement

🔵 **Indiana Academic Standards**
7.GM.2

Ⓟ**Ⓢ** **Process Standards**
1, 3, 4, 7

Angle-Angle (AA) Similarity

Words   If two angles of one triangle are congruent to two angles of another triangle, then the triangles are similar.

Symbols   If ∠A ≅ ∠F and ∠B ≅ ∠G, then △ABC ~ △FGH.

Model

In the figure below, ∠X ≅ ∠P and ∠Y ≅ ∠Q. If you extend the sides of each figure to form a triangle, you can see the two triangles are similar. So, triangle similarity can be proven by showing two pairs of corresponding angles are congruent.

STOP and Reflect

What do you know about the third pair of angles in the triangle?

Example

Tutor

1. **Determine whether the triangles are similar. If so, write a similarity statement.**

   Angle A and ∠E have the same measure, so they are congruent. Since 180 − 62 − 48 = 70, ∠G measures 70°. Two angles of △EFG are congruent to two angles of △ABC, so △ABC ~ △EFG.

Got it?   Do this problem to find out.

Show your work.

a. _____

   a.

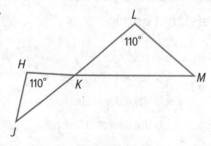

Use Indirect Measurement

One type of indirect measurement is *shadow reckoning*. Two objects and their shadows form two sides of right triangles. In shadow problems, you can assume that the angles formed by the Sun's rays with two objects at the same location are congruent. Since two pairs of corresponding angles are congruent, the two right triangles are similar. You can also use similar triangles that do not involve shadows to find missing measures.

Examples

Watch | Tutor

2. A fire hydrant 2.5 feet high casts a 5-foot shadow. How tall is a street light that casts a 26-foot shadow at the same time? Let *h* represent the height of the street light.

26 ft   *h* ft   2.5 ft   5 ft

Shadow   **Height**

hydrant → $\dfrac{5}{26} = \dfrac{2.5}{h}$ ← hydrant
street light →   ← street light

$5h = 26 \cdot 2.5$ Find the cross products.

$5h = 65$ Multiply.

$\dfrac{5h}{5} = \dfrac{65}{5}$ Divide each side by 5.

$h = 13$

The street light is 13 feet tall.

3. In the figure at the right, triangle *DBA* is similar to triangle *ECA*. Ramon wants to know the distance across the lake.

162 m   320 m   40 m   *d* m   A   D   E   B   C

$\dfrac{AB}{AC} = \dfrac{BD}{CE}$ $\overline{AB}$ corresponds to $\overline{AC}$ and $\overline{BD}$ corresponds to $\overline{CE}$.

$\dfrac{320}{482} = \dfrac{40}{d}$ Replace *AB* with 320, *AC* with 482, and *BD* with 40.

$320d = 482 \cdot 40$ Find the cross products.

$\dfrac{320d}{320} = \dfrac{19{,}280}{320}$ Multiply. Then divide each side by 320.

$d = 60.25$

The distance across the lake is 60.25 meters.

b. _____

b. At the same time a 2-meter street sign casts a 3-meter shadow, a nearby telephone pole casts a 12.3-meter shadow. How tall is the telephone pole?

Guided Practice

Check ✓

Determine whether the triangles are similar. If so, write a similarity statement. (Example 1)

1.

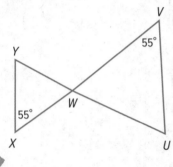

_____

_____

Show your work.

2.

_____

_____

3. How tall is the tree? (Example 2) _____

4. Find the distance from the house to the street light. (Example 3) _____

5. (e) **Building on the Essential Question** How do similar triangles make it easier to measure very tall objects?

_____

_____

_____

_____

_____

Rate Yourself!

Are you ready to move on?
Shade the section that applies.

YES ? NO

For more help, go online to access a Personal Tutor.

Tutor

Independent Practice

Go online for Step-by-Step Solutions

Determine whether the triangles are similar. If so, write a similarity statement. (Example 1)

1.

Show your work.

_____

_____

2.

_____

_____

3. How tall is the building? (Example 2)

4. How tall is the taller flagpole? (Example 2)

5 How far is it from the log ride to the pirate ship? (Example 3) _____

6. Find the height of the brace. (Example 3)

7 PS Reason Abstractly The Giant Wheel at Cedar Point in Ohio is one of the tallest Ferris wheels in the country at 136 feet tall. If the Giant Wheel casts a 34-foot shadow, write and solve a proportion to find the height of a nearby man who casts a $1\frac{1}{2}$-foot shadow.

_____

_____

H.O.T. Problems Higher Order Thinking

8. **PS** **Find the Error** Sara is finding the height of the lighthouse shown in the diagram. Find her mistake and correct it.

x ft

27 ft

60 ft

90 ft

$$\frac{27}{60} = \frac{x}{90}$$

$$27 \cdot 90 = 60x$$

$$x = 40.5$$

9. **PS** **Model with Mathematics** On a separate sheet of paper, draw two different triangles so that each one contains both of the angles shown. Then verify that they are similar by determining which transformation will map one onto the other.

10. **PS** **Persevere with Problems** You cut a circular hole $\frac{1}{4}$-inch in diameter in a piece of cardboard. With the cardboard 30 inches from your face, the Moon fits exactly into the hole. The Moon is about 240,000 miles from Earth. Is the Moon's diameter more than 1,500 miles? Justify your reasoning.

11. **PS** **Identify Structure** What measures must be known in order to calculate the height of tall objects using shadow reckoning?

12. **PS** **Reason Inductively** Mila wants to estimate the height of a statue in a local park. Mila's height and both shadow lengths are shown in the diagram. Is an estimate of 15 feet reasonable for the statue's height? Explain your reasoning.

$4\frac{1}{2}$ ft

6 ft

x ft

12 ft

Extra Practice

13. What is the height of the tree? _90 ft_

x ft   60 ft

63 ft   42 ft

> **Homework Help** → The triangles are similar. Write and solve a proportion.
>
> $$\frac{63}{42} = \frac{x}{60}$$
>
> $63 \cdot 60 = 42x$
>
> $90 = x$

14. Find the distance across the river. _____

D

140 m   300 m

A   B   350 m   E

x m

C

15. About how long is the log that goes across the creeks? _____

9 m

8 m   x m

12 m

16. How deep is the water 62 meters from the shore? _____

3 m   62 m

V W   Y

5 m

X

d m

Z

17. In the diagram shown at the right, $\triangle ABC \sim \triangle EDC$.

   a. Write a proportion that could be used to solve for the height h of the flag pole. _____

   b. What information would you need to know in order to solve this proportion?

_____

_____

_____

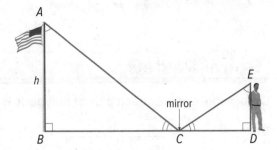

A

E

h

mirror

B   C   D

18. **PS Model with Mathematics** A 78-inch-tall man casts a shadow that is 54 inches long. At the same time, a nearby building casts a 48-foot-long shadow. Write and solve a proportion to find the height of the building.

_____

19. Horatio is 6 feet tall and casts a shadow 3 feet long. At the same time, a nearby tower casts a shadow that is 25 feet long.

Write a proportion Horatio can use to find the

height of the tower. [   ]

Using the proportion, the tower is [   ] feet tall.

20. Lenno is 5 feet tall and is using similar triangles and a mirror to find the height of a telephone pole. The horizontal distance between Lenno and the telephone pole is 28 feet. He places the mirror on the ground 7 feet from himself so that he can see the top of the pole in the mirror's reflection as shown in the figure below.

5 ft	7 ft	12 ft	14 ft
21 ft	28 ft	h ft	

Select values to label the diagram with the correct dimensions.

What is the height of the telephone pole? [   ]

Spiral Review

Determine whether each pair of polygons is similar. Explain.

21.

22.

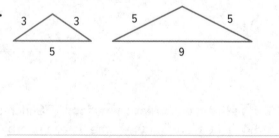

_____

_____

_____

_____

Inquiry Lab
Create Triangles

 Inquiry WHAT do you notice about the measures of the sides or the measures of the angles that form triangles?

Indiana Academic Standards
7.GM.1

PS Process Standards
1, 3, 5, 8

Dennis has a sailboat. The sail on his boat is in the shape of a triangle with side lengths of 6 feet, 8 feet, and 10 feet. These dimensions work to form a triangle, but not just any three lengths form a triangle. Complete the Activity below to determine which side lengths form triangles.

Hands-On Activity 1

Step 1 Measure and cut several plastic straws into lengths that equal 3, 4, 4, 5, 8, 8, 8, 13, 15, 15, 15, and 15 centimeters.

Step 2 Arrange three of the pieces that each measure 15 centimeters to see if you can form a triangle.

15 cm 15 cm

15 cm

So, you can form a triangle with side lengths of 15 centimeters, 15 centimeters, and 15 centimeters.

Step 3 Continue using pieces of straw to try to form triangles using the different combinations of side lengths given. Determine whether or not the lengths form a triangle. Complete the table.

Side 1	Side 2	Side 3	Do the sides form a triangle?
15 cm	15 cm	15 cm	yes
3 cm	4 cm	5 cm	
8 cm	8 cm	13 cm	
3 cm	4 cm	8 cm	
4 cm	4 cm	5 cm	
8 cm	3 cm	15 cm	
4 cm	8 cm	15 cm	

Investigate

Work with a partner. Try to create triangles using the given side lengths. Circle yes if you can make a triangle or no if you cannot.

1. 5 cm, 8 cm, 15 cm

   Yes   or   No

2. 13 cm, 8 cm, 15 cm

   Yes   or   No

3. 13 cm, 4 cm, 4 cm

   Yes   or   No

Analyze and Reflect

Work with a partner.

4. The table below contains the dimensions you used in Step 3 of the Activity. Transfer your results from the Investigation into the fourth column and then complete the fifth column.

Side 1	Side 2	Side 3	Do the sides form a triangle?	Is Side 1 + Side 2 greater than or less than Side 3?
15 cm	15 cm	15 cm	yes	greater than
3 cm	4 cm	5 cm		
8 cm	8 cm	13 cm		
3 cm	4 cm	8 cm		
4 cm	4 cm	5 cm		
8 cm	3 cm	15 cm		
4 cm	8 cm	15 cm		

5. What do you notice about the figures with a Side 1 and Side 2 sum that is

   less than the length of Side 3? _____

   _____

Create

6. Can you create a triangle that has the same shape as the triangle in the Activity, but different side lengths? Explain.

   _____

   _____

7. **PS Reason Inductively** Could you form a triangle using the side

   lengths of 7, 8, and 25 centimeters? Explain. _____

   _____

   _____

Hands-On Activity 2

Use angles of different sizes to determine which ones form a triangle.

Step 1 Draw two sets of angles measuring 30°, 45°, 60°, and 90° on different pieces of patty paper. Extend the rays of each angle to the edges of the patty paper.

30°

45°

60°

90°

Step 2 Try to form a triangle with one 90° angle and two 45° angles.

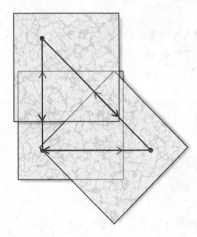

So, a 90° angle and two 45° angles form a triangle.

Step 3 Try to form triangles using the angle measures that are given in the table. Fill in *yes* or *no* in the fourth column of the table.

Angle 1	Angle 2	Angle 3	Do the angles form a triangle?
90°	45°	45°	yes
30°	60°	90°	
30°	45°	60°	
30°	30°	60°	

Work with a partner.

8. Draw another 60° angle on a piece of patty paper. Describe the angles and side lengths of the figure you form using three 60° angles.

_____

_____

9. Draw angles measuring 20°, 70°, and 90° on pieces of patty paper.

   a. Do the angles form a triangle? _____

   b. Can you create more than one triangle that is the same shape with different side lengths? What are the side lengths of your triangle?

_____

Analyze and Reflect
Collaborate

10. **PS** **Identify Repeated Reasoning** Refer back to the table in Step 3 of Activity 2. Compare the sum of the angle measures. Describe any patterns that are found.

_____

_____

Create
On Your Own

11. **PS** **Use Math Tools** Use a protractor to measure the three angles below. Would you be able to form a triangle from these angles? Explain.

_____

12. **Inquiry** WHAT do you notice about the measures of the sides or the measures of the angles that form triangles?

_____

_____

_____

Lesson 3
Triangles

Real-World Link

Ramps Julia practices jumping on a ski ramp. The front of the ramp is a triangle like the one shown below.

80°

x°

1. Draw an X through the type of angle that is not shown in the triangle.

right   acute   obtuse

2. Measure the unknown angle. Describe the relationship between the 80° angle and the unknown angle. _____

3. Draw a triangle with one obtuse angle.

Show your work.

4. Is it possible to draw a triangle with two obtuse angles? Explain.

_____

_____

Which PS **Process Standards** did you use?
Shade the circle(s) that applies.

① Persevere with Problems
② Reason Abstractly
③ Construct an Argument
④ Model with Mathematics

⑤ Use Math Tools
⑥ Attend to Precision
⑦ Make Use of Structure
⑧ Use Repeated Reasoning

> ## Classify Triangles

all acute angles

acute triangle

1 right angle

right triangle

1 obtuse angle

obtuse triangle

---

no congruent sides

scalene triangle

at least 2 congruent sides

isosceles triangle

3 congruent sides

equilateral triangle

> **Congruent Segments**
> The tick marks on the sides of the triangle indicate that those sides are congruent.

A **triangle** is a figure with three sides and three angles. The symbol for triangle is △.

Every triangle has at least two acute angles. One way you can classify a triangle is by using the third angle. Another way to classify triangles is by their sides. Sides with the same length are **congruent segments**.

Example

Tutor

1. **Draw a triangle with one obtuse angle and no congruent sides. Then classify the triangle.**

   Draw an obtuse angle.
   The two segments of the angle should have different lengths.

   Connect the two segments to form a triangle.

   The triangle is an obtuse scalene triangle.

Got it? Do this problem to find out.

Draw a triangle that satisfies the set of conditions below. Then classify the triangle.

   a. a triangle with one right angle and two congruent sides

a.

Example

2. **Classify the triangle on the house by its angles and by its sides.**

The triangle has one obtuse angle and two congruent sides. So, it is an obtuse isosceles triangle.

Got it? Do this problem to find out.

b. Classify the triangle shown by its angles and by its sides.

b. _____

Angles of a Triangle

Key Concept

Words	The sum of the measures of the angles of a triangle is 180°.	Model

Algebra $x + y + z = 180$

You can write and solve an equation to find the missing angle measure of a triangle.

Example

Tutor

3. **Find $m\angle Z$.**

The sum of the angle measures in a triangle is 180°.

$$m\angle Z + 43° + 119° = 180°$$ Write the equation.
$$m\angle Z + 162° = 180°$$ Simplify.
$$-162° = -162°$$ Subtract 162° from each side.
$$m\angle Z = 18°$$

So, $m\angle Z$ is 18°.

Got it? Do this problem to find out.

c. In $\triangle ABC$, if $m\angle A = 25°$ and $m\angle B = 108°$, what is $m\angle C$?

c. _____

Example

 Tutor

4. The Alabama state flag is shown. What is the missing measure in the triangle?

To find the missing measure, write and solve an equation.

110°
35°   x°

$$x + 110 + 35 = 180 \quad \text{The sum of the measures is 180.}$$
$$x + 145 = 180 \quad \text{Simplify.}$$
$$\underline{-145 = -145} \quad \text{Subtract 145 from each side.}$$
$$x = 35$$

The missing measure is 35°.

Guided Practice

 Check ✓

1. Draw a triangle with three acute angles and two congruent sides. Classify the triangle.

(Examples 1 and 2) _____

2. Find $m\angle T$ in $\triangle RST$ if $m\angle R = 37°$ and $m\angle S = 55°$. (Example 3) _____

 Show your work.

3. A triangle is used in the game of pool to rack the pool balls. Find the missing measure of the triangle. (Example 4)

_____

60°
60°   x°

4. **Building on the Essential Question** How can triangles be classified?

_____
_____
_____
_____

Independent Practice

Go online for Step-by-Step Solutions

Draw a triangle that satisfies each set of conditions. Then classify the triangle. (Example 1)

 1. a triangle with three acute angles and three congruent sides _____

2. a triangle with one right angle and no congruent sides _____

Classify the marked triangle by its angles and by its sides. (Example 2)

3.

_____

4.

5.

Find the value of x. (Examples 3 and 4)

6.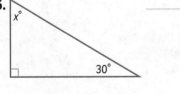

$x°$ $30°$

7. $33°$ $x°$ $29°$

8. $21°$ $x°$ $132°$

9. **PS Model with Mathematics** Refer to the graphic novel below. Classify the triangle formed by the cabin, ropes course, and mess hall by its angles and sides.

_____

10. Triangle *ABC* is formed by two parallel lines and two other intersecting lines. Find the measure of each angle *A*, *B*, and *C* of the triangle.

_____

 H.O.T. Problems Higher Order Thinking

11. (PS) **Persevere with Problems** Apply what you know about triangles to write and solve equations to find the missing angle measures in the figure.

_____

_____

12. (PS) **Model with Mathematics** Draw an acute scalene triangle. Describe the angles and sides of the triangle.

_____

_____

13. (PS) **Justify Conclusions** Determine whether each statement is *sometimes*, *always*, or *never* true. Justify your answer.

a. It is possible for a triangle to have two right angles.

_____

_____

_____

b. It is possible for a triangle to have two obtuse angles.

_____

_____

_____

14. (PS) **Reason Inductively** Miguel says that an equilateral triangle is sometimes an obtuse triangle. Jane says that an equilateral triangle is always an acute triangle. Is either of them correct? Explain your reasoning.

_____

_____

_____

Extra Practice

Classify the marked triangle in each object by its angles and by its sides.

15.

The triangle has all acute angles and two congruent sides. It is an acute isosceles triangle.

16.

_____

_____

17.

_____

_____

Draw a triangle that satisfies each set of conditions. Then classify the triangle.

18. a triangle with three acute angles and no

congruent sides _____

19. a triangle with one obtuse angle and two

congruent sides _____

Find the value of x.

20.

$x°$

$50°$

$65°$

_____

21.

$x°$

$34°$ $56°$

_____

22.

$53°$

$x°$

_____

23. Find $m\angle Q$ in $\triangle QRS$ if $m\angle R = 25°$ and $m\angle S = 102°$. _____

PS Reason Abstractly Find the value of x in each triangle.

24.

$x°$

$x°$ $x°$

25.

$x°$

$2x°$

26.

$x°$

$x°$

$25°$

27. Refer to the figure shown. Determine if each statement is true or false.

   a. To find $m\angle R$, subtract 30° from 90°.   ☐ True   ☐ False

   b. The measure of $\angle R$ is 120°.   ☐ True   ☐ False

   c. Triangle *RST* is an acute triangle.   ☐ True   ☐ False

28. In a right triangle, the measure of one of the angles is 43°. Sketch a diagram to represent this situation.

What is the measure of the other angle? ☐

Spiral Review

Find the area of each figure.

29.

5 in.

30.

4 ft

8 ft

31.

5 cm

7 cm

32.

6 m

5 m

4 m

33.

2 yd

9 yd

34.

6 in.

12 in.

Inquiry Lab
Draw Triangles

Indiana Academic
Standards
7.GM.1

PS Process
Standards
1, 3, 5

 HOW can you use technology to draw geometric shapes?

The Spirit Club is selling triangular-shaped pennants for Homecoming. Teresa is making a poster to advertise the pennants. She wants to use a computer program to draw a model of the pennant.

Hands-On Activity 1

You can use dynamic geometry software such as The Geometer's Sketchpad® to draw triangles given three angle measures. In this investigation, you will draw a triangle with angle measures of 30°, 60°, and 90°.

Step 1 First, click on **Edit**. Go to **Preferences**. Change the angle precision from *hundredths* to *units*. Next, use the **Straightedge (segment)** tool. Click and drag three times to create a triangle like the one shown.

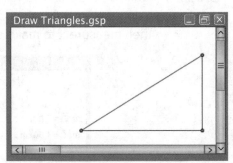

Step 2 Using the **Selection Arrow**, click on each of the vertex points *A*, *B*, and *C*. Then select **Measure** and **Angle**. Labels will automatically be assigned to the vertices. You found that the measure

of ∠*ABC* is ⬚.

Step 3 Click on points *B*, *C*, and *A*. Click **Measure** and **Angle** again. Repeat for points *B*, *A*, and *C*. The angle measures should be displayed on your screen.

Step 4 If the angles do not measure 30°, 60°, and 90°, use the **Selection Arrow** to move the vertices. Click and drag one or more points so that the angles move.

Hands-On Activity 2

You can also use The Geometer's Sketchpad® to draw triangles given three side measures. In this Activity, you will draw a triangle with side measures of 3 centimeters, 4 centimeters, and 5 centimeters.

Step 1 First, click on **Edit**. Go to **Preferences**. Check that the distance precision is set to hundredths. Using the **Straightedge (segment)** tool, click and drag to create a line segment with endpoints *A* and *B*. Use the **Selection Arrow** to select the segment. Click on **Measure** and **Length**. Then drag one of the endpoints so that the line segment measures 5 centimeters.

Step 2 Next, create a line segment from point *A* that is 4 centimeters long using the **Straightedge (segment)** tool. Draw the segment first and then measure it to make sure it is 4 centimeters.

Step 3 Finally, connect points *C* and *B* with a line segment that is 3 centimeters long.

You have created a triangle with side lengths of 3 centimeters, 4 centimeters, and 5 centimeters.

Investigate

Collaborate

PS Use Math Tools Work with a partner to construct each triangle. Once you have constructed a triangle, draw the text and image that appears on your display.

1. $\angle ABC = 90°$
   $\angle BCA = 70°$
   $\angle BAC = 20°$

Show your work.

2. $\angle ABC = 90°$
   $\angle BCA = 45°$
   $\angle BAC = 45°$

3. Explain the steps you would take to create a triangle if you were given the measures of all three angles.

4. $\overline{AB} = 4$ centimeters
   $\overline{AC} = 6$ centimeters
   $\overline{CB} = 9$ centimeters

5. $\overline{AB} = 2$ centimeters
   $\overline{AC} = 5$ centimeters
   $\overline{CB} = 4$ centimeters

6. **PS Justify Conclusions** Explain the steps you would take to create a triangle if you were given the lengths of all three sides.

Analyze and Reflect

Work with a partner to answer each of the following questions.

7. Is it possible to use dynamic geometry software to draw a triangle with angles of 50°, 65°, and 70°? Explain.

_____

_____

8. Is it possible to use dynamic geometry software to draw a triangle with side measures of 3, 6, and 10 centimeters? Explain.

_____

_____

_____

Create

On Your Own

9. **PS** **Reason Inductively** You know the rule to find the sum of the interior angles of a triangle. Does a similar rule exist for the sum of the interior angles of a quadrilateral? Use dynamic geometry software to draw four different quadrilaterals and complete the table below to find out. (*Hint:* Do not draw more than one square or rectangle.)

_____

_____

	m∠1	m∠2	m∠3	m∠4	Sum of Angles
Quadrilateral 1					
Quadrilateral 2					
Quadrilateral 3					
Quadrilateral 4					

10. **Inquiry** HOW can you use technology to draw geometric shapes?

_____

_____

_____

Problem-Solving Investigation
Make a Model

Case #1 Science Project

Indiana Academic Standards
7.GM.3

Process Standards
1, 4, 6

Jordan is making a model of Mount Saint Helens for a science project. The height of the actual volcano is about 2,500 meters. She uses a scale of 250 meters equals 1 centimeter.

What is the height of the volcano in Jordan's model?

 Understand *What are the facts?*

- The height of the actual volcano is about 2,500 meters.
- The scale for her model is 250 meters = 1 centimeter.

 Plan *What is your strategy to solve this problem?*

Draw a model that represents the actual volcano and Jordan's volcano to help you visualize the problem.

 Solve *How can you apply the strategy?*

The scale is 250 meters = 1 centimeter.
Write and solve a proportion using the scale.

$$\frac{250 \text{ m}}{1 \text{ cm}} = \frac{\boxed{} \text{ m}}{x \text{ cm}}$$

$$250 \cdot x = 1 \cdot \boxed{}$$

$$x = \boxed{} \text{ cm}$$

2,500 m

So, Jordan's model has a height of _____.

 Check *Does the answer make sense?*

Multiply the height of the model by 250 to see if it matches the actual height.

Analyze the Strategy

Be Precise The height of Mount Saint Helens is about 8,500 feet. What scale could Jordan use to represent the model in the U.S. Customary System?

_____

Case #2 Portraits

Alicia created a portrait that is 10 inches wide by 13 inches long. She wants to put it in a frame that is $2\frac{1}{4}$ inches wide on each side.

What is the area of the framed portrait?

1 Understand

Read the problem. What are you being asked to find?

I need to find _____.

2 Plan

What is your strategy to solve this problem?

I will use the _____ strategy.

3 Solve

How can you apply the strategy?

I will _____.

The inner rectangle is the portrait and the outer rectangle is the frame.

Label the combined length and width of the portrait and the frame.

The area of the framed portrait is _____

4 Check

Estimate the product of the length and width of the framed portrait to determine if your answer is reasonable.

_____

_____

Work with a small group to solve the following cases.
Show your work on a separate piece of paper.

Collaborate

Case #3 Tables

Members of Student Council are setting up tables end-to-end for an awards banquet. Each table will seat one person on each side.

How many square tables will they need to put together for 32 people? Explain your method.

Case #4 Tile

The diagram shows the design of a tile border around a rectangular swimming pool that measures 10.5 meters by 6 meters. Each tile is a square measuring 1.5 meter on each side.

Explain a method you could use to find the area of just the tile border. Then solve.

Case #5 Classes

Faith, Sarah, and Guadalupe take French, Spanish, and German. No person's language class begins with the same letter as their first name. Sarah's best friend takes French.

Which language does each person take?

Use any strategy!

Case #6 Money

Corri received money for her birthday. She let Lakisha borrow $4.50 and spent half of the remaining money. The next day she received $10 from her uncle. After spending $12.50 at the movies, she still had $7.75 left.

How much money did she receive for her birthday?

Mid-Chapter Check

Vocabulary Check

1. **PS** **Be Precise** Define *complementary angles*. Give an example of two angles that would be complementary. (Lesson 2)

   _____

   _____

2. Fill in the blank in the sentence below with the correct term. (Lesson 3)

   A _____ triangle is made up of one right angle and no congruent sides.

Skills Check and Problem Solving

Refer to the figure below for Exercises 3–5. (Lessons 1 and 2)

3. Identify a pair of vertical angles.

   _____

4. Identify a pair of supplementary angles.

   _____

5. Suppose $m\angle 1 = 127°$. Find the measures of the other angles.

   _____

6. What is $m\angle A$ in $\triangle ABC$ if $m\angle B = 35°$ and $m\angle C = 92°$? _____

7. **PS** **Reason Inductively** Classify the triangle that satisfies each set of conditions.

   a. one right angle and two congruent sides _____

   b. one obtuse angle and no congruent sides _____

   c. three acute angles and three congruent sides _____

Inquiry Lab

Investigate Online Maps and Scale Drawings

 Inquiry HOW is the zoom feature of an online map like the scale of a drawing?

Indiana Academic Standards
7.GM.3

PS Process Standards
1, 3, 4, 5

Maps and blueprints are *scale drawings* of the locations and buildings they represent. Unlike maps printed on paper, online map services allow users the opportunity to view a location from different distances.

Maps	Directions	Info

Start Here   **Country** [ ]

Business or Name
[Name of your School]

Address or location
[ ]

City   **State**   **Zip Code**
[Your Town]   [ ]   [ ]

Hands-On Activity 1

Step 1   Use the online map service provided to you by your teacher. Locate your school on a map.

Step 2   Measure the length of the scale bar in centimeters on the online map. Find the scale distance of the map. Write these values in the Original View table in Step 4.

Step 3   Click on the satellite or aerial view. Use the zoom feature to zoom in until your school shows up on the map.

Step 4   Measure the length of the scale bar in centimeters. Find the new scale distance for the map. Write these values in the Zoom View table.

Original View	
Scale Bar	
Scale Distance	

Zoom View	
Scale Bar	
Scale Distance	

What happens when you use the zoom feature?

_____

Describe the appearance of the map as you zoomed in.

_____

Investigate

PS Use Math Tools Work with a partner to answer the following questions about using an online map service.

1. Locate the local public library on the map. Write the scale bar and scale distance values in the Original View table below Exercise 2.

2. Click on the satellite or aerial view. Use the zoom feature to zoom in until the building shows up on the map. Write the scale bar and scale distance values in the Zoom View table.

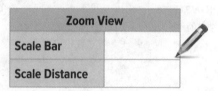

Original View	
Scale Bar	
Scale Distance	

Zoom View	
Scale Bar	
Scale Distance	

Analyze and Reflect

Work with a partner to answer the following questions about using an online map.

3. Refer to Activity 1. Write a ratio $\frac{\text{scale bar}}{\text{scale distance}}$ for the original view and the zoom view.

    Original View: _____   Zoom View: _____

4. How many times bigger is the zoom view?

    _____

    _____

    _____

5. How does zooming in affect the scale on the map? _____

    _____

6. When using the zoom feature on an online map, what changes and what stays

    the same? _____

    _____

    _____

    _____

Hands-On Activity 2

The diagram shown represents a garden. The scale is 1 centimeter = 30 meters. That means that each square on the grid measures 1 centimeter by 1 centimeter or 30 meters by 30 meters.

Step 1 Write the length and width of the drawing of the garden.

Length: _____ centimeters   Width: _____ centimeters

Step 2 Use the scale to find the dimensions of the garden.

Length: _____ meters   Width: _____ meters

Step 3 On the grid below, draw the garden so that the scale is 1 centimeter = 10 meters. Write the dimensions of your drawing.

Length: _____ centimeters   Width: _____ centimeters

Step 4 Use the scale on your drawing to compute the dimensions of the garden. How do the dimensions compare to the dimensions in Step 2?

Length: _____ meters   Width: _____ meters

Collaborate

Work with a partner to answer the following questions about reproducing a scale drawing.

7. Recreate the drawing of the baseball diamond below using the new scale.

current scale: 1 unit = 15 ft
new scale: 1 unit = 30 ft

8. A drawing of the Statue of Liberty is 3 inches tall. The scale is 1 inch = 50 feet. How tall would the drawing be if the scale were

0.5 inch = 100 feet? _____

Analyze and Reflect

Collaborate

9. (PS) **Reason Inductively** The triangle shown in the drawing has an area of 40 square feet. What is the scale of the drawing? _____

Create

On Your Own

10. (PS) **Model with Mathematics** Using a separate piece of grid paper, create a map of your classroom or a room in your home. Identify the scale you used.

_____

11. (Inquiry) How is the zoom feature of an online map like the scale of a drawing?

_____

_____

_____

Real-World Link

Room Model Architects make detailed drawings of rooms and buildings. Conner made a drawing of a bedroom. Follow the steps below to make a model of a room of your choosing.

Essential Question

HOW does geometry help us describe real-world objects?

Vocabulary

scale drawing
scale model
scale
scale factor

Indiana Academic Standards
7.GM.3

PS Process Standards
1, 2, 3, 4, 5

Step 1 Measure the length of three objects in the room. Record each length to the nearest $\frac{1}{2}$ foot in the table below.

Object	Length (ft)	Length (units)

Step 2 Let 1 unit represent 2 feet. So, 4 units = 8 feet. Convert all your measurements to units. Record these values.

Step 3 On grid paper, make a drawing of your room like the one shown.

Which PS **Process Standards** did you use?
Shade the circle(s) that applies.

① Persevere with Problems
② Reason Abstractly
③ Construct an Argument
④ Model with Mathematics

⑤ Use Math Tools
⑥ Attend to Precision
⑦ Make Use of Structure
⑧ Use Repeated Reasoning

Use a Scale Drawing or a Scale Model

Scale drawings and **scale models** are used to represent objects that are too large or too small to be drawn or built at actual size. The **scale** gives the ratio that compares the measurements of the drawing or model to the measurements of the real object. The measurements on a drawing or model are proportional to the measurements on the actual object.

Example

Tutor

1. **What is the actual distance between Hagerstown and Annapolis?**

Step 1   Use a centimeter ruler to find the map distance between the two cities. The map distance is about 4 centimeters.

Step 2   Write and solve a proportion using the scale. Let d represent the actual distance between the cities.

$$
\begin{array}{c}
\text{Scale} \qquad\qquad \text{Length} \\
\begin{array}{cc}
\text{map} \longrightarrow \\
\text{actual} \longrightarrow
\end{array}
\dfrac{1\,\text{centimeter}}{24\,\text{miles}} = \dfrac{4\,\text{centimeter}}{d\,\text{miles}}
\begin{array}{cc}
\longleftarrow \text{map} \\
\longleftarrow \text{actual}
\end{array}
\end{array}
$$

$$1 \times d = 24 \times 4 \qquad \text{Cross products}$$

$$d = 96 \qquad \text{Simplify.}$$

The distance between the cities is about 96 miles.

Got it?   **Do this problem to find out.**

a. On the map of Arkansas shown, find the actual distance between Clarksville and Little Rock. Use a ruler to measure.

Scale

A map scale can be written in different ways, including the following:

1 cm = 20 mi

1 cm : 20 mi

$\dfrac{1\ cm}{20\ mi}$

Show your work.

a. _____

Example

2. **A graphic artist is creating an advertisement for this cell phone. If she uses a scale of 5 inches = 1 inch, what is the length of the cell phone on the advertisement?**

Write a proportion using the scale. Let *a* represent the length of the advertisement cell phone.

4 in.

	Scale	**Length**	
advertisement →	5 inches	*a* inches	← advertisement
actual →	1 inch	4 inches	← actual

$$\frac{5 \text{ inches}}{1 \text{ inch}} = \frac{a \text{ inches}}{4 \text{ inches}}$$

$$5 \cdot 4 = 1 \cdot a \qquad \text{Cross products}$$

$$20 = a \qquad \text{Simplify.}$$

The length of the cell phone on the advertisement is 20 inches long.

> **Scale**
> The scale is the ratio of the drawing/model measure to the actual measure. It is not always the ratio of a smaller measure to a larger measure.

Got it? Do this problem to find out.

Show your work.

b. A scooter is $3\frac{1}{2}$ feet long. Find the length of a scale model of the scooter if the scale is 1 inch = $\frac{3}{4}$ feet.

b. _____

Find a Scale Factor

A scale written as a ratio without units in simplest form is called the **scale factor.**

Example

3. **Find the scale factor of a model sailboat if the scale is 1 inch = 6 feet.**

$$\frac{1 \text{ inch}}{6 \text{ feet}} = \frac{1 \text{ inch}}{72 \text{ inches}} \qquad \text{Convert 6 feet to inches.}$$

$$= \frac{1}{72} \qquad \text{Divide out the common units.}$$

The scale factor is $\frac{1}{72}$.

Got it? Do this problem to find out.

c. What is the scale factor of a model car if the scale is 1 inch = 2 feet?

c. _____

4. A floor plan for a home is shown at the left where $\frac{1}{2}$ inch represents 3 feet of the actual home. What is the actual area of bedroom 1?

Length of Bedroom 1.

$$\frac{\frac{1}{2}\text{ in.}}{3\text{ ft}} = \frac{4\text{ in.}}{w} \quad \begin{array}{l}\leftarrow \text{ floor plan} \\ \leftarrow \text{ actual}\end{array}$$

$$\frac{1}{2}w = 12 \qquad \text{Find cross products.}$$

$$w = 24 \qquad \text{Divide each side by } \frac{1}{2}.$$

Width of Bedroom 1.

$$\frac{\frac{1}{2}\text{ in.}}{3\text{ ft}} = \frac{1\text{ in.}}{x} \quad \begin{array}{l}\leftarrow \text{ floor plan} \\ \leftarrow \text{ actual}\end{array}$$

$$\frac{1}{2}x = 3 \qquad \text{Find cross products.}$$

$$x = 6 \qquad \text{Divide each side by } \frac{1}{2}.$$

So, the area of bedroom 1 is 24 × 6 or 144 square feet.

Got it? Do this problem to find out.

d. What is the actual area of bedroom 3?

Show your work.

d. _____

Guided Practice

1. On a map, the distance from Akron to Cleveland measures 2 centimeters. What is the actual distance if the scale of the map shows that 1 centimeter is equal to 30 kilometers? (Example 1)

_____

2. An engineer makes a model of a bridge using a scale of 1 inch = 3 yards. The length of the actual bridge is 50 yards. What is the length of the model? (Example 2)

_____

3. Julie is constructing a scale model of her room. The rectangular room is $10\frac{1}{4}$ inches by 8 inches. If 1 inch represents 2 feet of the actual room, what is the scale factor and the actual area of the room? (Examples 3 and 4)

_____

4. **Building on the Essential Question** Explain how you could use a map to estimate the actual distance between Miami, Florida, and Atlanta, Georgia.

_____

_____

Rate Yourself!

How well do you understand scale drawings? Circle the image that applies.

Clear   Somewhat   Not So
          Clear   Clear

For more help, go online to access a Personal Tutor.

Independent Practice

Go online for Step-by-Step Solutions
eHelp

PS Use Math Tools Find the actual distance between each pair of locations in South Carolina. Use a ruler to measure. (Example 1)

1. Columbia and Charleston _____

2. Hollywood and Sumter _____

 Show your work.

Find the length of each model. Then find the scale factor. (Examples 2 and 3)

36 m

0.5 cm = 1.5 m

4.
87 ft

2 in. = 15 ft

_____

_____

5. A model of an apartment is shown where $\frac{1}{4}$ inch represents 3 feet in the actual apartment. Find the actual area of the master bedroom. (Example 4)

_____

$1\frac{1}{2}$ in.   1 in.

Master Bedroom

$\frac{3}{4}$ in.

6. **(PS) Model with Mathematics** Refer to the graphic novel frames below. The scale on the map shows that 1 centimeter is equal to 75 yards. If the red line represents the path they took, how far have Raul, Caitlyn, and Jamar traveled since they left the lake? Each square on the map is 1 centimeter long.

H.O.T. Problems Higher Order Thinking

7. **(PS) Model with Mathematics** On the grid paper, create a scale drawing of a room in your home. Include the scale that you used.

8. **(PS) Reason Abstractly** A statue of Thomas Jefferson was made using a scale of 3 feet = 1 foot. Write an expression to represent the height of the statue if Thomas Jefferson is *x* feet in height. Then find his actual height if the height of the statue is 19 feet.

9. **(PS) Justify Conclusions** Determine whether the following statement is *always, sometimes,* or *never* true. Justify your reasoning.

   If the scale factor of a scale drawing is greater than one, the scale drawing is larger than the actual object.

Extra Practice

PS **Use Math Tools** Find the actual distance between each pair of cities in New Mexico. Use a ruler to measure.

10. Carlsbad and Artesia 50 km _____

$$\frac{1 \text{ cm}}{25 \text{ km}} = \frac{2 \text{ cm}}{d \text{ km}}$$
$$1 \times d = 25 \times 2$$
$$d = 50$$

11. Hobbs and Eunice _____

12. Artesia and Eunice _____

13. Lovington and Carlsbad _____

14. Find the length of the model. Then find the scale factor. The length of an actual bird is shown at the right.

_____

$5\frac{7}{8}$ in.

1 in. = 0.5 in.

Copy and Solve **Show your work on a separate piece of paper.**

15. A model of a tree is made using a scale of 1 inch = 25 feet. What is the height of the actual tree if the height of the model is $4\frac{3}{8}$ inches?

16. A map of Bakersfield has a scale of 1 inch = 5 miles. If the city is $5\frac{1}{5}$ inches across on the map, what is the actual distance across the city?

17. Tyson is creating a scale drawing of the area of his school. The rectangular drawing shows the length as 20 inches and the width as 19 inches. The drawing uses a scale of 1 inch = 3 feet. What is the actual area of the school in square feet?

18. A landscape designer created a scale drawing of a bench that will be in a garden as shown. The actual width of the bench is 6 feet, and the actual height is 3 feet. Fill in each box to complete the following statements.

— 2 in. —

a. The scale of the drawing is ☐ inch(es) = ☐ feet.

b. The height of the scale drawing is ☐ inch(es).

19. A scale drawing of a doctor's office is shown. What are the actual dimensions of the doctor's office? Explain how you found your answer.

2 in. Doctor's Office 2 in.

3 in. Key 1 in. = 20 ft

20. A carpenter sawed a piece of wood into 3 pieces. The ratio of wood pieces is 1:3:6. The longest piece is 2.5 feet longer than the shortest piece. Use the *draw a diagram* strategy to find the length of the original piece.

Solve each proportion.

21. $\dfrac{2}{5} = \dfrac{b}{25}$

22. $\dfrac{3}{7} = \dfrac{a}{49}$

23. $\dfrac{2}{9} = \dfrac{x}{99}$

24. Dante has 60 baseball cards. This is at least six more than three times as many cards as Anna. Write and solve an inequality to represent the situation.

Inquiry Lab
Scale Drawings

WHAT happens to the size of a scale drawing when it is reproduced using a different scale?

Indiana Academic Standards
7.GM.3

PS Process Standards
1, 3, 5

The owner of the miniature golf course wants to create a sign with an image of the 18th hole on it. Use the dimensions shown to create a scale drawing using the Geometer's Sketchpad®. Use the scale 1 centimeter = 3 meters.

Hands-On Activity

Step 1 Determine the length the 6 meter side and the 12 meter side will be in the drawing.

Scale	Length		Scale	Length

$$\frac{1 \text{ cm}}{3 \text{ m}} = \frac{x \text{ cm}}{6 \text{ m}} \qquad\qquad \frac{1 \text{ cm}}{3 \text{ m}} = \frac{x \text{ cm}}{12 \text{ m}}$$

$$1 \cdot 6 = 3 \cdot x \qquad\qquad\qquad 1 \cdot 12 = 3 \cdot x$$

$$x = \boxed{} \qquad\qquad\qquad x = \boxed{}$$

So, the 6 meter side will be $\boxed{}$ centimeters and the 12 meter side will be $\boxed{}$ centimeters in the drawing.

Step 2 Create the drawing using a dynamic geometry software. Then fill in the correct length for each line segment.

Investigate

Work with a partner. Use a dynamic geometry software.

1. **PS Use Math Tools** The owner wants a different size image of the 18th hole to place on the scorecards. Use the scale 1 centimeter = 6 meters. Fill in the new lengths of the line segments and draw the new scale drawing on the screen below. (*Hint:* You don't have to redraw the figure. Try clicking and dragging on the sides of your first drawing to adjust the side lengths.)

Analyze and Reflect

2. What happened to the size of the scale drawing when the scale changed from 1 centimeter = 3 meters to 1 centimeter = 6 meters?

Create

3. **PS Reason Inductively** Suppose you drew the miniature golf hole again at the scale 1 centimeter = 2 meters. Would the size of your drawing be larger or smaller than the drawing in the Activity? Explain.

4. **Inquiry** WHAT happens to the size of a scale drawing when it is reproduced using a different scale?

Draw Three-Dimensional Figures

New York City In art class, Rasheed studied buildings known for their unusual architecture. He studied the Flatiron Building shown.

Three-dimensional figures, such as the Flatiron Building, have length, width, and height. They can be viewed from different perspectives, including the *side* view and the *top* view.

1. What is the two-dimensional figure that makes up the side view?

_____

2. What is the two-dimensional figure that makes up the top view?

_____

3. Sketch the side view of the Flatiron Building.

4. Sketch the top view of the Flatiron Building.

 Show your work.

5. The top view, side view, and front view of a three-dimensional figure are shown below. Sketch the figure.

top	side	front

Which PS **Process Standards** did you use?
Shade the circle(s) that applies.

① Persevere with Problems

② Reason Abstractly

③ Construct an Argument

④ Model with Mathematics

⑤ Use Math Tools

⑥ Attend to Precision

⑦ Make Use of Structure

⑧ Use Repeated Reasoning

Draw a Three-Dimensional Figure

You can draw different views of three-dimensional figures. The most common views drawn are the top, side, and front views.

The top, side, and front views of a three-dimensional figure can be used to draw a corner view of the figure.

Examples

1. Draw a top, a side, and a front view of the figure at the right.

The top view is a triangle.

The side and front view are rectangles.

2. Draw a top, a side, and a front view of the figure at the right.

The top view is a circle.

The side and front view are triangles.

Got it? Do this problem to find out.

a. Draw a top, a side, and a front view of the figure at the right.

a. _____

Example

Tutor

3. Draw a top, a side, and a front view of the video console shown.

The top view is a rectangle.

The side and front views are also rectangles.

Got it? Do this problem to find out.

Show your work.

b. Draw a top, a side, and a front view of the tent shown.

b. _____

Example

Watch ▶ Tutor 💬

4. Draw a corner view of the three-dimensional figure whose top, side, and front views are shown.

top   side   front

Step 1 Use the top view to draw the base of the figure, a 1-by-3 rectangle.

Step 2 Add edges to make the base a solid figure.

top

Step 3 Use the side and front views to complete the figure.

front   side

Got it? Do this problem to find out.

c. Draw a corner view of the three-dimensional figure whose top, side, and front views are shown.

top   side   front

c. _____

Example

Tutor

5. Draw a corner view of the three-dimensional figure whose top view, side view, and front view are shown.

top   side   front

Step 1 Use the top view to draw the base of the figure, a 2-by-4 rectangle.

Step 2 Add edges to make the base a solid figure.

Step 3 Use the side and front views to complete the figure.

Guided Practice

Check ✓

1. Draw a top, a side, and a front view of the figure. (Examples 1–3)

Show your work.

2. Draw a corner view of the three-dimensional figure whose top view, side view, and front view are shown. (Examples 4–5)

top   side   front

3. (e) **Building on the Essential Question** How does drawing the different views of a three-dimensional figure help you have a better understanding of the figure?

Independent Practice

Go online for Step-by-Step Solutions

Draw a top, a side, and a front view of each figure. (Examples 1–2)

2.

 Show your work.

3 Draw a top, a side, and a front view of the eraser shown. (Example 3)

Draw a corner view of each three-dimensional figure whose top view, side view, and front view are shown. (Examples 4–5)

4. top   side   front

5. top   side   front

6. Name a real-world object that has a top view of a triangle, and a side and front

view that are each rectangles. _____

7. **Model with Mathematics** The Quetzalcoatl pyramid in Mexico is shown. Use the photo to sketch views from the top, side, and front of the pyramid.

Show your work.

 H.O.T. Problems Higher Order Thinking

8. **Model with Mathematics** Choose an object in your classroom or in your home. Sketch any view of the object. Choose among a top, a side, or a front view.

9. **Which One Doesn't Belong?** Identify the figure that does not have the same characteristic as the other three. Explain your reasoning.

10. **Persevere with Problems** Draw a three-dimensional figure in which the front and top views each have a line of symmetry but the side view does not.

11. **Reason Inductively** Determine whether each statement is *always*, *sometimes*, or *never* true.

   a. The bases of a cylinder have different radii. _____

   b. Two planes intersect in a single point. _____

   c. Three planes do not intersect in a point. _____

Extra Practice

Draw a top, a side, and a front view of each figure.

12.

top   side   front

13.

Homework Help

Draw a corner view of each three-dimensional figure whose top view, side view, and and front view are shown.

14. top side front

15. top   side   front

Draw a top, a side, and a front view of each figure.

16.

17.

18. **PS Find the Error** Raul drew the side, top, and front view of the figure shown at the right. Find his mistake and correct it.

side   top   front

19. The top, side, and front view of a figure made of cubes are shown.

top

front

side

Which of the following can be represented by these views? Select all that apply.

20. Draw the front, top, and side views of the three-dimensional figure shown at the right.

Spiral Review

Identify each figure as a *line segment*, *line*, or *ray*. Then name each figure using symbols.

21.
W   X

_____

22.
R

Q

_____

23. E _____ F

_____

Describe each pair of lines as *intersecting*, *perpendicular*, or *parallel*. Choose the most specific term.

24.

_____

25.

_____

26.

_____

Cross Sections

Vocabulary Start-Up

A **prism** is a three-dimensional figure with at least two parallel, congruent faces called **bases** that are polygons. A **pyramid** is a three-dimensional figure with one base that is a polygon. Its other faces are triangles.

Write *prism* or *pyramid* on the line below each figure.

_____   _____

_____   _____

Essential Question

HOW does geometry help us describe real-world objects?

Vocabulary

prism
bases
pyramid
plane
coplanar
parallel
polyhedron
edge
face
vertex
diagonal
skew lines
cylinder
cone
cross section

PS Process Standards
1, 3, 4

Real-World Link

The Rock and Roll Hall of Fame is shown below. Is the shape of the building a *prism* or *pyramid*? Explain.

_____

_____

Which PS **Process Standards** did you use?
Shade the circle(s) that applies.

① Persevere with Problems   ⑤ Use Math Tools
② Reason Abstractly   ⑥ Attend to Precision
③ Construct an Argument   ⑦ Make Use of Structure
④ Model with Mathematics   ⑧ Use Repeated Reasoning

Identify Three-Dimensional Figures

A **plane** is a flat surface that goes on forever in all directions. The figure at the right shows rectangle *ABCD*. Line segments *AB* and *DC* are **coplanar** because they lie in the same plane. They are also **parallel** because they will never intersect, no matter how far they are extended.

Just as two lines in a plane can intersect or be parallel, there are different ways that planes may be related in space.

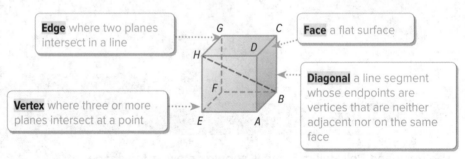

Intersect in a Line

Intersect at a Point

No Intersection

These are called *parallel planes*.

Intersecting planes can form three-dimensional figures. A **polyhedron** is a three-dimensional figure with flat surfaces that are polygons. Prisms and pyramids are both polyhedrons. Some terms associated with three-dimensional figures are *edge, face, vertex,* and *diagonal.*

Edge where two planes intersect in a line

Face a flat surface

Diagonal a line segment whose endpoints are vertices that are neither adjacent nor on the same face

Vertex where three or more planes intersect at a point

Notice in the figure above, $\overline{GC}$ and $\overline{DA}$ do not intersect. These segments are not parallel because they do not lie in the same plane. Lines that do not intersect and are not coplanar are called **skew lines**.

There are also solids that are not polyhedrons. A **cylinder** is a three-dimensional figure with two parallel congruent circular bases connected by a curved surface. A **cone** has one circular base connected by a curved side to a single vertex.

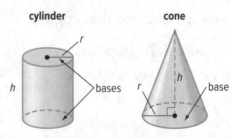

cylinder

cone

Examples

Tutor

Identify the figure. Name the bases, faces, edges, and vertices. Then, identify a pair of skew lines.

1.

The figure has one base that is a pentagon, so it is a pentagonal pyramid.

base: *RSTUV*

faces: *RSTUV, QVR, QRS, QST, QTU, QUV*

edges: $\overline{QR}, \overline{QS}, \overline{QT}, \overline{QU}, \overline{QV}, \overline{VR}, \overline{RS}, \overline{ST}, \overline{TU}, \overline{UV}$

vertices: *Q, R, S, T, U, V*

skew lines: $\overline{QV}$ and $\overline{TS}$

2.

The figure has rectangular bases that are parallel and congruent, so it is a rectangular prism.

bases: *ABCD* and *EFGH, ABFE* and *DCGH, ADHE* and *BCGF*

faces: *ABCD, EFGH, ABFE, DCGH, ADHE, BCGF*

edges: $\overline{AB}, \overline{BC}, \overline{CD}, \overline{AD}, \overline{EF}, \overline{FG}, \overline{GH}, \overline{EH}, \overline{AE},$ $\overline{BF}, \overline{CG}, \overline{DH}$

vertices: *A, B, C, D, E, F, G, H*

skew lines: $\overline{AE}$ and $\overline{FG}$

> ### Common Error
> In the drawing of a rectangular prism, the bases do not have to be on the top and bottom. Any two parallel rectangles are bases. In a triangular pyramid, any face is a base.

> **Got it?** Do this problem to find out.

a.

figure name: _____

base: _____

faces: _____

edges: _____

vertices: _____

skew lines : _____

Identify Cross Sections

The intersection of a solid and a plane is called a **cross section** of the solid.

Example

3. Describe the shape resulting from a vertical, angled, and horizontal cross section of a square pyramid.

Vertical Slice

The cross section is a triangle.

Angled Slice

The cross section is a trapezoid.

Horizontal Slice

The cross section is a square.

Got it? Do this problem to find out.

b. _____

b. Describe the shape resulting from a vertical, angled, and horizontal cross section of a cylinder.

Guided Practice

1. Identify the figure. Then name the bases, faces, edges, and vertices. Then, identify a pair of skew lines. (Examples 1–2)

figure name: _____

bases: _____

faces: _____

edges: _____

vertices: _____

skew lines: _____

2. Describe the shape resulting from the cross section shown. (Example 3) _____

3. @ **Building on the Essential Question** How can knowing the shape of the base of a three-dimensional figure help you name the figure?

_____

_____

_____

Rate Yourself!

Are you ready to move on? Shade the section that applies.

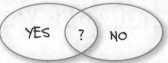

YES   ?   NO

For more help, go online to access a Personal Tutor.

Independent Practice

Go online for Step-by-Step Solutions

Identify each figure. Name the bases, faces, edges, and vertices. Then, identify a pair of skew lines. (Examples 1–2)

 1.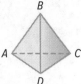

figure name: _____

bases: _____

faces: _____

_____

edges: _____

_____

vertices: _____

skew lines: _____

2.

figure name: _____

bases: _____

faces: _____

_____

edges: _____

_____

vertices: _____

skew lines _____

Describe the shape resulting from each cross section. (Example 3)

 3.

_____

4.

_____

5.

_____

6. A basketball is shaped like a *sphere*.

   a. Draw a basketball with a vertical, angled, and horizontal slice.

   b. Describe the cross section made by each slice.

   _____

   c. Is the basketball a polyhedron? Explain.

   _____

7. **PS Use a Counterexample** State whether the following conjecture is *true* or *false*. If *false*, provide a counterexample.

Two planes in three-dimensional space
can intersect at one point.

_____

_____

8. Draw and label a hexagonal prism. Then identify each of the following.

a. parallel planes _____

b. skew lines _____

c. intersecting planes _____

Show your work.

H.O.T. Problems Higher Order Thinking

9. **PS Model with Mathematics** Draw the cross sections of a polyhedron, cylinder, or cone. Exchange papers with another student. Identify the three-dimensional figures represented by the cross sections.

Show your work.

PS Persevere with Problems Determine whether each statement is *always*, *sometimes*, or *never* true. Explain your reasoning.

10. A pyramid has parallel faces.

_____

_____

_____

11. A prism has 2 bases and 4 faces.

_____

_____

_____

12. A parallelogram cannot be a cross section of a triangular prism.

_____

_____

_____

13. A pyramid has a rectangular base.

_____

_____

_____

Extra Practice

Identify each figure. Then name the bases, faces, edges, and vertices. Then identify a pair of skew lines.

14.

figure name: triangular prism _____

bases: RSV and UTW _____

faces: RSV, UTW, RSTU, SVWT, VRUW _____

edges: RS, SV, RV, UT, TW, UW, RU, VW, ST _____

vertices: R, S, T, U, V, W _____

skew lines: Sample answer: TU and WV _____

15.

figure name: _____

bases: _____

faces: _____
_____

edges: _____
_____

vertices: _____

skew lines: _____

Describe the shape resulting from each cross section. (Example 4)

16.

17.

18.

19. (PS) **Find the Error** Hannah is identifying the figure at the right. Find her mistake and correct it.

_____
_____
_____

The figure has a triangular base. It is a triangular pyramid.

20. The figure shown is a square pyramid. Which of the following are cross sections of the pyramid? Select all that apply.

21. Match each number of faces, edges, and vertices to the correct solid figure.

Figure 1
Figure 2
Figure 3

Figure 1

Figure 2

Figure 3

a. 4 faces, 6 edges, 4 vertices

b. 5 faces, 8 edges, 5 vertices

c. 5 faces, 9 edges, 6 vertices

Spiral Review

Name each polygon.

22.

23.

24.

25. Find the measure of the missing angle of the polygon. _____

21ST CENTURY CAREER
in Design Engineering

Roller Coaster Designer

If you have a passion for amusement parks, a great imagination, and enjoy building things, you might want to consider a career in roller coaster design. Roller coaster designers combine creativity, engineering, mathematics, and physics to develop rides that are both exciting and safe. In order to analyze data and make precise calculations, a roller coaster designer must have a solid background in high school math and science.

College & Career
READINESS

Is This the Career for You?

Are you interested in a career as a roller coaster designer? Take some of the following courses in high school to get started in the right direction.

◆ Algebra   ◆ Calculus
◆ Geometry   ◆ Physics
◆ Trigonometry

Turn the page to find out how math relates to a career in Design Engineering.

PS A Thrilling Ride

Use the information in the table to solve each problem.

1. In a scale drawing of SheiKra, a designer uses a scale of 1 inch = 16 feet. What is the height of the roller coaster in the drawing? _____

2. On a model of Montu, the height of the loop is 13 inches. What is the scale? _____

3. In a scale drawing of Montu, the height of the roller coaster is 10 inches. What is the scale factor? _____

4. SheiKra has a hill that goes through a tunnel. On a model of the roller coaster, the hill is 23 inches tall and the scale is 1 inch = 6 feet. What is the actual height of the tunnel hill? _____

5. An engineer is building a model of SheiKra. She wants the model to be about 32 inches high. Choose an appropriate scale for the model. Then use it to find the loop height of the model. _____

Busch Gardens Tampa		
Roller Coaster	Coaster Height (ft)	Loop Height (ft)
SheiKra	200	145
Montu	150	104

PS Career Project

It's time to update your career portfolio! Describe a roller coaster that you, as a roller coaster designer, would create. Include the height and angle of the tallest drop, the total length, maximum speed, number of loops and tunnels, and color scheme. Be sure to include the name of your roller coaster.

_____

_____

_____

_____

What problem-solving skills might you use as a roller coaster designer?

• _____
• _____
• _____
• _____
• _____

Chapter Review

Vocabulary Check

Complete the crossword puzzle using the vocabulary list at the beginning of the chapter.

Across

2. a three-dimensional figure with two parallel, congruent bases that are polygons

4. a triangle with an angle greater than 90 degrees and less than 180 degrees

8. a three-dimensional figure with two parallel congruent circular bases connected by a curved surface

11. a triangle with three congruent sides

12. segments with the same length

14. used to represent an object that is too large to be built at actual size (2 words)

15. two angles with a sum of 90 degrees

Down

1. angles that share a common vertex, a common side, and do not overlap

3. two angles with a sum of 180 degrees

5. a figure with three sides and three angles

6. the ratio that compares the measurements of a model and the real object

7. opposite angles that are formed by the intersection of two lines

8. a three-dimensional figure with one circular base connected by a curved side to a single vertex

9. an angle less than 90 degrees

10. where two rays meet to form an angle

13. a 90 degree angle

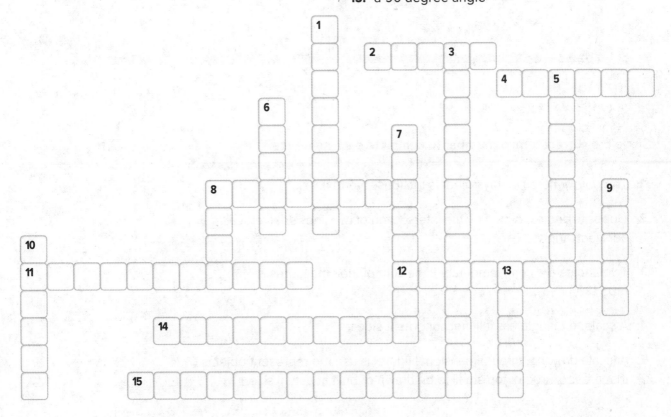

Use Your FOLDABLES

Use your Foldable to help review the chapter.

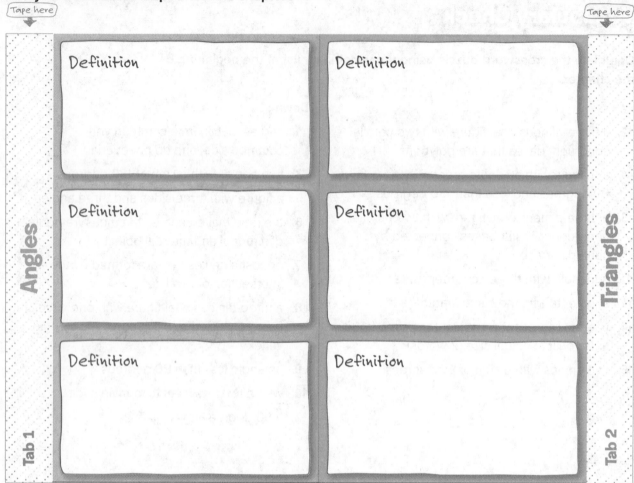

Got it?

Circle the correct term or number to complete each sentence.

1. The point where two rays meet is the (base, vertex).

2. Opposite angles formed by the intersection of two lines are (vertical, adjacent) angles.

3. Two angles are complementary if the sum of their measures is (90°, 180°).

4. A scalene triangle has (all, no) congruent sides.

5. A (scale drawing, three-dimensional figure) is used to represent objects that are too large or too small to be drawn or built at actual size.

Power Up! Performance Task

Stacking Triangles

Thompson has drawn two different triangles.

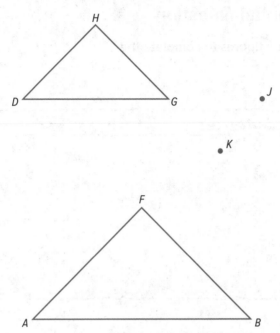

Write your answers on another piece of paper. Show all of your work to receive full credit.

Part A

Triangle *DHG* is a scale drawing of triangle *AFB*. Use a ruler. Measure and label the side lengths of triangle *AFB* and triangle *DHG*. What scale factor was used to make triangle *DHG*?

Part B

Use a scale factor of 2 to make a new scale drawing of triangle *DHG*. Label the new triangle *XYZ*.

Part C

Extend line *DG* though point *J* and extend line *HG* through point *K*. Find the measure of angle *HGJ* and angle *JGK*. Name a pair of complementary or supplementary angles. Justify your response.

Reflect

Use what you learned about geometric figures to complete the
graphic organizer.

How do polygons help us describe real-world objects?

Essential Question

HOW does geometry
help us describe
real-world objects?

How do polyhedrons help us describe real-world objects?

Answer the Essential Question. HOW does geometry help us describe
real-world objects?

Chapter 8
Measure Figures

Essential Question

How do measurements help you describe real-world objects?

Indiana Academic Standards
7.GM.5, 7.GM.6, 7.GM.7

PS Process Standards
1, 2, 3, 4, 5, 6, 8

Math in the Real World

Soccer is a sport that is played on a rectangular field. The dimensions of a regulation size soccer field are 100 yards long and 60 yards wide.

What is the area of the soccer field shown?

$A =$ ☐ square yards

100 yd

60 yd

FOLDABLES
Study Organizer

1 Cut out the Foldable on page FL9 of this book.

2 Place your Foldable on page 700.

3 Use the Foldable throughout this chapter to help you learn about measuring figures.

Vocabulary

center	lateral face	semicircle
circle	lateral surface area	slant height
circumference	pi	surface area
composite figure	radius	volume
diameter	regular pyramid	

Study Skill: Studying Math

Power Notes *Power notes* are similar to lesson outlines, but they are simpler to organize. Power notes use the numbers 1, 2, 3, and so on. You can have more than one detail under each power. You can even add drawings or examples to your power notes.

Power 1: This is the main idea.
  Power 2: This provides details about the main idea.
    Power 3: This provides details about Power 2.
      and so on...

Complete the following sample of power notes for this chapter.

1: Circles

  2: Circumference

  3: _____

  3: _____

  2: Area

  3: _____

What Do You Already Know?

Place a checkmark below the face that expresses how much you know about each concept. Then scan the chapter to find a definition or example of it.

😞 I have no clue.   😐 I've heard of it.   🙂 I know it!

Integers

Concept	😞	😐	🙂	Definition or Example
area of a circle				
area of composite figures				
lateral surface area				
pi (π)				
total surface area				
volume				

When Will You Use This?

Here are a few examples of how volume and surface area are used in the real world.

Activity 1 When wrapping a present, how do you determine how much paper to use? Describe a method that you could use to make sure that you cut the right size piece of wrapping paper.

_____

_____

_____

Activity 2 Go online at **connectED.mcgraw-hill.com** to read the graphic novel *The Dunk Tank*. How many square feet of metal sheeting do they have to build the dunk tank?

_____

Caitlyn, Dario, and Hannah in

The Dunk Tank

The school carnival is coming up soon. It's our job to design a dunk tank.

Are You Ready?

Try the Quick Check below.
Or, take the Online Readiness Quiz.

 Check ✓

Quick Review

Example 1

Find the area of the rectangle.

10 m

4 m

$A = \ell w$ Area of a rectangle
$A = (10)(4)$ Replace ℓ with 10 and w with 4.
$A = 40$ Simplify.

The area of the rectangle is 40 square meters.

Example 2

Find the area of the triangle.

5 in.   13 in.

12 in.

$A = \frac{1}{2}bh$ Area of a triangle
$A = \frac{1}{2}(12)(5)$ Replace b with 12 and h with 5.
$A = \frac{1}{2}(60)$ Multiply.
$A = 30$ Simplify.

The area of the triangle is 30 square inches.

Quick Check

Area Find the area of each figure.

1.

14 m

3 m

 Show your work.

$A = $ _____

2.

14 yd   10 yd

5 yd

$A = $ _____

3.

17 mm

9 mm

$A = $ _____

4. Anita's yard is in the shape of a triangle. It has a height of 35 feet and a base of 50 feet. What is the area of the yard?

_____

How Did You Do?

Which problems did you answer correctly in the Quick Check?
Shade those exercise numbers below.

1 2 3 4

Inquiry Lab
Circumference

 HOW is the circumference of a circle related to its diameter?

Indiana Academic Standards
7.GM.5

PS Process Standards
1, 3, 6

The distance around a flying disc, or its *circumference*, is 37.7 centimeters. The distance across the disc through its center, or its *diameter*, is 12 centimeters. How is the circumference of a circular object, such as a flying disc, related to its diameter?

 Hands-On Activity

Step 1 Cut a piece of string the length of the circumference of a circular object such as a jar lid. Use a centimeter ruler to measure the length of the string to the nearest tenth of a centimeter. Record this measurement in the table below.

Object	Circumference (C)	Diameter (d)	$\frac{C}{d}$
Disc	37.7 cm	12 cm	

Step 2 Measure and record the diameter of the lid.

Step 3 Use a calculator to find the ratio of the circumference of the flying disc to its diameter. Repeat for the circular object you measured in Steps 1 and 2. Round answers to the nearest hundredth.

Step 4 Repeat Steps 1 through 3 for other circular objects.

Describe the ratios $\frac{C}{d}$ you found. Identify the number that is closest to the value of each ratio. _____

_____

Write a rule in the form $\frac{C}{d} \approx$ ■ , where ■ is the number you identified in the question above. _____

question above. _____

Investigate

Collaborate

PS Make a Prediction Work with a partner. Measure the diameter of two different circular objects. Predict each circumference. Check your predictions by measuring. Then find each ratio $\frac{C}{d}$. Record your values to the nearest hundredth in the table below.

	Object	Diameter (d)	Predicted Circumference	Measured Circumference (C)	Ratio $\frac{C}{d}$
1.					
2.					

Analyze and Reflect

Collaborate

3. **PS Reason Inductively** How do the ratios $\frac{C}{d}$ in the table compare to the ones in the Activity? Identify the number that is closest to the value of all of the ratios.

_____

_____

Create

On Your Own

4. **PS Reason Abstractly** Write a formula in the form $\frac{C}{d} = $ ■ , that gives the approximate ratio of the circumference C of a circle to its diameter d, where ■ is the number you identified in Exercise 3. _____

5. **PS Reason Abstractly** Multiply both sides of your formula by d to write an equivalent formula in the form C = ■ × d *that gives the approximate circumference C if you know the diameter d of a circle.* _____

_____

6. **PS Reason Abstractly** The radius of a circle is one half of its diameter. Write a formula that relates the circumference C of a circle to its radius r.

_____

7. **Inquiry** HOW is the circumference of a circle related to its diameter?

_____

_____

Circumference

Vocabulary Start-Up

A **circle** is the set of all points in a plane that are the same distance from a point, called the **center**. The **circumference** is the distance around a circle. The **diameter** is the distance across a circle through its center. The **radius** is the distance from the center to any point on the circle.

Fill in each box with one of the following terms: *center*, *diameter*, and *radius*.

 ### Real-World Link

1. The table shows the approximate measurements of two sizes of hula hoops.

Size	Radius (in.)	Diameter (in.)	Circumference (in.)
child	14	28	88
adult	20	40	126

a. Describe the relationship between the diameter and radius of each hula hoop. _____

_____

b. Describe the relationship between the circumference and diameter of each hula hoop. _____

_____

Which PS **Process Standards** did you use?
Shade the circle(s) that applies.

① Persevere with Problems   ⑤ Use Math Tools

② Reason Abstractly   ⑥ Attend to Precision

③ Construct an Argument   ⑦ Make Use of Structure

④ Model with Mathematics   ⑧ Use Repeated Reasoning

Essential Question

HOW do measurements help you describe real-world objects?

Vocabulary

circle
center
circumference
diameter
radius
pi π

Indiana Academic Standards
7.GM.5

Process Standards
1, 3, 4, 6, 8

Radius and Diameter

Words   The diameter *d* of a circle is twice its radius *r*. The radius *r* of a circle is half of its diameter *d*.

Symbols $d = 2r$ $r = \dfrac{d}{2}$

Work Zone

Examples

Tutor

1. **The diameter of a circle is 14 inches. Find the radius.**

•14 in.

$r = \dfrac{d}{2}$ Radius of circle

$r = \dfrac{14}{2}$ Replace *d* with 14.

$r = 7$ Divide.

The radius is 7 inches.

- -

STOP and Reflect

The diameter of a circle is 36 inches. Circle the radius.

72 in.   18 in.

2. **The radius of a circle is 8 feet. Find the diameter.**

8 ft

$d = 2r$ Diameter of circle

$d = 2 \cdot 8$ Replace *r* with 8.

$d = 16$ Multiply.

The diameter is 16 feet.

Show your work.

a. _____

b. _____

Got it? Do these problems to find out.

c. _____

Find the radius or diameter of each circle with the given dimension.

  a. $d = 23$ cm   **b.** $r = 3$ in.

  c. $d = 16$ yd   **d.** $r = 5.2$

d. _____

Circumference

Words   The circumference of a circle is equal to π times its diameter or π times twice its radius.

Model

Symbols $C = \pi d$ or $C = 2\pi r$

In the Inquiry Lab, you learned that $\frac{C}{d} \approx 3$. The exact ratio is represented by the Greek letter **π (pi)**. The value of π is 3.1415926... . The decimal never ends, but it is often approximated as 3.14.

Another approximation for π is $\frac{22}{7}$. Use this value when the radius or diameter is a multiple of 7 or has a multiple of 7 in its numerator if the radius is a fraction.

Estimation
To estimate the circumference of a circle, you can use 3 for π since π ≈ 3.

Example

3. **Find the circumference of a circle with a radius of 21 inches.**

Since 21 is a multiple of 7, use $\frac{22}{7}$ for π.

$C = 2\pi r$ Circumference of a circle

$C \approx 2 \cdot \frac{22}{7} \cdot 21$ Replace π with $\frac{22}{7}$ and r with 21.

$C \approx 2 \cdot \frac{22}{\cancel{7}} \cdot \frac{\cancel{21}^{3}}{1}$ Divide by the GCF, 7.

$C \approx 132$ Simplify.

The circumference of the circle is about 132 inches.

Got it?   Do these problems to find out.

Find the circumference of each circle. Use $\frac{22}{7}$ for π.

e.

70 in.

f.

$\frac{7}{8}$ ft

Show your work.

e. _____

f. _____

Example

4. Big Ben is a famous clock tower in London, England. The diameter of the clock face is 23 feet. Find the circumference of the clock face. Round to the nearest tenth.

$C = \pi d$ Circumference of a circle

$C \approx 3.14(23)$ Replace π with 3.14 and d with 23.

$C \approx 72.2$ Multiply.

So, the distance around the clock is about 72.2 feet.

Got it? Do this problem to find out.

Show your work.

g. A circular fence is being placed to surround a tree. The diameter of the fence is 4 feet. How much fencing is used? Use 3.14 for π. Round to the nearest tenth if necessary.

g. _____

Guided Practice

Check ✓

Find the radius or diameter of each circle with the given dimension. (Examples 1 and 2)

1. $d = 3$ m _____

Show your work.

2. $r = 14$ ft _____

3. $d = 20$ in. _____

Find the circumference of each circle. Use 3.14 or $\frac{22}{7}$ for π. Round to the nearest tenth if necessary. (Examples 3 and 4)

4. _____

15 m

5. _____

7 yd

6. **ⓔ** **Building on the Essential Question** A circle has a circumference of about 16.3 meters and a diameter of about 5.2 meters. What is the relationship between the circumference and diameter of this circle?

_____

_____

_____

Rate Yourself!

How confident are you about finding the circumference? Check the box that applies.

For more help, go online to access a Personal Tutor.

Tutor

Independent Practice

Go online for Step-by-Step Solutions

Find the radius or diameter of each circle with the given dimensions.
(Examples 1 and 2)

1. $d = 5$ mm _____

2. $d = 24$ ft _____

3. $r = 17$ cm _____

Find the circumference of each circle. Use 3.14 or $\frac{22}{7}$ for π. Round to the nearest tenth if necessary. (Example 3)

4.

8 ft

5

13 cm

6.

3.5 mi

7. The largest tree in the world by volume is in Sequoia National Park. The diameter at the base is 36 feet. If a person with outstretched arms can reach 6 feet, how many people would it take to reach around the base of the tree? (Example 4)

8. The Belknap shield volcano is located in the Cascade Range in Oregon. The volcano is circular and has a diameter of 5 miles. What is the circumference of this volcano. Round your answer to the nearest tenth? (Example 4)

9. **PS** **Be Precise** Refer to the circle at the right.

a. Find the circumference of the circle. Use 3 as the estimate of π.

10 mm

b. Find the circumference of the circle using 3.14 for π.

c. Another estimate of π is 3.14159. Find the circumference using this estimate.

d. What do you notice about the estimate used for π and the circumference of the circle?

Copy and Solve For Exercises 10–14, show your work on a separate piece of paper.

Find the diameter given each circumference. Use 3.14 for π.

10. a satellite dish with a circumference of 957.7 meters

11. a basketball hoop with a circumference of 56.52 inches

12. a nickel with a circumference of about 65.94 millimeters

Find the distance around each figure. Use 3.14 for π.

13.

100 cm

14.

5 ft
5 ft

H.O.T. Problems Higher Order Thinking

15. ^{PS} **Justify Conclusions** Determine if the circumference of a circle with a radius of 4 feet will be greater or less than 24 feet. Explain.

_____

_____

_____

16. ^{PS} **Model with Mathematics** Draw and label a circle that has a diameter more than 5 inches, but less than 10 inches. Estimate its circumference and then find its circumference using a calculator. Compare your results.

_____

_____

Show your work.

17. ^{PS} **Persevere with Problems** Analyze how the circumference of a circle would change if the diameter was doubled. Provide an example to support your explanation.

_____

_____

_____

18. ^{PS} **Justify Conclusions** Determine whether the relationship between the circumference of a circle and its diameter is a direct variation. If so, identify the constant of proportionality. Justify your response.

_____

_____

_____

Extra Practice

Find the radius or diameter of each circle with the given dimensions.

19. $d = 7$ in. _3.5 in.___

Homework Help →

$r = \dfrac{d}{2}$

$r = \dfrac{7}{2}$ or 3.5

20. $d = 30$ m _____

21. $r = 36$ ft _____

Find the circumference of each circle. Use 3.14 or $\dfrac{22}{7}$ for π.

22.

5 in.

_____

23.

21 ft

_____

24.

$\dfrac{14}{15}$ in.

_____

25. a button with a radius of 21 millimeters

_____

26. a dunk tank with a radius of 36 inches

_____

27. The diameter of a music CD is 12 centimeters. Find the circumference

of a CD to the nearest tenth. _____

28. At a local park, Sara can choose between two circular paths to walk.
One path has a diameter of 120 yards, and the other has a radius of
45 yards. How much farther can Sara walk on the longer path than

the shorter path if she walks around the path once? _____

29. **PS** **Identify Repeated Reasoning** The diagram at the right is made up
of circles with the same center. The innermost circle has a diameter of
1 unit. Each circle moving outward has a diameter one more unit than
the previous. Without calculating, how much longer is the circumference

of each circle? _____

_____

30. A bicycle tire has a radius of 12.5 inches. Select values to complete the equation below to find the circumference of the wheel. Use 3.14 for π.

0.5	4
2	12.5
3.14	25

$C \approx$ [ ] × [ ] × [ ]

How far does the tire roll in one complete revolution?

[ ]

31. A circle with center at point O is shown. Determine if each statement is true or false.

a. $\overline{ON}$ is a radius of the circle.   ☐ True   ☐ False

b. $\overline{QM}$ is a diameter of the circle.   ☐ True   ☐ False

c. To find the circumference, multiply the length of $\overline{OL}$ by π.   ☐ True   ☐ False

Spiral Review

Find the area of each trapezoid.

32. _____

11 cm
14 cm
34 cm

33. _____

5.4 m
2.8 m
3.7 m

34. _____

83 mm
31 mm
47 mm

35. Find the area of glass used on the side of the parallelogram-shaped building shown.

_____

98 ft
377 ft

36. Find the area of a triangle with a base of 25 inches and a height of 30 inches.

_____

Inquiry Lab
Area of Circles

 Inquiry HOW are the circumference and area of a circle related?

Indiana Academic Standards
7.GM.5

PS Process Standards
1, 3, 6

Mrs. Allende wants to create a family message center on a wall in her house. There are 4 family members, including Mrs. Allende. She decides to paint 1 circle for each family member using magnetic paint. Each circle will have a 12-inch radius. How do you find the area of a circle?

Hands-On Activity

Let's develop a formula for finding the area of a circle.

Step 1 Fold a paper plate in half four times to divide it into 16 equal sections.

Step 2 Label the radius *r* as shown. Let *C* represent the circumference of the circle.

Step 3 Cut out each section. Reassemble the sections to form a parallelogram-shaped figure.

What expressions represent the measurements of the base and the height?

Base: _____   Height: _____

Substitute these values into the formula for the area of a parallelogram,

$A = b \times h$. Write the new formula. _____

Replace *C* with the expression for the circumference of a circle, $2\pi r$. Simplify the equation and describe what it represents.

_____

Investigate

Work with a partner. Use the circle to draw and label a parallelogram that would result from cutting and reassembling the circle. Use 3.14 for π.

1.

4 in.

2.

7 cm

Base: _____   Base: _____

Height: _____   Height: _____

Area of Parallelogram: _____   Area of Parallelogram: _____

Analyze and Reflect

3. **PS** **Reason Inductively** Use the formula you wrote on the previous page to find the area of the circles in Exercises 1 and 2 above. Use 3.14 for π.

Area of circle in Exercise 1: _____

Area of circle in Exercise 2: _____

4. Compare the area of the circles you found in Exercise 3 to the area of the parallelograms in Exercises 1 and 2. What do you notice? Explain.

_____

_____

Create

5. **PS** **Model with Mathematics** Find a real-world example of a circle. Measure the radius of the circle. Draw a resulting parallelogram from reassembling the circle. Then calculate the circle's area. _____

6. **Inquiry** HOW are the circumference and area of a circle related?

_____

_____

Area of Circles

Pets Adrienne bought an 8-foot leash for her dog.

1. Adrienne wants to find the distance the dog runs when it runs one circle with the leash fully extended. Should she calculate the circumference or area? Explain.

   _____

   _____

   _____

2. Suppose she wants to find the amount of running room the dog has with the leash fully extended. Should she calculate the circumference or area? Explain.

   _____

   _____

   _____

3. Describe a real-world situation that would involve finding the area of a circle.

   _____

   _____

4. Describe a real-world situation that would involve finding the circumference of a circle.

   _____

   _____

 Essential Question

HOW do measurements help you describe real-world objects?

 Vocabulary

semicircle

Indiana Academic Standards
7.GM.5

PS **Process Standards**
1, 3, 4

Which **PS** Process Standards did you use?
Shade the circle(s) that applies.

① Persevere with Problems   ⑤ Use Math Tools

② Reason Abstractly   ⑥ Attend to Precision

③ Construct an Argument   ⑦ Make Use of Structure

④ Model with Mathematics   ⑧ Use Repeated Reasoning

Key Concept

Find the Area of a Circle

Words	The area A of a circle equals the product of π and the square of its radius r.	Model

Symbols $A = \pi r^2$

Work Zone

Examples

Tutor

1. Find the area of the circle. Use 3.14 for π.

2 in.

Estimate $3 \times 2 \times 2 = 12$

$A = \pi r^2$ Area of a circle

$A \approx 3.14 \cdot 2^2$ Replace r with 2.

$A \approx 3.14 \cdot 4$ $2^2 = 2 \cdot 2$ or 4

$A \approx 12.56$ Multiply.

Check for Reasonableness $12.56 \approx 12$ ✓

The area of the circle is approximately 12.56 square inches.

2. Find the area of a circle with a radius of 14 centimeters. Use $\frac{22}{7}$ for π.

Estimate $3 \times 14 \times 14 = 588$

$A = \pi r^2$ Area of a circle

$A \approx \frac{22}{7} \cdot 14^2$ Replace π with $\frac{22}{7}$ and r with 14.

$A \approx \frac{22}{7} \cdot 196$ $14^2 = 14 \cdot 14$ or 196

$A \approx \frac{22}{\underset{1}{7}} \cdot \overset{28}{196}$ Divide by the GCF, 7.

$A \approx 616$ Multiply.

Check for Reasonableness $616 \approx 588$ ✓

The area of the circle is approximately 616 square centimeters.

STOP and Reflect

Cross out the formula that is not used for finding the area of a circle.

$A = \pi r^2$ $A = 3.14 r^2$

$A = \frac{22}{7} r^2$ $A = \frac{1}{2} bh$

Got it? Do this problem to find out.

Show your work.

a. Find the area of a circle with a radius of 3.2 centimeters. Round to the nearest tenth.

a. _____

Example

Tutor

3. Find the area of the face of the Virginia quarter with a diameter of 24 millimeters. Use 3.14 for π. Round to the nearest tenth if necessary.

The radius is $\frac{1}{2}$(24) or 12 millimeters.

$A = \pi r^2$ Area of a circle

$A \approx 3.14 \cdot 12^2$ Replace r with 12.

$A \approx 452.16$ Multiply.

The area is approximately 452.2 square millimeters.

Got it? Do this problem to find out.

b. The bottom of a circular swimming pool with a diameter of 30 feet is painted blue. How many square feet are blue?

b. _____

Area of Semicircles

A **semicircle** is half of a circle. The formula for the area of a semicircle is $A = \frac{1}{2}\pi r^2$.

Example

Tutor

4. Find the area of the semicircle. Use 3.14 for π. Round to the nearest tenth.

16 in.

$A = \frac{1}{2}\pi r^2$ Area of a semicircle

$A \approx \frac{1}{2}(3.14)8^2$ Replace r with 8.

$A \approx 0.5(3.14)(64)$ $8^2 = 8 \cdot 8$ or 64

$A \approx 100.5$ Simplify.

The area of the semicircle is approximately 100.5 square inches.

Got it? Do this problem to find out.

c. Find the approximate area of a semicircle with a radius of 6 centimeters.

c. _____

Calculating with π

When evaluating expressions involving π, using the π key on a calculator will result in a different approximation.

Show your work.

Tutor

Example

5. On a basketball court, there is a semicircle above the free-throw line that has a radius of 6 feet. Find the area of the semicircle. Use 3.14 for π. Round to the nearest tenth.

$A = \frac{1}{2}\pi r^2$ Area of a semicircle

$A \approx 0.5(3.14)(6^2)$ Replace π with 3.14 and r with 6.

$A \approx 0.5(3.14)(36)$ $6^2 = 6 \cdot 6$ or 36

$A \approx 56.5$ Multiply.

So, the area of the semicircle is approximately 56.5 square feet.

Guided Practice

Check ✓

Find the area of each circle. Round to the nearest tenth. Use 3.14 or $\frac{22}{7}$ for π. (Examples 1–3)

1.

 Show your work.

5 cm

2.

7 in.

3. diameter = 16 m

_____

4. Rondell draws the semicircle shown at the right. What is the area of the semicircle?

Use 3.14 for π. (Examples 4 and 5)

_____

 14 yd

5. **Building on the Essential Question** Name one way the circumference and area of a circle are the same and

one way they are different. _____

_____

_____

_____

Rate Yourself!

Are you ready to move on? Shade the section that applies.

YES   ?   NO

For more help, go online to access a Personal Tutor. Tutor

Independent Practice

Go online for Step-by-Step Solutions

eHelp

Find the area of each circle. Round to the nearest tenth. Use 3.14 or $\frac{22}{7}$ for π. (Examples 1–3)

1.

Show your work.

6 cm

_____

2.

28 in.

_____

3.

11 ft

_____

4. diameter = 10.5 in.

_____

5. radius = 6.3 mm

_____

6. radius = $3\frac{1}{4}$ yd

_____

7. Refer to the pets problem at the beginning of this lesson. Find the area, to the nearest tenth, of grass that Adrianne's dog may run in if the leash is 9 feet long. (Example 3) _____

8. A rotating sprinkler that sprays water at a radius of 11 feet is used to water a lawn. Find the area of the lawn that is watered. Use 3.14 for π.

(Example 3) _____

Find the area of each semicircle. Round to the nearest tenth. Use 3.14 for π. (Example 4)

9.

12 in.

_____

10. 3.6 m

_____

11.

20.4 yd

_____

12. The tunnel opening shown is a semicircle. Find the area, to the nearest tenth, of the opening of the tunnel enclosed by the semicircle. (Example 5)

_____

23 ft

13. **PS Justify Conclusions** Harry's Pizzeria is having a sale on medium and large pizzas. Medium pizzas are 10 inches in diameter and cost $7.99. Large pizzas are 14 inches in diameter and cost $14.99. Which size pizza is the better deal? Explain. (*Hint*: Find the cost per square inch of each pizza.)

H.O.T. Problems Higher Order Thinking

14. **PS Model with Mathematics** Write a real-world problem that involves finding the area of two circles. Then solve your problem.

15. **PS Reason Inductively** If the length of the radius of a circle is doubled, how does that affect the circumference and area? Explain.

PS Persevere with Problems Find the area of the shaded region in each figure. Round to the nearest tenth.

16.

17.

18.

19. **PS Persevere with Problems** Explain how you could find the area of the quarter circle shown at the right. Then write a formula that could be used to find the area of a quarter circle and use the formula to find the area to the nearest tenth.

5 in.

Extra Practice

Find the area of each circle. Round to the nearest tenth. Use 3.14 or $\frac{22}{7}$ for π.

20.

$A = \pi r^2$
$A = 3.14 \cdot 4.2^2$
$A = 55.4 \text{ m}^2$

$3.14 \times 4.2 \times 4.2 = 55.4 \text{ m}^2$

21.

12.6 cm

22.
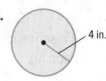
4 in.

23. diameter = 10.8 yd

24. radius = $3\frac{4}{5}$ ft

25. radius = 9.3 mm

26. Find the area of the Girl Scout patch shown if the diameter is 1.25 inches. Round to the nearest tenth.

Find the area of each semicircle. Round to the nearest tenth. Use 3.14 for π.

27.

9.6 ft

28.

4.1 mm

29.
12.8 in.

30. A window that is in the shape of a semicircle has a diameter of 28 inches. Find the area of the window. Round to the nearest tenth.

31. (PS) **Justify Conclusions** Which has a greater area, a triangle with a base of 100 feet and a height of 100 feet or a circle with diameter of 100 feet? Justify your selection.

32. A radio station sends a signal in a circular area with an 80-mile radius. Find the approximate area in square kilometers that receives the signal. (*Hint*: 1 square mile ≈ 2.6 square kilometers)

33. A large pizza at a restaurant has the dimensions shown. Find the area of the pizza. Use $\frac{22}{7}$ for π.

14 in.

[   ]

Why does it make sense to use $\frac{22}{7}$ as the estimate for π? Explain your reasoning.

[   ]

34. Refer to the figures shown below. Which figures have the same area? Select all that apply.

 16 cm

 4 cm

 6 cm

 8 cm

Spiral Review

35. A frame for a collage of pictures is in the shape of a trapezoid. The two bases are 15 inches and 20 inches. The height of the trapezoid is

12 inches. What is the area enclosed by the frame? _____

Find the area of each parallelogram. Round to the nearest tenth if necessary.

36.

10 in.

12 in.

_____

37.

5 cm

7.9 cm

_____

38.

8.7 m

11.5 m

_____

Area of Composite Figures

 Real-World Link

Stained Glass Windows An image of a stained glass window is shown below.

1. Identify two of the shapes that make up the window.

_____

_____

2. How could you find the area of the entire window except for the shapes you identified in Exercise 1?

_____

_____

_____

3. Draw a figure that is made up of a triangle and a rectangle on the grid below. Then find the area of your figure by counting square units.

Area: _____ square units

 Essential Question

HOW do measurements help you describe real-world objects?

Vocab
abc **Vocabulary**

composite figure

Indiana Academic Standards
7.GM.5

PS Process Standards
1, 2, 3, 4

Which PS Process Standards did you use?
Shade the circle(s) that applies.

① Persevere with Problems

② Reason Abstractly

③ Construct an Argument

④ Model with Mathematics

⑤ Use Math Tools

⑥ Attend to Precision

⑦ Make Use of Structure

⑧ Use Repeated Reasoning

Find the Area of a Composite Figure

A **composite figure** is made up of two or more shapes.

To find the area of a composite figure, decompose the figure into shapes with areas you know. Then find the sum of these areas.

Shape	Words	Formula
Parallelogram	The area A of a parallelogram is the product of any base b and its height h.	$A = bh$
Triangle	The area A of a triangle is half the product of any base b and its height h.	$A = \frac{1}{2}bh$
Trapezoid	The area A of a trapezoid is half the product of the height h and the sum of the bases, b_1 and b_2.	$A = \frac{1}{2}h(b_1 + b_2)$
Circle	The area A of a circle is equal to π times the square of the radius r.	$A = \pi r^2$

parallelogram

half of a circle or semicircle

trapezoid

rectangle

square

triangle

Example

Tutor

1. **Find the area of the composite figure.**

The figure can be separated into a semicircle and a triangle.

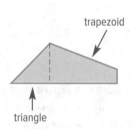
6 m
11 m

Area of semicircle

$A = \frac{1}{2}\pi r^2$

$A \approx \frac{1}{2} \cdot 3.14 \cdot 3^2$

$A \approx 14.1$

• 6 m

Area of triangle

$A = \frac{1}{2}bh$

$A = \frac{1}{2} \cdot 11 \cdot 6$

$A = 33$

6 m
11 m

The area of the figure is about $14.1 + 33$ or 47.1 square meters.

Show your work.

Got it? Do this problem to find out.

a. Find the area of the figure. Round to the nearest tenth if necessary.

20 in.
13 in.
20 in.
25 in.

a. _____

Example

Watch ▶ Tutor 💬

2. A miniature golf hole is composed of a trapezoid and a parallelogram. How many square feet of turf does the hole cover?

Area of trapezoid

$A = \frac{1}{2}h(b_1 + b_2)$

$A = \frac{1}{2}(3)(2 + 5)$

$A = 7.5$

Area of parallelogram

$A = bh$

$A = 6 \cdot 2.5$

$A = 15$

So, 7.5 + 15 or 22.5 square feet of turf will be needed.

Got it? Do this problem to find out.

b. Pedro's father is building a shed. How many square feet of wood are needed to build the back of the shed shown at the right?

b. _____

Show your work.

Find the Area of a Shaded Region

Use the areas you know to find the area of a shaded region.

Examples

Tutor 💬

3. Find the area of the shaded region.

Find the area of the rectangle and subtract the area of the four congruent triangles.

Area of rectangle

$A = \ell w$

$A = 12 \cdot 5$ $\ell = 12, w = 5$

$A = 60$ Simplify.

Area of triangles

$A = 4 \cdot \left(\frac{1}{2}bh\right)$

$A = 4 \cdot \frac{1}{2} \cdot 1 \cdot 1$ $b = 1, h = 1$

$A = 2$ Simplify.

The area of the shaded region is 60 − 2 or 58 square inches.

Congruent Triangles
Congruent triangles have corresponding sides and angles that are congruent.

4. The blueprint for a hotel swimming area is represented by the figure shown. The shaded area represents the pool. Find the area of the pool.

Find the area of the entire rectangle and subtract the section that is not shaded.

Area of the entire rectangle	**Area not shaded**
$A = \ell w$	$A = \ell w$
$A = 42 \cdot 25$ or 1,050	$A = 22 \cdot 20$ or 440

The area of the shaded region is $1,050 - 440$ or 610 square meters.

 Got it? Do this problem to find out.

c. _____

c. A diagram for a park is shown. The shaded area represents the picnic sections. Find the area of the picnic sections.

Guided Practice

1. Mike installed the window shown. How many square feet is the window? Round to the nearest tenth. Use 3.14 for π.

 (Examples 1 and 2) _____

2. A triangle is cut from a rectangle. Find the area of the shaded region.

(Examples 3 and 4) _____

3. **Building on the Essential Question** Is your answer to Exercise 1 an exact or approximate answer? Explain.

_____

_____

_____

Rate Yourself!

How confident are you about finding the area of composite figures? Check the box that applies.

For more help, go online to access a Personal Tutor.

Independent Practice

Go online for Step-by-Step Solutions

Find the area of each figure. Round to the nearest tenth if necessary. (Example 1)

1.

12 cm
4.5 cm
2 cm
5 cm

Show your work.

2.

6 yd   6 yd
16 yd
8 yd
24 yd

3.

15 cm
8 cm

4.

7 m
15 m

5.

6.4 ft
7 ft
3.6 ft
9 ft

6.

3 yd
8 yd
10 yd

7. Daniel is constructing a deck like the one shown. What is the area of the deck? (Example 2)

5 ft
3.5 ft
12 ft

Find the area of the shaded region. Round to the nearest tenth if necessary. (Examples 3 and 4)

8.

10 yd
6 yd
9 yd
15 yd

9.

13 cm
3 cm
7 cm
4 cm
2 cm
1 cm

10. **Persevere with Problems** Zoe's mom is carpeting her bedroom and needs to know the amount of floor space. How many square feet of carpeting are needed for the room? If she is also installing baseboards on the bottom of all the walls, how many feet of baseboards are needed? _____

 H.O.T. Problems Higher Order Thinking

11. **Persevere with Problems** The composite figure shown is made from a rectangle and part of a circle. Find the approximate area and perimeter of the entire figure. Round to the nearest tenth.

_____

8 ft   4 ft

12. **Reason Abstractly** The side length of the square in the figure at the right is *x* units. Write expressions that represent the perimeter and area of the figure.

_____

x

13. **Persevere with Problems** In the diagram shown at the right, a 2-foot-wide flower border surrounds the heart-shaped pond. What is the area of the border?

_____

12 ft

12 ft

14. **Model with Mathematics** Find a real-world object that is a composite figure. Measure the dimensions of the figure. Draw a model of the figure with appropriate labels. Then find the area

of the composite figure. _____

Show your work.

Extra Practice

Find the area of each figure. Round to the nearest tenth if necessary.

15.

7 m

7 m

87.5 m² _____

Homework Help

Area of circle

$A = \pi r^2$

$A = 3.14 \cdot 3.5^2$ or 38.5

Area of square

$A = lw$

$A = 7 \cdot 7$ or 49

$38.5 + 49 = 87.5$

16. _____

12 in.

11 in.

17 in.

16 in.

17.   _____

10 cm

6 cm

10 cm

20 cm

18. _____

12 cm

12 cm

6 cm

18 cm

19. A necklace comes with a gold pendant. What is the area of the pendant in square centimeters? _____

1 cm

2 cm

3 cm

1 cm

Find the area of the shaded region. Round to the nearest tenth if necessary.

20.

2 cm

2 cm

8 cm

16 cm

_____

21.

5 ft

12 ft

25 ft

_____

22. The Patel's backyard has a rectangular vegetable garden and a triangular pet exercise area.

16 ft   28 ft   21 ft   48 ft   32 ft   181 ft

Match each part of the yard with the correct area.

Pet Exercise Area: [   ] ft²

Vegetable Garden Area: [   ] ft²

Total Backyard Area: [   ] ft²

106	672
224	1,092
458	7,520
544	8,688

How much of the backyard is not being used for the vegetable garden or pet exercise area?

[   ]

23. The figure is made up of a square and four semicircles. Fill in each box to complete each statement. Round to the nearest hundredth.

6 cm   6 cm

a. The area of the square is [   ] cm².

b. The area of each semicircle is about [   ] cm².

c. The total area of the figure is about [   ] cm².

Spiral Review

24. What is the area of a triangle with a base of 52 feet and a height of 38 feet? _____

25. Find the area of the parallelogram at the right. Round to the nearest tenth. _____

1.6 cm   2.3 cm

26. Find the height of a parallelogram with an area of 104 square yards and a base of 8 yards.

_____

27. Find the base of a parallelogram with a height of 3.2 meters and an area of 15.04 square meters.

_____

Volume of Prisms

Vocabulary Start-Up

Recall that a prism is a polyhedron with two parallel, congruent bases. The bases of a *rectangular prism* are rectangles, and the bases of a *triangular prism* are triangles.

Write *rectangular prism* or *triangular prism* on the line below each figure.

_____   _____

 Essential Question

HOW do measurements help you describe real-world objects?

 Vocabulary

volume

Indiana Academic Standards
7.GM.6

PS **Process Standards**
1, 2, 3, 4

Real-World Link

1. Suppose you observed the camping tent shown from directly above. What geometric figure would you see?

_____

2. What formula would you use to find the area of the figure?

_____

Which **Process Standards did you use?**
Shade the circle(s) that applies.

① Persevere with Problems   ⑤ Use Math Tools

② Reason Abstractly   ⑥ Attend to Precision

③ Construct an Argument   ⑦ Make Use of Structure

④ Model with Mathematics   ⑧ Use Repeated Reasoning

Volume of a Rectangular Prism

Words The volume *V* of a rectangular prism is the product of the length *ℓ*, the width *w*, and the height *h*. It is also the area of the base *B* times the height *h*.

Model

Symbols $V = \ell wh$ or $V = Bh$

The **volume** of a three-dimensional figure is the measure of space it occupies. It is measured in cubic units such as cubic centimeters (cm^3) or cubic inches (in^3).

It takes 2 layers of 36 cubes to fill the box. So, the volume of the box is 72 cubic centimeters.

Work Zone

Decomposing Figures

Think of the volume of the prism as consisting of three congruent slices. Each slice contains the base area, 20 square centimeters, and a height of 1 centimeter.

Example

1. Find the volume of the rectangular prism.

$V = \ell wh$ Volume of a prism

$V = 5 \cdot 4 \cdot 3$ $\ell = 5$, $w = 4$, and $h = 3$

$V = 60$ Multiply.

The volume is 60 cubic centimeters or 60 cm^3.

Got it? Do this problem to find out.

Show your work.

a. Find the volume of the rectangular prism shown below.

a. _____

Volume of a Triangular Prism

Words	The volume V of a triangular prism is the area of the base B times the height h.	**Model**

Symbols $V = Bh$, where B is the area of the base.

Height
Do not confuse the height of the triangular base with the height of the prism.

The diagram below shows that the volume of a triangular prism is also the product of the area of the base B and the height h of the prism.

Tutor

Example

2. **Find the volume of the triangular prism shown.**

The area of the triangle is $\frac{1}{2} \cdot 6 \cdot 8$, so replace B with $\frac{1}{2} \cdot 6 \cdot 8$.

$V = Bh$ Volume of a prism

$V = \left(\frac{1}{2} \cdot 6 \cdot 8\right)h$ Replace B with $\frac{1}{2} \cdot 6 \cdot 8$.

$V = \left(\frac{1}{2} \cdot 6 \cdot 8\right)9$ The height of the prism is 9.

$V = 216$ Multiply.

The volume is 216 cubic feet or 216 ft^3.

6 ft

9 ft

8 ft

Before finding the volume of a prism, identify the base. In Example 2, the base is a triangle, so you replace B with $\frac{1}{2}bh$.

Got it? Do this problem to find out.

b. Find the volume of the triangular prism.

Show your work.

b. _____

7 in.

5 in.

4 in.

Example

3. Which lunch box holds more food?

Find the volume of each lunch box. Then compare.

Lunch Box A

$V = \ell wh$

$V = 7.5 \cdot 3.75 \cdot 10$

$V = 281.25 \text{ in}^3$

Lunch Box B

$V = \ell wh$

$V = 8 \cdot 3.75 \cdot 9.5$

$V = 285 \text{ in}^3$

Since $285 \text{ in}^3 > 281.25 \text{ in}^3$, Lunch Box B holds more food.

Guided Practice

Check ✓

Find the volume of each prism. Round to the nearest tenth if necessary.
(Examples 1–2)

1.

2.

Show your work.

3. One cabinet measures 3 feet by 2.5 feet by 5 feet. A second measures 4 feet by 3.5 feet by 4.5 feet. Which volume is greater? Explain. (Example 3)

_____

_____

4. **Building on the Essential Question** Compare and contrast finding the volume of a rectangular prism and

a triangular prism. _____

_____

_____

Rate Yourself!

How confident are you about finding volume for prisms? Check the box that applies.

☐ ☐ ☐ ☐ ☐

For more help, go online to access a Personal Tutor.

Tutor

FOLDABLES Time to update your Foldable!

Independent Practice

Go online for Step-by-Step Solutions

Find the volume of each prism. Round to the nearest tenth if necessary.
(Examples 1–2)

1. 4 m, 6 m, 8 m

2. 9 ft, 11 ft, 8 ft

3 9 m, 6 m, 4 m

Show your work.

4. Which container holds more detergent? Justify your answer. (Example 3)

13 in., 12 in., 8 in. — Soapy Suds

8 in., 9 in., 13 in. — CLEAN & BRIGHT

_____

_____

5. **PS** **Model with Mathematics** Refer to the graphic novel frame below. The table shows possible dimensions for the dunk tank.

Length (ft)	Width (ft)	Height (ft)	Surface Area (ft²)
2	12	4	136
4	4	8	144
4	7	6	160
8	5	4	144
10	4	3	124

We only have 160 square feet of metal sheeting.

a. Find the volume of each given dunk tank.

_____

b. Which dimensions are reasonable for a dunk tank? Explain.

_____

_____

6. The diagram shows the dimensions of an office. It costs about $0.11 per year to air condition one cubic foot of space. On average, how much does it cost to air condition the office for one month? _____

 H.O.T. Problems Higher Order Thinking

7. (PS) **Reason Inductively** A rectangular prism is shown.

a. Suppose the length of the prism is doubled. How does the volume change? Explain your reasoning. _____

_____

_____

b. Suppose the length, width, and height are each doubled. How does the volume change? _____

_____

c. Which will have a greater effect on the volume of the prism: doubling the height or doubling the width? Explain your reasoning.

_____

_____

_____

8. (PS) **Persevere with Problems** The prism shown has a base that is a trapezoid. Find the volume of the prism. _____

9. (PS) **Model with Mathematics** Find the volume of a real-world object that is in the shape of a rectangular or triangular prism using appropriate units. Draw a model of the prism including the dimensions. _____

Extra Practice

Find the volume of each prism. Round to the nearest tenth if necessary.

10.

10 ft

3 ft   3 ft

90 ft³

$V = lwh$

$V = 3 \cdot 3 \cdot 10$

$V = 90$

11. _____

12.5 cm

4.2 cm   4.5 cm

12. _____

2.8 yd

4.5 yd   6 yd

13. _____

3.4 mm

4.8 mm   2.5 mm

14. A toy company makes rectangular sandboxes that measure 6 feet by 5 feet by 1.2 feet. A customer buys a sandbox and 40 cubic feet of sand. Did the customer buy too much or too little sand? Justify your answer.

_____

_____

15. The base of a rectangular prism has an area of 19.4 square meters and the prism has a volume of 306.52 cubic meters. Write an equation that can be used to find the height h of the prism. Then find the height of the prism.

_____

_____

Find the volume of each prism.

16. _____

$5\frac{1}{2}$ ft

3 ft $2\frac{1}{4}$ ft

17. _____

$8\frac{3}{4}$ yd

4 yd $9\frac{1}{2}$ yd

18. **PS** **Reason Abstractly** Write a formula for finding the volume of a cube. Use an exponent and the variable s to represent the side lengths. Then use the formula to find the volume of a cube with side lengths of 7 inches.

_____

Power Up! Test Practice

19. The volume of a paperclip box is 1.5 cubic inches. Which of the following are possible dimensions of the box? Select all that apply.

☐ 2 in. by 1.5 in. by 0.5 in.   ☐ 3 in. by 0.5 in. by 1.5 in.

☐ 2 in. by 1 in. by 1 in.   ☐ 3 in. by 1 in. by 0.5 in.

20. The table shows the dimensions of 4 mailing containers. Sort the containers from least to greatest volume.

Container	Volume (ft³)
Least	
Greatest	

Container	ℓ (ft)	w (ft)	h (ft)
A	2	2	2
B	1	3	3
C	3	4	0.5
D	3	2	0.5

Which container has the greatest volume? ☐

Spiral Review

Find the perimeter of each figure.

21.
4.3 m hexagon (all sides 4.3 m)

22.
3 ft (all sides)

23.
8 cm, 2.6 cm, 4 cm, 4 cm, 4 cm, 6.6 cm

24. Write a formula for finding the perimeter of a square. Use your formula to find the perimeter of a square with side length of 0.5 inch.

PS Problem-Solving Investigation
Solve a Simpler Problem

Case #1 Playgrounds

Liam is helping to mulch the play area at the community center. The diagram shows the dimensions of the play area.

13 ft

7 ft

10 ft

8 ft

5 ft

What is the area of the play area to be mulched? Round to the nearest tenth if necessary.

ℹ️ **Indiana Academic Standards**
7.GM.5

PS **Process Standards**
1, 3

Understand *What are the facts?*

You know the shape and dimensions of the play area.

Plan *What is your strategy to solve this problem?*

Find the area of the two rectangles and the semi-circle, and then add.

Solve *How can you apply the strategy?*

Area of Rectangle 1

$A = \ell w$

$A = 5 \cdot 10$

$A = \boxed{}$

Area of Rectangle 2

$A = \ell w$

$A = 8 \cdot 7$

$A = \boxed{}$

Area of Semi-Circle

$A = \dfrac{\pi r^2}{2}$

$A = \dfrac{3.14 \cdot (3.5)^2}{2}$

$A = \boxed{}$

The total area is $\boxed{} + \boxed{} + \boxed{}$ or $\boxed{}$ square feet.

Check *Does the answer make sense?*

The play area is about 13 · 10 or 130 square feet. So, an answer

of $\boxed{}$ square feet is reasonable.

Analyze the Strategy

 Tutor

PS **Reason Inductively** Why is breaking this problem into simpler parts a good strategy to solve it?

_____

_____

Case #2 Wallpaper

Dora is painting a wall in her house.

What is the area that will be painted?

2 ft

3 ft

10 ft

12 ft

1 Understand

Read the problem. What are you being asked to find?

I need to find _____.

What information do you know?

The picture shows the wall is _____ long and _____ high.

There is a window that is _____ by _____.

2 Plan

Choose a problem-solving strategy.

I will use the _____ strategy.

3 Solve

Use your problem-solving strategy to solve the problem.

Find the area of the wall. Then subtract the area of the window.

The dimensions of the wall are [ ] feet by [ ] feet.

So, the area of the wall is [ ] × [ ] = [ ] ft².

The dimensions of the window are [ ] feet by [ ] feet.

So, the area of the window is [ ] × [ ] = [ ] ft².

[ ] – [ ] = [ ]

So, _____.

4 Check

Use information from the problem to check your answer.

Use estimation to check the reasonableness of your answer. The

area of the wall is approximately 10 × 12 = [ ] ft². The answer

is reasonable.

Work with a small group to solve the following cases.
Show your work on a separate piece of paper.

Collaborate

Case #3 Woodworking

Two workers can make two chairs in two days.

How many chairs can 8 workers working at the same rate make in 20 days?

_____

Case #4 Tips

Ebony wants to leave an 18% tip for a $19.82 restaurant bill. The tax is 6.25%, which is added to the bill before the tip.

How much money does Ebony spend at the restaurant? Explain.

_____

_____

_____

Case #5 Continents

The land area of Earth is 57,505,708 square miles.

To the nearest tenth, how much larger is the land area of Asia than North America? Explain.

_____

_____

_____

Continent	Percent of Earth's Land
Asia	30
Africa	20.2
North America	16.5

Case #6 Fountains

Mr. Flores has a circular fountain with a radius of 5 feet. He plans on installing a brick path around the fountain.

Use any strategy!

If each brick covers 2 square feet, how many bricks will he need to buy?.

_____

5 ft

9 ft

Mid-Chapter Check

Vocabulary Check

1. **PS Be Precise** Define *circumference*. Explain how to find the circumference of a circle. (Lesson 1)

_____

_____

_____

2. Fill in the blank in the sentence below with the correct term. (Lesson 3)

A _____ is made up of two or more shapes.

Skills Check and Problem Solving

Find the circumference and area of each circle. Use 3.14 for π. Round to the nearest tenth if necessary. (Lessons 1 and 2)

3. circumference = _____

   area = _____

   8 in.

4. circumference = _____

   area = _____

   4.5 cm

5. circumference = _____

   area = _____

   16.8 mi

6. The dimensions of a cardboard box are shown in the figure at the right. What is the volume of the box? (Lesson 4)

   _____

8 ft

5 ft

11 ft

7. **PS Persevere with Problems** The figure at the right represents the design for a new hole for a miniature golf course. The new turf to cover the hole costs $1.50 per square foot. How much will it cost to cover the entire area? (Lesson 3)

   _____

3 ft   7 ft

Inquiry Lab
Volume of Pyramids

 Inquiry **WHAT** is the relationship between the volume of a prism and the volume of a pyramid with the same base area and height?

Indiana Academic Standards
7.GM.6

PS **Process Standards**
1, 3, 5

A movie theater offers two different containers of popcorn: a square prism and a square pyramid. Both containers are 4 inches tall and have a base area of 16 square inches. Determine the container that holds more popcorn.

Hands-On Activity

Nets are two-dimensional patterns of three-dimensional figures.

Step 1 Draw the nets of the popcorn containers shown below onto card stock. Cut out and tape each net to form its shape. The prism and pyramid will be open. The pyramid is composed of ☐ congruent isosceles triangles with bases of 4 inches and heights of $4\frac{1}{2}$ inches.

4 in.

4 in.

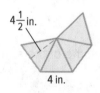

$4\frac{1}{2}$ in.

4 in.

Step 2 Fill the pyramid with rice. Pour the rice from the pyramid into the prism and repeat until the prism is full. Slide a ruler across the top to level the amount.

It took ☐ pyramids of rice to fill the prism.

So, the square _____ container holds more popcorn

than the square _____ container.

Investigate

Collaborate

PS **Use Math Tools** Work with a partner to repeat the Activity with the rectangular prism and the rectangular pyramid shown.

1. How many pyramids of rice did it take to fill the prism?

_____

2. What is true about the bases of your rectangular prism and rectangular pyramid? the heights?

_____

3. Refer to the Activity. What is true about the bases of the square prism and square pyramid? the heights?

_____

Analyze and Reflect

Collaborate

4. What fraction of the volume of the rectangular prism is the volume of the rectangular pyramid? _____

5. Refer to the Activity. What fraction of the volume of the square prism is the volume of the square pyramid? _____

Create

On Your Own

6. **PS** **Reason Inductively** How can you find volume of a pyramid given a prism with the same base area and height? Write a formula for the volume of a pyramid based on the formula for the volume of a prism.

_____

7. **Inquiry** WHAT is the relationship between the volume of a prism and the volume of a pyramid with the same base area and height?

_____

Volume of Pyramids

Real-World Link

Sand Sculpture Dion is helping his mother build a sand sculpture at the beach in the shape of a pyramid. The square pyramid has a base with a length and width of 12 inches each and a height of 14 inches.

1. Label the dimensions of the sand sculpture on the square pyramid below.

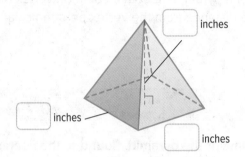

inches

inches

inches

2. What is the area of the base of the pyramid?

_____

3. What is the volume of a square prism with the same dimensions as the pyramid?

_____

 Essential Question

HOW do measurements help you describe real-world objects?

Vocab

Vocabulary

lateral face

Indiana Academic Standards
7.GM.6

PS Process Standards
1, 3, 4, 6

Which **PS Process Standards** did you use?
Shade the circle(s) that applies.

①Persevere with Problems ⑤Use Math Tools

②Reason Abstractly ⑥Attend to Precision

③Construct an Argument ⑦Make Use of Structure

④Model with Mathematics ⑧Use Repeated Reasoning

Volume of a Pyramid

Words The volume *V* of a pyramid is one third the area of the base *B* times the height of the pyramid *h*.

Model

Symbols $V = \frac{1}{3}Bh$

In a polyhedron, any face that is not a base is called a **lateral face**. The lateral faces of a pyramid meet at a common vertex. The height of a pyramid is the distance from the vertex perpendicular to the base.

Examples

Tutor

1. **Find the volume of the pyramid. Round to the nearest tenth.**

$V = \frac{1}{3}Bh$ Volume of a pyramid

$V = \frac{1}{3}(3.2 \cdot 1.4)2.8$ $B = 3.2 \cdot 1.4, h = 2.8$

$V \approx 4.2$ Simplify.

The volume is about 4.2 cubic inches.

2.8 in.
3.2 in.
1.4 in.

2. **Find the volume of the pyramid. Round to the nearest tenth.**

$V = \frac{1}{3}Bh$ Volume of a pyramid

$V = \frac{1}{3}\left(\frac{1}{2} \cdot 8.1 \cdot 6.4\right)11$ $B = \frac{1}{2} \cdot 8.1 \cdot 6.4, h = 11$

$V = 95.04$ Simplify.

The volume is about 95.0 cubic meters.

11 m
6.4 m
8.1 m

Got it? Do this problem to find out.

a. Find the volume of a pyramid that has a height of 9 centimeters and a rectangular base with a length of 7 centimeters and a width of 3 centimeters.

Show your work.

a. _____

Find the Height of a Pyramid

You can also use the formula for the volume of a pyramid to find a missing height.

Examples

3. The rectangular pyramid shown has a volume of 90 cubic inches. Find the height of the pyramid.

$V = \frac{1}{3}Bh$ Volume of a pyramid

$90 = \frac{1}{3}(9 \cdot 5)h$ $V = 90, B = 9 \cdot 5$

$90 = 15h$ Multiply.

$\dfrac{90}{15} = \dfrac{15h}{15}$ Divide by 15.

$6 = h$ Simplify.

5 in.   9 in.

The height of the pyramid is 6 inches.

- - - - - - - - - - - - - - - - - - - -

4. A triangular pyramid has a volume of 44 cubic meters. It has an 8-meter base and a 3-meter height. Find the height of the pyramid.

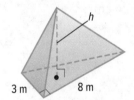

$V = \frac{1}{3}Bh$ Volume of a pyramid

$44 = \frac{1}{3}\left(\frac{1}{2} \cdot 8 \cdot 3\right)h$ $V = 44, B = \frac{1}{2} \cdot 8 \cdot 3$

$44 = 4h$ Multiply.

$\dfrac{44}{4} = \dfrac{4h}{4}$ Divide by 4.

$11 = h$ Simplify.

3 m   8 m

The height of the pyramid is 11 meters.

Multiplying Fractions

To find $\frac{1}{3} \cdot \frac{1}{2} \cdot 8 \cdot 3$,

multiply $\frac{1}{3} \cdot \frac{1}{2}$ and $8 \cdot 3$

to get $\frac{1}{6}$ and 24, then

find $\frac{1}{6}$ of 24.

Got it? Do these problems to find out.

Show your work.

b. A triangular pyramid has a volume of 840 cubic inches. The triangular base has a base length of 20 inches and a height of 21 inches. Find the height of the pyramid.

b. _____

c. A rectangular pyramid has a volume of 525 cubic feet. It has a base of 25 feet by 18 feet. Find the height of the pyramid.

c. _____

Example

5. Kamilah is making a model of the Food Guide Pyramid for a class project. Find the volume of the square pyramid.

12 in.

12 in.

12 in.

$V = \frac{1}{3}Bh$ Volume of a pyramid

$V = \frac{1}{3}(12 \cdot 12)12$ $B = 12 \cdot 12, h = 12$

$V = 576$ Multiply.

The volume is 576 cubic inches.

Guided Practice

Check ✓

Find the volume of each pyramid. Round to the nearest tenth if necessary. (Examples 1 and 2)

1. _____

25 yd

14 yd

23 yd

2. _____

2.9 cm

1.8 cm

2.2 cm

Find the height of each pyramid. (Examples 3 and 4)

3. square pyramid: volume 1,024 cm³; base edge 16 cm _____

4. triangular pyramid: volume 48 in³; base edge 9 in.; base height 4 in. _____

Show your work.

5. The Transamerica Pyramid is a skyscraper in San Francisco. The rectangular base has a length of 175 feet and a width of 120 feet. The height is 853 feet. Find the volume of the building. (Example 5) _____

6. @ **Building on the Essential Question** When you are finding the volume of a pyramid, why is it important to know the shape of the base of the pyramid?

_____

_____

Rate Yourself!

How well do you understand volume of pyramids? Circle the image that applies.

Clear   Somewhat Clear   Not So Clear

For more help, go online to access a Personal Tutor.

Tutor

FOLDABLES Time to update your Foldable!

Independent Practice

Go online for Step-by-Step Solutions

Find the volume of each pyramid. Round to the nearest tenth if necessary. (Examples 1 and 2)

1

10 ft
6 ft
8 ft

_____

2. _____

10.6 m
6.8 m
9.1 m

3. _____

6 ft
7 ft
6 ft

4. _____

11 cm
8 cm
14 cm

Find the height of each pyramid. (Examples 3 and 4)

5. rectangular pyramid: volume 448 in³; base edge 12 in.; base length 8 in.

_____

6. triangular pyramid: volume 270 cm³; base edge 15 cm; height of base 4 cm

_____

7 A glass pyramid has a height of 4 inches. Its rectangular base has a length of 3 inches and a width of 2.5 inches. Find the volume of glass used to create the pyramid. (Example 5)

_____

8. The Pyramid Arena in Memphis, Tennessee, is a square pyramid that is 321 feet tall. The base has 600-foot sides. Find the volume of the pyramid. (Example 5)

_____

9. **PS Reason Inductively** A rectangular pyramid has a length of 14 centimeters, a width of 9 centimeters, and a height of 10 centimeters. Explain the effect on the volume if each dimension were doubled.

_____

_____

10. Find the height of a square pyramid that has a volume of $25\frac{3}{5}$ meters and a base with 4 meter sides.

_____

H.O.T. Problems Higher Order Thinking

11. **PS Be Precise** A rectangular pyramid has a volume of 160 cubic feet. Find two possible sets of measurements for the base area and height

of the pyramid. _____

_____

_____

_____

12. **PS Persevere with Problems** A square pyramid and a cube have the same bases and volumes. How are their heights related? Explain.

_____

_____

13. **PS Reason Inductively** The two figures shown have congruent bases. How does the volume of the two square pyramids in Figure B compare to the volume of the square pyramid in Figure A?

_____

_____

Figure A   Figure B

14. **PS Reason Inductively** Determine whether the following statement is *true* or *false*. Explain your reasoning.

The volumes of a rectangular-based pyramid and a triangular-based pyramid with congruent heights and equal base areas are equal.

_____

_____

_____

_____

Extra Practice

Find the volume of each pyramid. Round to the nearest tenth if necessary.

15. 60 in^3 _____

12 in.

3 in.

10 in.

Homework Help →

$V = \dfrac{1}{3} Bh$

$V = \dfrac{1}{3}\left(\dfrac{1}{2} \cdot 10 \cdot 3\right) 12$

$V = 60$

16. _____

5 in.

4 in.

$6\dfrac{1}{2}$ in.

17. _____

15 yd

6 yd

13 yd

18. _____

8 cm

4.8 cm

4.8 cm

Find the height of each pyramid.

19. square pyramid: volume 297 ft^3; area of the base 81 ft^2

_____

20. hexagonal pyramid: volume 1,320 ft^3; area of the base 120 ft^2

_____

21. square pyramid: volume 550 in^3; area of the base 75 in^2

_____

22. rectangular pyramid: volume 3,800 m^3; area of the base 300 m^2

_____

23. An ancient stone pyramid has a height of 13.6 meters. The edges of the square base are 16.5 meters. Find the volume of the stone pyramid.

_____

24. The table shows the base dimensions and heights of 4 rectangular pyramids. Sort the pyramids from least to greatest volume.

Pyramid	ℓ (yd)	w (yd)	h (yd)
A	4	9	5
B	6	6	7
C	5	5	9
D	3	6	12

	Pyramid	Volume (yd³)
Least		
Greatest		

Which pyramid has the greatest volume? [ ]

25. The rectangular pyramid shown has a volume of 1,560 cubic inches. What is the height of the pyramid? Explain how you found your answer.

13 in.

15 in.

h

Spiral Review

Convert each length to feet. Then find the area of each figure in square feet.

26.

5 yd

3 yd

_____

27.

18 in.

24 in.

_____

28.

$12\frac{1}{2}$ yd

13 yd

_____

29.

72 in.

60 in.

66 in.

_____

Inquiry Lab

Nets of Three-Dimensional Figures

Inquiry HOW can models and nets help you find the surface area of prisms?

Indiana Academic Standards
7.GM.7

PS **Process Standards**
1, 3, 6

Nets are used to design and manufacture items such as boxes and labels. Find the shapes that make up the net of a cereal box.

Hands-On Activity 1

Make a net from a rectangular prism.

Step 1 Use an empty cereal box. Cut off one of the two top flaps. The remaining top flap is the top face.

Step 2 Label the top and bottom faces using a green marker. Label the front and back faces using a blue marker. Label the left and right faces using a red marker.

Step 3 Carefully cut along the three edges of the top face. Then cut down each vertical edge.

The net of a cereal box is made up of a total of ☐ rectangles.

What do you notice about the top and bottom faces, the left and right faces, and the front and back faces?

_____

Hands-On Activity 2

Make a triangular prism from a net.

Step 1 Draw a net on a piece of card stock with the dimensions shown below.

Step 2 Fold the net into a triangular prism. Tape together adjacent edges.

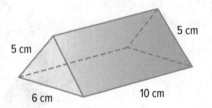

The triangular prism is made up of ☐ triangles and ☐ rectangles.

What is true about the triangular bases?

_____

How is the side of one of the rectangles related to the base of one of the triangles?

_____

Explain one way to find the total surface area of a triangular prism.

_____

_____

_____

Investigate

Collaborate

Work with a partner to solve each problem.

1. A net of a rectangular prism that is 24 inches by 18 inches by 4 inches is shown. The net of the prism is labeled with *top*, *bottom*, *side*, and *end*. Fill in the boxes to find the total area of the rectangular prism.

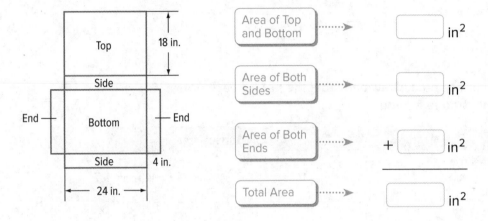

Area of Top and Bottom ┈┈┈➤ ☐ in²

Area of Both Sides ┈┈┈➤ ☐ in²

Area of Both Ends ┈┈┈➤ + ☐ in²

Total Area ┈┈┈➤ ☐ in²

2. Describe in words how you could find the total surface area of a rectangular prism.

_____

_____

3. A net of a triangular prism is shown. Fill in the boxes to find the total area of the triangular prism.

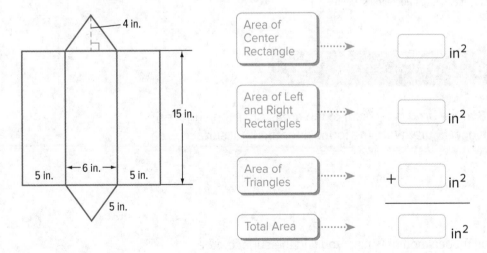

Area of Center Rectangle ┈┈┈➤ ☐ in²

Area of Left and Right Rectangles ┈┈┈➤ ☐ in²

Area of Triangles ┈┈┈➤ + ☐ in²

Total Area ┈┈┈➤ ☐ in²

4. Describe in words how you could find the total surface area of a triangular prism.

_____

_____

Analyze and Reflect

Work with a partner.

5. **PS Reason Inductively** Suppose Ladell wants to wrap a present in a container that is a rectangular prism. How can he determine the amount of wrapping paper that he will need? _____

_____

_____

Circle each correct surface area. Draw and label the net for each figure if needed. The first one is done for you.

Prism	Measures	Surface Area		
Rectangular	Length: 10 cm Width: 8 cm Height: 5 cm	170 cm^2	340 cm^2	400 cm^2
6. Rectangular	Length: 3 ft Width: 2 ft Height: 5 ft	30 ft^2	31 ft^2	62 ft^2
7. Rectangular	Length: 2 m Width: 1 m Height: 1.5 m	3 m^2	6.5 m^2	13 m^2
8. Triangular	Area of Top and Bottom Triangles: 3 mm^2 Area of Center Rectangle: 12 mm^2 Area of Left and Right Rectangles: 10 mm^2	25 mm^2	28 mm^2	38 mm^2
9. Triangular	Area of Top and Bottom Triangles: 6 in^2 Area of Center Rectangle: 50.4 in^2 Area of Left and Right Rectangles: 56 in^2	174.4 in^2	118.4 in^2	112.4 in^2

Create

10. **PS Be Precise** *Surface area* is the sum of the areas of all the surfaces of a three-dimensional figure. Write the formula for the total surface area of a rectangular prism.

_____

_____

11. **Inquiry** HOW can models and nets help you find the surface area

of prisms? _____

_____

_____

Surface Area of Cylinders

 Real-World Link

Bakery The Shiny Bright bakery is making a cake for Maria's quinceañera. The cake will be in the shape of a cylinder with a height of 4 inches and a diameter of 14 inches.

1. What are the shapes that make up the net of the cake? Sketch the net in the space provided.

_____

2. How is the length of the rectangle related to the circles that form the top and bottom of the cake?

_____

_____

3. Find the area of each part of the cake. Round to the nearest whole number.

Top: [ ] in²   Bottom: [ ] in²   Side: [ ] in²

4. Add the values from Exercise 3. What is the total

surface area of the cake? [ ] in²

  Essential Question

WHY are formulas important in math and science?

Vocab **Vocabulary**

lateral area
total surface area

Indiana Academic Standards
7.GM.7

PS Process Standards
1, 3, 4

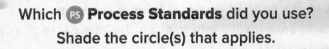

Which PS Process Standards did you use?
Shade the circle(s) that applies.

① Persevere with Problems

⑤ Use Math Tools

② Reason Abstractly

⑥ Attend to Precision

③ Construct an Argument

⑦ Make Use of Structure

④ Model with Mathematics

⑧ Use Repeated Reasoning

Key Concept > Surface Area of a Cylinder

Work Zone

Lateral Area

Words The lateral area *L.A.* of a cylinder with height *h* and radius *r* is the circumference of the base times the height.

Symbols $L.A. = 2\pi rh$

Total Surface Area

Words The surface area *S.A.* of a cylinder with height *h* and radius *r* is the lateral area plus the area of the two circular bases.

Symbols $S.A. = L.A. + 2\pi r^2$ or $S.A. = 2\pi rh + 2\pi r^2$

Model

area of base $= \pi r^2$

You can find the surface area of a cylinder using a net.

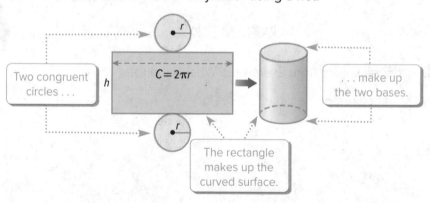

Two congruent circles . . .

$C = 2\pi r$

. . . make up the two bases.

The rectangle makes up the curved surface.

In the diagram above, the length of the rectangle is the same as the circumference of the circle, $2\pi r$. Also, the width of the rectangle is the same as the height of the cylinder.

The **lateral area** of a three-dimensional figure is the surface area of the figure, excluding the area of the base(s). So, the lateral area of a cylinder is the area of curved surface.

The **total surface area** of a three-dimensional figure is the sum of the areas of all its surfaces.

Example

Tutor

1. Find the surface area of the cylinder.
Round to the nearest tenth.

2 m

7 m

$S.A. = 2\pi rh + 2\pi r^2$ Surface area of a cylinder

$S.A. = 2\pi(2)(7) + 2\pi(2)^2$ Replace r with 2 and h with 7.

$S.A. \approx 113.1$ Simplify.

The surface area is about 113.1 square meters.

Got it? Do these problems to find out.

Show your work.

Find the surface area of each cylinder. Round to the nearest tenth.

a.

9 ft

3 ft

b.

|←14 cm→|

10 cm

a. _____

b. _____

Real World

Example

Tutor

2. A circular fence that is 2 feet high is to be built around the outside of a carousel. The distance from the center of the carousel to the edge of the fence will be 35 feet. What is the area of the fencing material that is needed to make the fence around the carousel?

You need to find the lateral area. The radius of the circular fence is 35 feet. The height is 2 feet.

$L.A. = 2\pi rh$ Lateral area of a cylinder

$L.A. = 2\pi(35)(2)$ Replace r with 35 and h with 2.

$L.A. \approx 439.8$ Simplify.

So, about 439.8 square feet of material is needed to make the fence.

Got it? Do these problems to find out.

c. Find the area of the label of a can of tuna with a radius of 5.1 centimeters and a height of 2.9 centimeters. Round to the nearest tenth.

c. _____

d. Find the total surface area of a cylindrical candle with a diameter of 4 inches and a height of 2.5 inches. Round to the nearest tenth.

d. _____

Find the total surface area of each cylinder. Round to the nearest tenth. (Example 1)

1.

Show your work.

6 yd

10 yd

2.

← 11 in. →

8 in.

3.

7.5 in.

6 in.

4.

24 cm

14 cm

5. Find the total surface area of a water tank with a height of 10 meters and a diameter of 10 meters. Round to the nearest tenth. (Example 1) _____

Find the lateral area of each cylinder. Round to the nearest tenth. (Example 2)

6.

← 6.2 in. →

6.8 in.

7.

5 ft

12 ft

8. Find the area of the label of a cylindrical potato chip container with a radius of 3.1 inches and a height of 9.2 inches. Round to the nearest tenth. (Example 2)

_____

9. ℮ **Building on the Essential Question** How is a calculation affected if you round π to 3.14 or use the π key on your calculator? Explain.

_____

_____

_____

Rate Yourself!

Are you ready to move on?
Shade the section that applies.

I have a few questions.

I'm ready to move on.

I have a lot of questions.

For more help, go online to access a Personal Tutor.

Tutor

FOLDABLES Time to update your Foldable!

Independent Practice

Go online for Step-by-Step Solutions

Find the total surface area of each cylinder. Round to the nearest tenth.
(Example 1)

1 _____

5 mm

2 mm

Show your work.

2. _____

12.5 m

9 m

3. _____

8.7 mm

5.6 mm

4. _____

$11\frac{1}{2}$ in.

4 in.

5. A cylindrical candle has a diameter of 4 inches and a height of
7 inches. To the nearest tenth, what is the total surface area of the

candle? (Example 1) _____

6. Find the total surface area of an unsharpened cylindrical pencil that has a
radius of 0.5 centimeter and a height of 19 centimeters. Round to the

nearest tenth. (Example 1) _____

Find the lateral area of each cylinder. Round to the nearest tenth. (Example 2)

7. _____

17 yd

20 yd

8. _____

7.6 mm

13 mm

9 Find the lateral area of a cylindrical copper pipe that has a diameter of
6.4 inches and a height of 12 inches. Round to the nearest tenth.

(Example 2) _____

10. **PS** **Model with Mathematics** An online store, Candles by Camilla, sells candles and other gifts. Each candle they sell is a cylinder with a height of 6 inches, and a diameter of 2.5 inches. Prior to shipping, each candle is wrapped in decorative wrapping paper, with no overlap. An order was placed online for a shipment of 70 candles.

    a. What is the least amount of paper that will be needed to wrap one candle with no overlap? _____

    b. How many square feet of wrapping paper will be needed to wrap all 70 candles? _____

H.O.T. Problems Higher Order Thinking

11. **PS** **Persevere with Problems** If the height of a cylinder is doubled, will its surface area also double? Explain your reasoning.

_____

_____

12. **PS** **Reason Inductively** Which has a greater surface area: a cylinder with radius 6 centimeters and height 3 centimeters or a cylinder with radius 3 centimeters and height 6 centimeters? Explain your reasoning.

_____

_____

_____

13. **PS** **Reason Inductively** A baker is icing a cylindrical cake with radius r and height h. The baker will ice the top and sides of the cake. Write an equation giving the total area A that the baker will ice. Explain why your equation is not the same as the formula for the total surface area of a cylinder.

_____

_____

_____

Extra Practice

Copy and Solve For Exercises 14–27, show your work and answers on a separate piece of paper.

Find the lateral area and the total surface area of each cylinder. Round to the nearest tenth.

14.

3 ft

18 ft

15.

22 cm

16 cm

16.

17.8 m

6 m

17. A lamp shade is in the shape of a cylinder with a height of 18 inches and a radius of $6\frac{3}{4}$ inches. Fabric will cover the lateral area of the lamp shade. Find the area of the fabric needed. Round to the nearest tenth.

PS Use Math Tools Estimate the surface area of each cylinder.

18.

4.8 cm

2.2 cm

19.

8.2 m

3.7 m

20.

12.8 ft

6.5 ft

21. The mail tube shown is made of cardboard and has plastic end caps. Approximately what percent of the surface area of the mail tube is cardboard?

2.5 in.

15 in.

22. **PS Persevere with Problems** A hot cocoa canister is a cylinder with a height of 24.5 centimeters and a diameter of 13 centimeters.

    a. What is the lateral area of the hot cocoa canister to the nearest tenth?

    b. How does the lateral area change if the height is divided by 2?

13 cm

24.5 cm

23. Maria is comparing how much wrapping paper it would take to wrap the containers below.

Complete each statement with the correct answers. Round answers to the nearest square inch.

Container I   **Container II**

a. The minimum amount of wrapping paper needed for

Container I is [   ] square centimeters.

b. The minimum amount of wrapping paper needed for

Container II is [   ] square centimeters.

c. Container [   ] requires [   ] more square

centimeters of wrapping paper than Container [   ].

24. Stacey has a cylindrical paper clip holder with a diameter of 2 inches and a height of 1.5 inches. Label the net of the cylinder below with the correct dimensions.

To the nearest tenth, what is the surface area of the paper clip holder? [   ]

Spiral Review

Find the surface area of each prism.

25.

0.8 ft
2.1 ft
3.4 ft

26.

5 m
14 m
5 m
4.3 m
5 m

27. Mrs. Jones is filling cone-shaped treat bags with candy. Each bag has a height of 6 inches and a radius of 0.75 inch. What is the volume of each bag? Round to the nearest tenth.

Surface Area of Prisms

Real-World Link

Message Board Members of a local recreation center are permitted to post messages on 8.5-inch by 11-inch paper on the board. Assume the signs are posted vertically and do not overlap, as shown below.

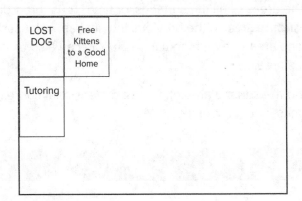

1. Suppose 6 messages fit across the board widthwise.

   What is the width of the board in inches? ☐ inches

2. Suppose 3 messages fit down the board lengthwise.

   What is the length of the board in inches? ☐ inches

3. What is the area in square inches of the message board?

4. Messages can also be posted on the other side of the board. What is the total area of the front and back of the board in square inches?

Essential Question

HOW do measurements help you describe real-world objects?

Vocab
Vocabulary

surface area

Indiana Academic Standards
7.GM.7

PS Process Standards
1, 3, 4, 6

Which **PS Process Standards** did you use?
Shade the circle(s) that applies.

① Persevere with Problems
② Reason Abstractly
③ Construct an Argument
④ Model with Mathematics
⑤ Use Math Tools
⑥ Attend to Precision
⑦ Make Use of Structure
⑧ Use Repeated Reasoning

Surface Area of a Rectangular Prism

Work Zone

Words The surface area *S.A.* of a rectangular prism with base ℓ, width *w*, and height *h* is the sum of the areas of its faces.

Model

Symbols $S.A. = 2\ell h + 2\ell w + 2hw$

The sum of the areas of all the surfaces, or faces, of a three-dimensional figure is the **surface area**. In the previous Inquiry Lab, you used a net to find the surface area of a rectangular prism. You can also use a formula to find surface area.

When you find the surface area of a three-dimensional figure, the units are square units, not cubic units.

Example

Watch Tutor

1. **Find the surface area of the rectangular prism shown at the right.**

13 in.

7 in.

9 in.

Replace ℓ with 9, *w* with 7, and *h* with 13.

surface area $= 2\ell h + 2\ell w + 2hw$

$= 2 \cdot 9 \cdot 13 + 2 \cdot 9 \cdot 7 + 2 \cdot 13 \cdot 7$

$= 234 + 126 + 182$ Multiply first. Then add.

$= 542$

The surface area of the prism is 542 square inches.

Got it? Do these problems to find out.

 Show your work.

Find the surface area of each rectangular prism.

a. _____

b. _____

a.

6 m

10 m

3 m

b. 11 mm

11 mm

11 mm

Tutor

Example

2. Domingo built a toy box 60 inches long, 24 inches wide, and 36 inches high. He has 1 quart of paint that covers about 87 square feet of surface. Does he have enough to paint the outside of the toy box? Justify your answer.

Step 1 Find the surface area of the toy box.

Replace ℓ with 60, w with 24, and h with 36.

$$\text{surface area} = 2\ell h + 2\ell w + 2hw$$
$$= 2 \cdot 60 \cdot 36 + 2 \cdot 60 \cdot 24 + 2 \cdot 36 \cdot 24$$
$$= 8{,}928 \text{ in}^2$$

Step 2 Find the number of square inches the paint will cover.

$$1 \text{ ft}^2 = 1 \text{ ft} \times 1 \text{ ft} \qquad \text{Replace 1 ft with 12 in.}$$
$$= 12 \text{ in.} \times 12 \text{ in.} \qquad \text{Multiply.}$$
$$= 144 \text{ in}^2$$

So, 87 square feet is equal to 87×144 or 12,528 square inches.

Since $12{,}528 > 8{,}928$, Domingo has enough paint.

> **Consistent Units**
>
> Since the surface area of the toy box is expressed in inches, convert 87 ft^2 to square inches so that all measurements are expressed using the same units.

Got it? Do this problem to find out.

Show your work.

c. The largest corrugated cardboard box ever constructed measured about 23 feet long, 9 feet high, and 8 feet wide. Would 950 square feet of paper be enough to cover the box? Justify your answer.

c. _____

Surface Area of Triangular Prisms

To find the surface area of a triangular prism, it is more efficient to find the area of each face and calculate the sum of all of the faces rather than using a formula.

Example

3. Marty is mailing his aunt the package shown. How much cardboard is used to create the shipping container?

14 in.
3.6 in.   3.6 in.
RUSH MAIL
4 in.
3 in.

Find the area of each face and add.

The area of each triangle is $\frac{1}{2} \cdot 4 \cdot 3$ or 6.

The area of two of the rectangles is $14 \cdot 3.6$ or 50.4. The area of the third rectangle is $14 \cdot 4$ or 56.

The sum of the areas of the faces is $6 + 6 + 50.4 + 50.4 + 56$ or 168.8 square inches.

Show your work.

Got it? Do this problem to find out.

d. Find the surface area of the triangular prism.

2.5 cm
2 cm
4 cm
3 cm

d. _____

Guided Practice

Check ✓

Find the surface area of each prism. (Examples 1–3)

1.

Show your work.

4 ft
6 ft   3 ft

_____

2.

5 m   3 m
6 m
4 m

_____

3. ℯ **Building on the Essential Question** Why is the surface area of a three-dimensional figure measured in square units rather than in cubic units?

_____

_____

_____

Rate Yourself!

Are you ready to move on?
Shade the section that applies.

YES   ?   NO

For more help, go online to access a Personal Tutor.

FOLDABLES Time to update your Foldable!

Independent Practice

Go online for Step-by-Step Solutions

eHelp

Find the surface area of each rectangular prism. Round to the nearest tenth if necessary. (Example 1)

1.

8 cm
9 cm
5 cm

Show your work.

2. _____

12 ft
1.7 ft
6.4 ft

3. When making a book cover, Anwar adds an additional 20 square inches to the surface area to allow for overlap. How many square inches of paper will Anwar use to make a book cover for a book 11 inches long, 8 inches wide, and 1 inch high? (Example 2) _____

Find the surface area of each triangular prism. (Example 3)

4. _____

10 cm
8 cm
3 cm
12 cm

5. _____

13 in.
5 in.
4 in.
12 in.

6. **PS Model with Mathematics** Refer to the graphic novel frame below. What whole number dimensions would allow the students to maximize the volume while keeping the surface area at most 160 square feet? Explain. _____

_____

We are designing a dunk tank. Remember, we want to maximize the volume and minimize the surface area.

7. Write a formula for the surface area *S.A.* of a cube in which each side measures *x* units.

_____

8. A company will make a cereal box with whole number dimensions and a volume of 100 cubic centimeters. If cardboard costs $0.05 per 100 square centimeters, what is the least cost to make 100 boxes?

_____

H.O.T. Problems Higher Order Thinking

9. PS **Reason Inductively** Determine if the following statement is *true* or *false*. Explain your reasoning.

> *If you double one of the dimensions of a rectangular prism, the surface area will double.*

_____

_____

_____

10. PS **Reason Inductively** A prism with a base that is a regular hexagon is shown. How would you find the surface area of the hexagonal prism if the area of the base of the prism is *x* square centimeters?

_____

_____

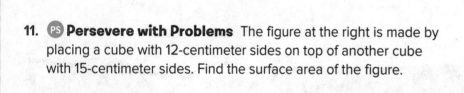

y cm

8 cm

11. PS **Persevere with Problems** The figure at the right is made by placing a cube with 12-centimeter sides on top of another cube with 15-centimeter sides. Find the surface area of the figure.

_____

12 cm

12 cm

15 cm

15 cm

12. PS **Model with Mathematics** Draw and label a rectangular prism that has a total surface area between 100 and 200 square units. Then find the surface area of your prism. _____

area of your prism. _____

Show your work.

Extra Practice

Find the surface area of each prism. Round to the nearest tenth if necessary.

13.

15 mm
8.5 mm
12.3 mm

833.1 mm^2

S.A. $= 2lh + 2lw + 2hw$

$= 2 \cdot 12.3 \cdot 15 + 2 \cdot 12.3 \cdot 8.5 + 2 \cdot 15 \cdot 8.5$

$= 369 + 209.1 + 255$

$= 833.1$

14.

3 in.
$4\frac{3}{4}$ in.
$6\frac{1}{4}$ in.

15.

3 ft   4 ft
7 ft
5 ft

16.

24 m
17.2 m
14 m
10 m

17. If one gallon of paint covers 350 square feet, will 8 gallons of paint be enough to paint the inside and outside of the fence shown once? Explain.

60 ft
6 ft
45 ft

_____

_____

_____

18. The attic shown is a triangular prism. Insulation will be placed inside all walls, not including the floor. Find the surface area that will be covered with insulation.

30 ft
15 ft
15 ft
21.2 ft

_____

19. **PS Be Precise** To the nearest tenth, find the approximate amount of plastic covering the outside of the CD case.

7.5 in.
5 in.
0.4 in.
5.6 in.

_____

20. A cardboard box has the dimensions shown. Select the correct values to complete the formula to find the surface area of the box.

2 ft

1.6 ft

2.5 ft

1.6

2

2.5

$SA =$ ▭ · ▭ · ▭ + ▭ · ▭ ·

▭ + ▭ · ▭ · ▭

How much cardboard is needed to make the box? ▭

21. A triangular prism has the dimensions shown. Fill in each box to complete each statement.

5 in. 5 in.

10 in.

5 in. 5 in.

7.1 in.

a. The area of each triangular base is ▭ square inches.

b. The area of each of the two congruent rectangular faces is ▭ square inches.

c. The area of the third rectangular face is ▭ square inches.

d. The total surface area of the prism is ▭ square inches.

Spiral Review

Describe the shape resulting from a vertical, horizontal, and angled cross section for each figure.

22.

vertical: _____

horizontal: _____

angled: _____

23.

vertical: _____

horizontal: _____

angled: _____

24.

vertical: _____

horizontal: _____

angled: _____

25.

vertical: _____

horizontal: _____

angled: _____

Inquiry Lab
Relate Surface Area and Volume

 HOW does the shape of a rectangular prism affect its volume and surface area?

🛈 **Indiana Academic Standards**
7.GM.6

🅿️🅂 **Process Standards**
1, 3, 4

You can arrange blocks in many ways. How can you arrange 8 blocks to create the least possible surface area?

What do you know? _____

_____

What do you need to find? _____

_____

Hands-On Activity 1

🛠️ Tools

Step 1   Create a rectangular prism using 8 centimeter cubes. Record the dimensions in the table below. Find and record the volume and surface area of the prism.

Rectangular Prism	Length (cm)	Width (cm)	Height (cm)	Volume (cm³)	Surface Area (cm²)
1	2	2			
2					
3					

Step 2   Repeat Step 1 for as many different rectangular prisms as you can create with 8 cubes.

Does the volume change when the prism changes? Explain.

_____

_____

The rectangular prism measuring ☐ × ☐ × ☐ has the least surface area.

Hands-On Activity 2

Suppose you make structures in the shape of the ones shown below. What is the volume of each structure? Which structure has the lesser surface area? Draw a net if necessary.

Figure 1

Figure 2

Step 1 Use centimeter cubes to create the rectangular prism shown in Figure 1. Write its dimensions, volume, and surface area in the table below.

Rectangular Prism	Length (cm)	Width (cm)	Height (cm)	Volume (cm³)	Surface Area (cm²)
Figure 1	3				
Figure 2					

Step 2 Use centimeter cubes to create the rectangular prism shown in Figure 2. Write its dimensions, volume, and surface area in the table.

Step 3 Compare the volume and surface areas of Figure 1 and Figure 2.

What do you notice about the volume of Figure 1 and Figure 2?

_____

The surface area of Figure 1 is ☐ square centimeters.

The surface area of Figure 2 is ☐ square centimeters.

Compare the surface areas using an inequality.

☐ square centimeters < ☐ square centimeters

So, Figure ☐ has the lesser surface area.

Investigate

Collaborate

Work with a partner. Compare the two figures that have the same volume. Then determine which figure has a greater surface area. Draw a net if necessary.

1.

7 ft

2 ft

6 ft

Show your work.

4 ft

3 ft

7 ft

Figure 1   **Figure 2**

Surface Area: _____   Surface Area: _____

_____

_____

2.

$\frac{1}{2}$ yd

2 yd

$\frac{1}{8}$ yd

0.5 yd

1 yd

0.25 yd

Figure 1   **Figure 2**

Surface Area: _____   Surface Area: _____

_____

_____

3.

$3\frac{4}{25}$ ft

3 ft

$\frac{2}{5}$ ft

2 ft

Figure 1

0.5 ft

10 ft

0.4 ft

0.6 ft

Figure 2

Surface Area: _____   Surface Area: _____

_____

_____

Analyze and Reflect

Work with a partner to solve the following problems. Draw a net if necessary.

4. Monique sews together pieces of fabric to make rectangular gift boxes. She only uses whole numbers. What are the dimensions of a box with a volume of 50 cubic inches that has the greatest amount of surface area?

_____

5. Thomas is creating a decorative container to fill with colored sand. He uses only whole numbers. The top of the container is open. What are the dimensions of the rectangular prism that holds 100 cubic inches with the least amount of surface area?

_____

6. **PS Construct an Argument** Zack needs to melt a stick of butter that measures 5 inches by 1 inch by 1 inch. He is going to put the butter in a pan on top of the stove. Explain why cutting the butter into smaller pieces

will help the butter melt faster. _____

_____

_____

Create

On Your Own

7. **PS Model with Mathematics** Draw a sketch of a triangular prism with a volume of 120 cubic units and a surface area of 184 square units.

Show your work.

8. **Inquiry** HOW does the shape of a rectangular prism affect its volume and surface area?

_____

_____

_____

_____

Surface Area of Pyramids

Vocabulary Start-Up

Pyramids Ancient Egyptians built pyramids, such as the one shown in the photo below. A right square pyramid has a square base and four isosceles triangles that make up the lateral faces. The **lateral surface area** is the sum of the areas of all its lateral faces. The height of each lateral face is called **slant height**.

1. Fill in the blanks on the diagram below with the terms *slant height* and *lateral face*.

2. Draw a net of a square pyramid.

Essential Question

HOW do measurements help you describe real-world objects?

Vocabulary

lateral surface area
slant height
regular pyramid

🔵 **Indiana Academic Standards**
7.GM.6

PS **Process Standards**
1, 3, 4, 5

Which **PS** **Process Standards** did you use?
Shade the circle(s) that applies.

① Persevere with Problems
② Reason Abstractly
③ Construct an Argument
④ Model with Mathematics

⑤ Use Math Tools
⑥ Attend to Precision
⑦ Make Use of Structure
⑧ Use Repeated Reasoning

Surface Area of a Pyramid

Lateral Area

Words   The lateral surface area *L.A.* of a regular pyramid is half the perimeter *P* of the base times the slant height *ℓ*.

Model

slant height *ℓ*

Symbols $L.A. = \frac{1}{2}P\ell$

Total Surface Area

Words   The total surface area *S.A.* of a regular pyramid is the lateral area *L.A.* plus the area of the base *B*.

Symbols $S.A. = B + L.A.$ or $S.A. = B + \frac{1}{2}P\ell$

A **regular pyramid** is a pyramid with a base that is a regular polygon.

Model of Regular Square Pyramid

vertex

slant height

lateral face

base

Net of Regular Square Pyramid

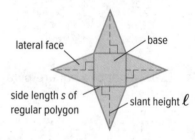

lateral face

base

side length *s* of regular polygon

slant height *ℓ*

To find the lateral area *L.A.* of a regular pyramid, refer to the net. The lateral area is the sum of the areas of the triangles.

$L.A. = 4\left(\frac{1}{2}s\ell\right)$ Area of the lateral faces

$L.A. = \frac{1}{2}(4s)\ell$ Commutative Property of Multiplication

$L.A. = \frac{1}{2}P\ell$ The perimeter of the base *P* is 4*s*.

The total surface area of a regular pyramid is the lateral surface area *L.A.* plus the area of the base *B*.

$$S.A. = B + \frac{1}{2}P\ell$$

slant height *ℓ*

area of the base *B*

perimeter of the base *P*

Examples

1. Find the total surface area of the pyramid. Round to the nearest tenth.

$S.A. = B + \frac{1}{2}P\ell$ — Surface area of a pyramid

$S.A. = 16 + \frac{1}{2}(16 \cdot 9)$ — $B = 4 \cdot 4, P = 4 \cdot 4$ or $16, \ell = 9$

$S.A. = 88$ — Simplify.

The surface area is 88 square inches.

9 in.

4 in.

4 in.

> **Perimeter of a Square**
>
> The formula for the perimeter of a square is $P = 4s$.

---

2. Find the total surface area of the pyramid with a base area of 111 square meters.

$S.A. = B + \frac{1}{2}P\ell$ — Surface area of a pyramid

$S.A. = 111 + \frac{1}{2}(48 \cdot 20)$ — $B = 111, P = 16 + 16 + 16$ or $48, \ell = 20$

$S.A. = 591$ — Simplify.

The surface area of the pyramid is 591 square meters.

20 m

16 m

16 m   16 m

---

3. Find the total surface area of the pyramid.

$S.A. = B + \frac{1}{2}P\ell$ — Surface area of a pyramid

$S.A. = 43.5 + \frac{1}{2}P\ell$ — $B = \frac{1}{2} \cdot 10 \cdot 8.7$ or 43.5

$S.A. = 43.5 + \frac{1}{2}(30 \cdot 12)$ — $P = 10 + 10 + 10$ or $30, \ell = 12$

$S.A. = 223.5$ — Simplify.

The surface area is 223.5 square feet.

10 ft   12 ft

8.7 ft

10 ft   10 ft

Got it? Do these problems to find out.

a. Find the surface area of a square pyramid that has a slant height of 8 centimeters and a base length of 5 centimeters.

b. Find the total surface area of the pyramid shown.

12 m   15 m

10.4 m

12 m   12 m

show your work.

a. _____

b. _____

Example

4. Sal is wrapping gift boxes that are square pyramids for party favors. They have a slant height of 3 inches and base edges 2.5 inches long. How many square inches of card stock are used to make one gift box?

$S.A. = B + \frac{1}{2}P\ell$ Surface area of a pyramid

$S.A. = 6.25 + \frac{1}{2}(10 \cdot 3)$ $B = 2.5^2$ or 6.25, $P = 4(2.5)$ or 10, $\ell = 3$

$S.A. = 21.25$ Simplify.

So, 21.25 square inches of card stock are used to make one gift box.

Got it? Do this problem to find out.

Show your work.

c. Amado purchased a bottle of perfume that is in the shape of a square pyramid. The slant height of the bottle is 4.5 inches and the base is 2 inches. Find the surface area.

c. _____

Guided Practice

Check ✓

Find the total surface area of each pyramid. Round to the nearest tenth.

(Examples 1–3)

1.

6.1 cm
6.4 cm
6.4 cm

Show your work.

_____

2.

9 mm   7.8 mm
7.8 mm
9 mm   9 mm

_____

3. The Washington Monument is an obelisk with a square pyramid top. The slant height of the pyramid is 55.5 feet, and the square base has sides of 34.5 feet. Find the lateral area of the pyramid. (Example 4)

_____

_____

4. @ **Building on the Essential Question** Justify the formula for the surface area of a pyramid.

_____

_____

Rate Yourself!

ow confident are you about finding the surface area of pyramids? Check the box that applies.

For more help, go online to access a Personal Tutor.

Tutor

FOLDABLES Time to update your Foldable!

Independent Practice

Go online for Step-by-Step Solutions

Find the total surface area of each pyramid. Round to the nearest tenth. (Examples 1–3)

1 7 in.

Show your work.

5 in.   5 in.

2. 15 mm

17 mm   17 mm

17 mm

$A \approx 125 \text{ mm}^2$

3.

15.9 in.

8.2 in.

8.2 in.

4. 6 m   8.3 m

6 m   6 m

5.2 m

5. A triangular pyramid has a slant height of 0.75 foot. The equilateral triangular base has a perimeter of 1.2 feet and an area of about 0.07 square foot. Find the approximate surface area. (Example 4)

_____

6. The gemstone shown is a square pyramid that has a base with sides 3.4 inches long. The slant height of the pyramid is 3.8 inches. Find the surface area of the gemstone. (Example 4)

_____

7 Isaac is building a birdhouse for a class project. The birdhouse is a regular hexagonal pyramid. The base has side lengths of 3 inches and an area of about 24 square inches. The slant height is 6 inches. Find the approximate surface area of the birdhouse. (Example 4)

_____

8. **Persevere with Problems** A square pyramid has a surface area of 175 square inches. The square base has side lengths of 5 inches. Find the slant height of the pyramid.

9. A square pyramid has a lateral area of 107.25 square centimeters and a slant height of 8.25 centimeters. Find the length of each side of its base.

H.O.T. Problems Higher Order Thinking

10. **PS** **Justify Conclusions** Suppose you could climb to the top of the Great Pyramid of Giza in Egypt. Which path would be shorter, climbing a lateral edge or the slant height? Justify your response.

11. **PS** **Model with Mathematics** Draw a rectangular pyramid and a square pyramid. Explain the differences between the two.

Rectangular Pyramid   **Square Pyramid**

12. **PS** **Persevere with Problems** The total height of the figure shown is 20 inches and the slant height is 17 inches. Which has a greater surface area, the prism or the pyramid? Explain your reasoning.

5 in.   16 in.   16 in.

Extra Practice

Find the total surface area of each pyramid. Round to the nearest tenth.

13.

12 m
9 m
9 m
9 m
35.1 m²

197.1 m^2

$S.A. = B + \frac{1}{2}Pl$

$S.A. = 35.1 + \frac{1}{2}(27 \cdot 12)$

$S.A. = 197.1$

14.

3.5 in.
2 in.
2 in. _____

Homework Help

15.

18 cm
15 cm   15 cm _____

16.

2 m   4 m
2 m   2 m
1.7 m _____

17. A square pyramid has a slant height of $4\frac{2}{3}$ feet. The base has side lengths of $2\frac{1}{4}$ feet. Find the surface area. _____

18. A building in San Francisco is shaped like a square pyramid. It has a slant height of 856.1 feet and each side of its base is 145 feet long. Find the lateral area of the building. _____

19. **PS Use Math Tools** Complete the organizer below to help you remember what each part of the formula for the surface area of a pyramid represents.

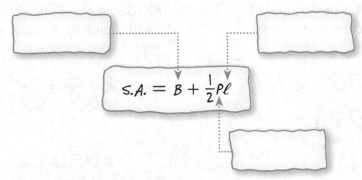

$$S.A. = B + \frac{1}{2}Pl$$

20. The base of a square pyramid has a perimeter of 28 centimeters. The height of the pyramid is 2.1 centimeters longer than the side length of the base. Label the net of the pyramid with the correct dimensions.

2.1 cm	7 cm
4 cm	9.1 cm
4.9 cm	28 cm

What is the total surface area of the pyramid?

21. An entertainment company is constructing a tent in the shape of a square pyramid, without a floor, to be used at a party. Determine if each statement is true or false.

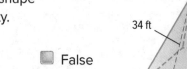

a. The area of the ground covered by the tent is 625 square feet.　☐ True　☐ False

b. The area of each triangular face of the tent is 425 square feet.　☐ True　☐ False

c. The amount of material needed to make the tent is 2,325 square feet.　☐ True　☐ False

Spiral Review

Find the surface area of each prism.

22.

60 cm
35 cm
51 cm

23.

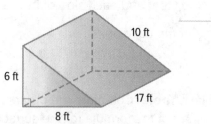

10 ft
6 ft
17 ft
8 ft

24. The volume of the prism shown below is 140 cubic meters. Find the height of the prism.

h
4 m
7 m

25. The volume of the prism shown below is 10,360 cubic feet. Find the width of the prism.

14 ft
w
74 ft

Inquiry Lab
Composite Figures

 Inquiry HOW can you find the volume and surface area of a composite figure?

A company made a model of a new office building. The building is composed of rectangular prisms. You can use centimeter cubes to find the volume of the building model.

Indiana Academic Standards
7.GM.6

PS Process Standards
1, 3, 4

Hands-On Activity 1

The model is a *composite figure* because it is made from two rectangular prisms.

Step 1 Model the top and bottom rectangular prisms using cubes.

Bottom

Top

Step 2 Count the cubes to find the dimensions. Write the dimensions in the table below. Then use the cube models to find the volume of both prisms. Write these measures in the table below step 3.

Step 3 Use the table to find the volume of the entire building model. Write these measures in the composite row of the table.

Model	Length (cm)	Width (cm)	Height (cm)	Volume (cm³)
Bottom	6	1		
Top				
Composite				

Mr. Wendell's class made a model of a house. The model was composed of a rectangular prism and a triangular prism. Determine the volume and surface area of the model house.

Hands-On Activity 2

Step 1 Use a rectangular prism to model the bottom of the house. Use a triangular prism to model the top of the house.

Step 2 Complete the tables below using the models from Step 1.

Prism	Length (cm)	Width (cm)	Height (cm)
Rectangular	4	3	

Prism	Length (cm)	Base (cm)	Height (cm)
Triangular	4	3	

Step 3 Use the information from the tables and the models to find the total volume of the model house.

☐ cm³   +   ☐ cm³   =   ☐ cm³

Volume of Rectangular Prism   Volume of Triangular Prism   Total Volume

Step 4 Use the information from the tables and the models to find the total surface area of the model house.

☐ cm²   +   ☐ cm²   –   ☐ cm²   =   ☐ cm²

Surface Area of Rectangular Prism   Surface Area of Triangular Prism   Areas where Prisms Connect   Total Surface Area

The total volume of the model house is ☐ cubic centimeters. The total surface area is ☐ square centimeters.

Investigate

Collaborate

Work with a partner.

1. **Model with Mathematics** Use the top, side, and front views to build a figure using centimeter cubes.

 Show your work.

top   side   front

a. Make a sketch of the figure you built.

 Show your work.

b. Find the volume and surface area of the figure.

Volume: _____   Surface Area: _____

Refer to the figure at the right for Exercises 2–4.

2. The figure is comprised of a _____ and a square _____.

9 cm

10 cm

10 cm   10 cm

3. Complete the following to find the volume of the figure.

a. The volume of the cube is [_____] cubic centimeters.

b. The volume of the square pyramid is 250 cubic centimeters.

c. So, the volume of the composite figure is [_____] cubic centimeters.

4. Complete the following to find the surface area of the figure.

a. The surface area of the cube is [_____] square centimeters.

b. The surface area of the square pyramid is [_____] square centimeters.

c. The area where the figures overlap is [_____] square centimeters.

d. The surface area of the composite figure is [_____] square centimeters.

Analyze and Reflect

PS Reason Inductively Work with a partner. Write each of the following statements in the correct location. One statement is done for you.

5. *measured in square units*

6. *measured in cubic units*

7. *involves adding measures of each figure*

8. *involves subtracting where figures overlap*

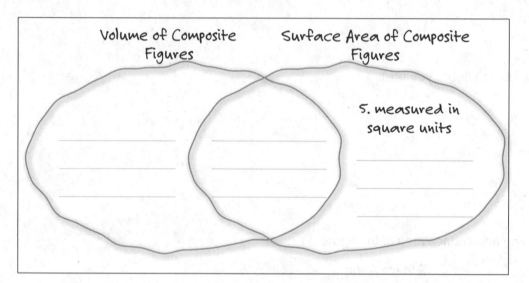

Volume of Composite Figures

Surface Area of Composite Figures

5. measured in square units

On Your Own

Create

9. **PS Model with Mathematics** Describe a real-world situation where it might be necessary to use a model or a drawing to find the volume or surface area.

_____

_____

_____

10. **Inquiry** HOW can you find the volume and surface area of a composite figure?

_____

_____

_____

_____

21ST CENTURY CAREER
in Landscape Architecture

Landscape Architect

Do you have an artistic side, and do you enjoy being outdoors? If so, a career in landscape design might be a perfect fit for you. Landscape architects design outside areas such as yards, parks, playgrounds, campuses, shopping centers, and golf courses. Their designed areas are not only meant to be beautiful, but also functional and compatible with the natural environment. A landscape architect must be proficient in mathematics, science, and the use of computer-aided design.

College & Career READINESS

Is This the Career for You?

Are you interested in a career as a landscape architect? Take some of the following courses in high school.

◆ Algebra
◆ Botany
◆ Drafting/Illustrative Design Technology
◆ Geometry
◆ Architectural Design

Find out how math relates to a career in Landscape Architecture.

Volume of a Composite Figure

The volume of a composite figure can be found by decomposing the figure into solids whose volumes you know how to find.

Examples

1. **Find the volume of the composite figure.**

Find the volume of each prism.

$V = \ell wh$

$V = 8 \cdot 6 \cdot 16$ or 768

$V = \ell wh$

$V = 8 \cdot 6 \cdot 8$ or 384

The volume is 768 + 384 or 1,152 cubic inches.

2. **Find the volume of the composite figure.**

Find the volume of the cube and the pyramid. Round to the nearest tenth.

$V = \ell wh$

$V = 8 \cdot 8 \cdot 8$ or 512

$V = \frac{1}{3}Bh$

$V = \frac{1}{3}(8 \cdot 8)5$ or 106.7

The volume is 512 + 106.7 or 618.7 cubic feet.

Show your work.

Got it? Do this problem to find out.

a. Find the volume of the composite figure.

a. _____

Surface Area of a Composite Figure

You can also find the surface area of composite figures by finding the areas of the faces that make up the composite figure.

Examples

3. Find the surface area of the figure in Example 1.

The surface is made up of three different polygons.

$A = \ell w + \ell w$

$A = (8 \cdot 16) + (8 \cdot 8)$

$A = 128 + 64$ or 192

$A = \ell w$

$A = 6 \cdot 16$

$A = 96$

$A = \ell w$

$A = 6 \cdot 8$

$A = 48$

The total surface area is $2(192) + 2(96) + 4(48)$ or 768 square inches.

- -

4. Find the surface area of the composite figure in Example 2.

The figure is made up of two different polygons.

$A = \ell w$

$A = 8 \cdot 8$ or 64

$A = \frac{1}{2}bh$

$A = \frac{1}{2} \cdot 8 \cdot 6.4$ or 25.6

The total surface area is $5(64) + 4(25.6)$ or 422.4 square feet.

Surface Area

To make it easier to see each face, sketch the faces and label the dimensions of each.

Got it? Do this problem to find out.

Show your work.

b. Find the surface area of the steps that are represented by the composite figure shown.

b. _____

Find the volume of each composite figure. Round to the nearest
tenth if necessary. (Examples 1 and 2)

1.

7 in.

8 in.

6 in.

13 in.

Show your work.

2.

4 m

2 m

4 m

6 m

4 m

Find the surface area of each composite figure. Round to the nearest tenth
if necessary. (Examples 3 and 4)

3.

3 cm

7 cm

7 cm

9 cm

18 cm

4.

9 cm

2 cm

2 cm

2 cm   4 cm   2 cm   4 cm

5. 🅔 **Building on the Essential Question** How do the
previous lessons in this chapter help you find the surface
area and volume of a composite figure?

_____

_____

_____

_____

Independent Practice

Go online for Step-by-Step Solutions

Find the volume of each composite figure. Round to the nearest tenth if necessary. (Examples 1 and 2)

1.

1.14 m
0.7 m
1.14 m
0.8 m
1.1 m
1.8 m

_____

2.

2.5 m
3 m
2 m
4 m

_____

Show your work.

Find the surface area of each composite figure. Round to the nearest tenth if necessary. (Examples 3 and 4)

3.

15 ft
20 ft
20 ft
20 ft

_____

4.

2 m
6 m
6 m
9 m
16 m

_____

5 Find the volume of the figure at the right in cubic feet. Round to the nearest tenth. (Examples 1 and 2)

12 in.
5 in.
10 in.
24 in.

_____

6. (PS) **Reason Inductively** The swimming pool at the right is being filled with water. Find the number of cubic feet that it will take to fill the swimming pool. (*Hint:* The area of a trapezoid is $A = \frac{1}{2}h(b_1 + b_2)$.) (Examples 1 and 2)

30 ft
3 ft
12 ft
8 ft
14 ft

_____

Copy and Solve **For Exercises 7–8, show your work on a separate piece of paper. Round to the nearest tenth.** (Examples 1–4)

7. Find the surface area of the figure in Exercise 1.

8. Find the volume of the figure in Exercise 4.

9. A carryout container is shown. The bottom base is a 4-inch square and the top base is a 4-inch by 6-inch rectangle. The height of the container is 5 inches. Find the volume of food

that it holds. _____

10. Refer to the house shown. Find the surface area and volume of the house. Do not include the bottom of the house when

calculating the surface area. _____

H.O.T. Problems Higher Order Thinking

11. **PS** **Model with Mathematics** Draw a composite figure that is made up of a cube and a square pyramid. Label its dimensions and find the volume

of the figure. _____

Show your work.

12. **PS** **Persevere with Problems** Draw an example of a composite figure that has a volume between 250 and 300 cubic units.

13. **PS** **Construct an Argument** Will the surface area of the figure at the right be greater than or less than 180 square inches? Explain

your reasoning. _____

_____

_____

Extra Practice

Find the volume of each composite figure. Round to the nearest tenth if necessary.

14.

4 in.

7 in.

10 in.

5 in.

450 in^3

15.

7 in.

5 in.

4 in.

8 in.

Rectangular Prism

$V = lwh$

$V = 5 \cdot 10 \cdot 7$

$V = 350$

Triangular Prism

$V = Bh$

$V = \frac{1}{2} \cdot 10 \cdot 4 \cdot 5$

$V = 100$

Total Volume $= 350 + 100$ or 450 in^3

Find the surface area of each composite figure. Round to the nearest tenth if necessary.

16.

4 yd

5 yd

4 yd

5 yd

9 yd

17.

6.1 cm

5 cm

5 cm

6 cm

7 cm

18. (PS) **Find the Error** Seth is finding the surface area of the composite figure shown. Find his mistake and correct it.

6 cm

6 cm

4 cm

5 cm

6 cm

6 cm

$V = \frac{1}{3}Bh + s^3$

$V = \frac{1}{3} \cdot 36 \cdot 4 + 6^3$

$V = 264 \text{ cm}^3$

19. Refer to the composite figure with the dimensions shown. Fill in the boxes to complete each statement.

   a. The volume of the composite figure is [_____].

   b. The total surface area of the composite figure is [_____].

20. Refer to the composite figure with the dimensions shown.

Select the correct values to complete the expression to find the volume of the figure.

$V =$ [____] $\cdot \dfrac{1}{3} \cdot$ [____] $\cdot$ [____] $\cdot$ [____]

What is the volume of the composite figure?

[_____]

    2
    3
    4
    6
    8

Spiral Review

Draw a net for each figure.

21.

Show your work.

22.

6 mm
6 mm
6 mm

23.

24.

21ST CENTURY CAREER
in Landscape Architecture

Landscape Architect

Do you have an artistic side, and do you enjoy being outdoors? If so, a career in landscape design might be a perfect fit for you. Landscape architects design outside areas such as yards, parks, playgrounds, campuses, shopping centers, and golf courses. Their designed areas are not only meant to be beautiful, but also functional and compatible with the natural environment. A landscape architect must be proficient in mathematics, science, and the use of computer-aided design.

College & Career READINESS

Explore college and careers at ccr.mcgraw-hill.com

Is This the Career for You?

Are you interested in a career as a landscape architect? Take some of the following courses in high school.

◆ Algebra
◆ Botany
◆ Drafting/Illustrative Design Technology
◆ Geometry
◆ Architectural Design

Find out how math relates to a career in Landscape Architecture.

ⓅⓈ Planting in Circles

For each problem, use the information in the designs.

1. In Design 2, what is the radius of the larger grassy area? _____

2. The small circular fountain in Design 1 is surrounded by a stone wall. Find the circumference of the wall. Use $\frac{22}{7}$ for π.

   _____

3. Find the circumference of the smaller grassy area in Design 2. Use 3.14 for π.

   _____

4. In Design 2, how much greater is the lawn area in the larger circle than in the smaller circle? Use 3.14 for π. _____

5. In Design 2, the smaller circle is surrounded by a path 1 meter wide. What is the outer circumference of the path? Use the π key on a calculator and round to the nearest tenth.

   _____

6. In Design 1, the area of the large circular patio is about 201.1 square feet. What is the radius of the patio? Round to the

   nearest foot. _____

Design 1

10 m

4 m

Design 2

ⓅⓈ Career Project

It's time to update your career portfolio! Download free landscaping software from the Internet and use it to create your own landscape design. Include a list of all the plants, materials, and hard elements used in your design. Also, provide an estimate of the total cost of the landscaping project.

_____

_____

_____

_____

What is something you really want to do in the next ten years?

- _____
- _____
- _____
- _____
- _____

Chapter Review

Vocabulary Check

Complete each sentence using the vocabulary list at the beginning of the chapter. Then (circle) the word that completes the sentence in the word search.

1. The distance across a circle through its center is called the _____.

2. The _____ is the distance from the center to any point on the circle.

3. A _____ is the set of all points in a plane that are the same distance from a point.

4. The point in a circle from which all other points are equidistant is called the _____.

5. The distance around a circle is the _____.

6. The ratio of circumference to diameter is called _____.

7. A _____ is half of a circle.

8. A _____ figure is made up of two or more shapes.

9. The _____ of a three-dimensional figure is the measure of the space it occupies.

10. The sum of the areas of all the faces of a three-dimensional figure is the _____ area.

11. The triangular faces of a pyramid that are not bases are _____ faces.

12. The height of each lateral face of a pyramid is called the _____ height.

```
G U H M I R H X P E S F S S Q W C P A C O Q
P I B A E V O L U M E E V W Z A X S D O O C
P G J T V C T Y A G E R M R Q A Q I E M I O
C N N C D E D Z M M L R L I I N A D P P I D
M E Z C K G H N L O C P I V C M C W Z O C Z
C H C I R C U M F E R E N C E I P M C S N P
X E O V G B L H V Z I B B T P T R S O I C N
S Y V T D K L A B W C O E E T J L C V T D L
S P M T Y S U Z R I T R J Q O R Y B L E Y Q
Y P V S Z B E Z O E H N W G J C T T Q E H S
P R D B T T L D W T T N W Y X Z S V J X L J
E K A J N J G W C M P A C D M K L M O S L P
A I Y D A Z X F Q F C X L Y M Y A W X F Z F
V X Y M I N H P I W D U Z L A T N Q L O Q J
Z U O Y M U U K K K L I C E W H T A J M U H
E C A F R U S G Z E X K W S T R X J X K I K
```

Use Your FOLDABLES

Use your Foldable to help review the chapter.

Tape here →   ← Tape here

Volume

Volume =

Surface area =

Volume =

Surface area =

5 cm   4 cm   3 cm

3.2 in.   2.9 in.   12 in.   3 in.

height = 2.8 in.

Surface Area

Tab 1   Tab 2

Got it?

Circle the correct term or number to complete each sentence.

1. The diameter of a circle is (twice, three times) its radius.

2. The area of a circle equals the product of pi and the square of its (radius, diameter).

3. The volume of a rectangular prism can be found by multiplying the area of the base times the (length, height).

4. To find the surface area of a triangular prism, find the area of each face and calculate the (sum, product) of all the faces.

Power Up! Performance Task

Juice Box Packaging

Supreme Packaging Company manufactures juice boxes for juice
companies. They are examining different ways to make the juice boxes
using various lengths, widths, and heights. The measurements of one
juice box are shown.

Write your answers on another piece of paper. Show all of your
to receive full credit.

Part A

What is the volume of the juice box shown? The company received an order to
make a jumbo juice box that has twice the volume as the one shown. Could you
double the current dimensions to make the jumbo juice box at the suggested
volume? Explain.

Part B

Draw and label a net to find the surface area of the original juice box. It costs
Supreme Packaging $0.02 per square inch to create one juice box. The company
groups eight juice boxes together as one package. How much does it cost to
create one package?

Part C

An artist created the picture of the citrus fruit on the label. The picture is a circle
and has an area of 12.56 square inches. Will the artist's picture fit on the juice box
label? Explain. Use 3.14 for π.

Reflect

Answering the Essential Question

Use what you learned about measuring figures to complete the graphic organizer.

Circumference

Area

Essential Question

HOW do measurements help you describe real-world objects?

Volume

Surface Area

Answer the Essential Question. HOW do measurements help you describe real-world objects?

_____

_____

UNIT PROJECT

Watch ▶

Turn Over a New Leaf The flatness of leaves serves an important purpose. In this project you will:

- **Collaborate** with your classmates as you research the primary function of leaves.

- **Share** the results of your research in a creative way.

- ℮ **Reflect** on how you use different measurements to solve real-life problems.

Collaborate

⏻ **Go Online** Work with your group to research and complete each activity. You will use your results in the Share section on the following page.

1. Suppose you have a cube that is 10 centimeters on each side. Find the volume, surface area, and surface area to volume ratio.

2. Disassemble the cube from Exercise 1 into centimeter cubes. Arrange the cubes in a 50-by-20-by-1 prism. Find the volume, surface area, and surface area to volume ratio.

3. Compare and contrast the volume, surface area, and surface area to volume ratio from Exercises 1 and 2.

4. Trace the outline of a leaf onto centimeter grid paper. Estimate the volume of the leaf. (Assume the height of your leaf is 0.1 centimeter.) Estimate the surface area. (You can ignore the edge of the leaf.) Find the surface area to volume ratio.

5. Do research to find the primary function of a leaf. Explain how the surface area to volume ratio of a leaf aids in its function.

6. Find examples from nature or man-made objects that have a small surface area to volume ratio. Explain the benefits.

With your group, decide on a way to share what you have learned about the surface area to volume ratio of leaves. Some suggestions are listed below, but you could also think of other creative ways to present your information. Remember to show how you used mathematics to complete each of the activities in this project!

- Create a digital presentation that compares two types of leaves. Use what you learned about surface area to volume ratios in your presentation.
- Imagine you discovered a new type of leaf. Create an annotated diagram of your leaf. The annotations should include the type of information you learned in this project.

Check out the note on the right to connect this project with other subjects.

 with Science

Environmental Literacy Write a paragraph detailing facts about the leaves you researched. Some questions to consider are:

- What are the names of the trees that dropped these leaves?
- Are these types of trees common in your state?

Reflect

On Your Own

6. **Answer the Essential Question** How can you use different measurements to solve real-life problems?

   a. How did what you learned about geometric figures help you use different measurements to solve real-life problems in this project?

   _____

   _____

   _____

   b. How did what you learned about measuring figures to help you use different measurements to solve real-life problems in this project?

   _____

   _____

   _____

UNIT 5
Statistics and Probability

Essential Question

WHY is learning mathematics important?

Chapter 9
Probability

Probability describes the likelihood of an event occurring. In this chapter, you will develop probability models and find probabilities of simple and compound events.

Chapter 10
Statistics

Statistics can be used to draw conclusions about a population. In this chapter, you will use random samples to make predictions and compare populations.

Math Genes A *Punnett Square* is a diagram that is used to predict the genetic traits of offspring.

A pea plant can be tall (described by TT, TS, or ST) or short (described by SS). Complete the Punnett Square below. What percent of the outcomes indicate that the offspring will be short? _____

At the end of Chapter 10, you'll complete a project in which you use pets' traits to make predictions about their offspring. Put on your lab coat and grab your math tool kit to begin this adventure!

Chapter 9
Probability

 Essential Question

HOW can you predict the outcome of future events?

Indiana Academic Standards
7.DSP.5, 7.DSP.6, 7.DSP.7

PS Process Standards
1, 3, 4, 5

Math in the Real World

Probability is the likelihood or chance of an event occurring.

At the beginning of a football game, a coin is tossed to determine which team receives the ball first. Fill in the table below to indicate the number of times a team would expect to win the coin toss based on the number of games played.

HOME	Number of Games	Number of Coin Toss Wins	AWAY
	4		
	10		
	22		
	50		

FOLDABLES
Study Organizer

 1 Cut out the Foldable on page FL11 of this book.

 2 Place your Foldable on page 786.

3 Use the Foldable throughout this chapter to help you learn about probability.

What Tools Do You Need?

Vocabulary

complementary events	outcome	simple event
compound event	permutation	simulation
dependent events	probability	theoretical probability
experimental probability	random	tree diagram
fair	relative frequency	uniform probability model
Fundamental Counting Principle	sample space	unfair
independent events		

Review Vocabulary

Fractions, Decimals, and Percents Equivalent rational numbers are numbers that have the same value. For example, three-fourths is equivalent to 0.75 or 75%.

A probability can be expressed as a fraction, decimal, or percent. For each rational number, write the missing equivalent values. Write fractions in simplest form.

What Do You Already Know?

List three things you already know about probability in the first section. Then list three things you would like to learn about probability in the second section.

Probability

What I know	What I want to find out

When Will You Use This?

Here are a few examples of how probability is used in the real world.

Activity 1 Have you ever read something like "The chances of winning are 75%." or "30% of the people surveyed said that they prefer vanilla ice cream."? Use the Internet to find an example like the ones given. Describe your example and what it means to you.

_____

_____

_____

_____

Activity 2 Go online at **connectED.mcgraw-hill.com** to read the graphic novel **Radio Surveys**. What type of information do Jamar and Theresa want to learn from their survey?

_____

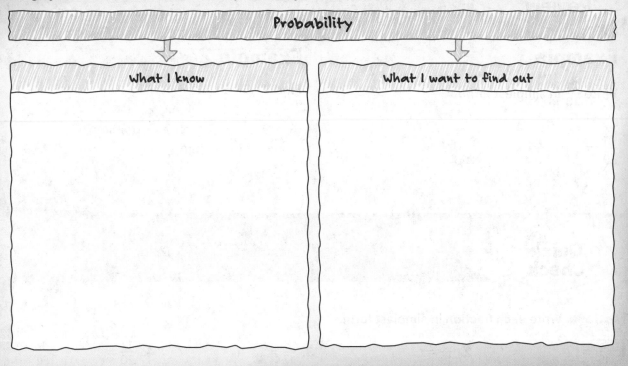

Jamar and Theresa in

Radio Surveys

WGRV FM 92.8

Are you ready for our first task as radio station interns?

I'm ready! It's gonna be fun! What should we do first?

Are You Ready?

Try the Quick Check below.
Or, take the Online Readiness Quiz.

 Check ✓

Quick Review

Example 1

Write $\frac{21}{28}$ in simplest form.

$$\frac{21}{28} = \frac{3}{4}$$

Divide the numerator and denominator by the GCF, 7.

Example 2

Find $7 \cdot 6 \cdot 5 \cdot 4$.

$$7 \cdot 6 \cdot 5 \cdot 4 = 42 \cdot 5 \cdot 4$$
$$= 210 \cdot 4$$
$$= 840$$

Multiply from left to right.

Quick Check

Fractions Write each fraction in simplest form.

1. $\frac{5}{15} =$ _____

2. $\frac{3}{18} =$ _____

3. $\frac{8}{12} =$ _____

4. $\frac{12}{20} =$ _____

Show your work.

Products Find each product.

5. $6 \cdot 5 =$ _____

6. $10 \cdot 9 \cdot 8 =$ _____

7. $4 \cdot 3 \cdot 2 \cdot 1 =$ _____

8. Suppose you listen to 9 songs each hour for 5 hours every day this week. How many songs will you have listened to this week?

_____

How Did You Do?

Which problems did you answer correctly in the Quick Check?
Shade those exercise numbers below.

① ② ③ ④ ⑤ ⑥ ⑦ ⑧

Probability of Simple Events

Vocabulary Start-Up

Probability is the chance that some event will occur. A **simple event** is one outcome or a collection of outcomes. What is an **outcome**?

Math Definition		Real-World Definition
A possible result in a probability experiment.	Outcome	_____

Real-World Link

For a sledding trip, you randomly select one of the four hats shown. Complete the table to show the possible outcomes.

Hat Selection Outcomes			
Outcome 1	green hat	Outcome 3	
Outcome 2		Outcome 4	

1. Write a ratio that compares the number of blue hats to the total number of hats. _____

2. Describe a hat display in which you would have a better chance of selecting a red hat.

   _____

   _____

Which **PS Process Standards** did you use?
Shade the circle(s) that applies.

① Persevere with Problems
② Reason Abstractly
③ Construct an Argument
④ Model with Mathematics
⑤ Use Math Tools
⑥ Attend to Precision
⑦ Make Use of Structure
⑧ Use Repeated Reasoning

Probability

Words	The probability of an event is a ratio that compares the number of favorable outcomes to the number of possible outcomes.
Symbols	$P(event) = \dfrac{\text{number of favorable outcomes}}{\text{number of possible outcomes}}$

STOP and Reflect

In the space below, describe an example of a simple event that is certain to occur.

The probability of a chance event is a number between 0 and 1 that expresses the likelihood of the event occurring. Greater numbers indicate greater likelihood. A probability near 0 indicates an unlikely event, a probability around $\frac{1}{2}$ indicates an event that is neither unlikely nor likely, and a probability near 1 indicates a likely event.

Probability can be written as a fraction, decimal, or percent.

Impossible	Unlikely	As likely to happen as not	Likely	Certain
0	$\frac{1}{4}$	$\frac{1}{2}$	$\frac{3}{4}$	1
0	0.25	0.5	0.75	1
0%	25%	50%	75%	100%

Outcomes occur at **random** if each outcome is equally likely to occur.

Example

There are six equally likely outcomes if a number cube with sides labeled 1 through 6 is rolled.

1. **Find $P(6)$ or the probability of rolling a 6.**

There is only one 6 on the number cube.

$P(6) = \dfrac{\text{number of favorable outcomes}}{\text{number of possible outcomes}}$

$= \dfrac{1}{6}$

The probability of rolling a 6 is $\frac{1}{6}$, or about 17%, or about 0.17.

Show your work.

Got it? Do this problem to find out.

a. _____

a. A coin is tossed. Find the probability of the coin landing on heads. Write your answer as a fraction, percent, and decimal.

Example

Tutor

2. **Find the probability of rolling a 2, 3, or 4 on the number cube.**

The word *or* indicates that the number of favorable outcomes needs to include the numbers 2, 3, and 4.

$$P(2, 3, \text{ or } 4) = \frac{\text{number of favorable outcomes}}{\text{number of possible outcomes}}$$

$$= \frac{3}{6} \text{ or } \frac{1}{2} \quad \text{Simplify.}$$

The probability of rolling a 2, 3, or 4 is $\frac{1}{2}$, 50%, or 0.5.

Got it? Do these problems to find out.

The spinner at the right is spun once. Find the probability of each event. Write each answer as a fraction, percent, and decimal.

   b. *P*(F)   **c.** *P*(D or G)   **d.** *P*(vowel)

Show your work.

b. _____

c. _____

d. _____

Find Probability of the Complement

Complementary events are two events in which either one or the other must happen, but they cannot happen at the same time. For example, a coin can either land on heads or *not* land on heads. The sum of the probability of an event and its complement is 1 or 100%.

Example

Tutor

Complement

In everyday language complement means the quantity required to make something complete. This is similar to the math meaning.

3. **Find the probability of *not* rolling a 6 in Example 1.**

The probability of *not* rolling a 6 and the probability of rolling a 6 are complementary. So, the sum of the probabilities is 1.

$$P(6) + P(not\ 6) = 1 \quad \text{\small $P(6)$ and $P(not\ 6)$ are complements.}$$

$$\frac{1}{6} + P(not\ 6) = 1 \quad \text{\small Replace $P(6)$ with $\frac{1}{6}$.}$$

$$\frac{1}{6} + \frac{5}{6} = 1 \quad \text{\small THINK } \frac{1}{6} \text{ plus what number equals 1?}$$

The probability of *not* rolling a 6 is $\frac{5}{6}$, or about 83% or 0.83.

Got it? Do this problem to find out.

   e. A bag contains 5 blue, 8 red, and 7 green marbles. A marble is selected at random. Find the probability the marble is *not* red.

e. _____

Example

4. Mr. Harada surveyed his class and discovered that 30% of his students have blue eyes. Identify the complement of this event. Then find its probability.

The complement of having blue eyes is *not* having blue eyes. The sum of the probabilities is 100%.

$P(\text{blue eyes}) + P(\textit{not} \text{ blue eyes}) = 100\%$ *P*(blue eyes) and *P*(*not* blue eyes) are complements.

$30\% + P(\textit{not} \text{ blue eyes}) = 100\%$ Replace *P*(blue eyes) with 30%.

$30\% + 70\% = 100\%$ **THINK** 30% plus what number equals 100%?

So, the probability that a student does *not* have blue eyes is 70%, 0.7, or $\frac{7}{10}$.

Guided Practice

A letter tile is chosen randomly. Find the probability of each event. Write each answer as a fraction, percent, and decimal. (Examples 1–3)

1. $P(D)$ _____

2. $P(S, V, \text{ or } L)$ _____

3. $P(\textit{not } D)$ _____

4. The probability of choosing a "Go Back 1 Space" card in a board game is 25%. Describe the complement of this event and find its probability. (Example 4) _____

_____

_____

_____

5. **Building on the Essential Question** Explain the relationship between the probability of an event and its complement. Give an example.

_____

_____

_____

_____

Rate Yourself!

How confident are you about finding the probability of simple events? Shade the ring on the target.

For more help, go online to access a Personal Tutor.

FOLDABLES Time to update your Foldable!

Independent Practice

Go online for Step-by-Step Solutions

The spinner shown is spun once. Find the probability of each event. Write each answer as a fraction, percent, and decimal. (Examples 1–3)

1. *P*(blue)

_____

2. *P*(red or yellow)

_____

3 *P*(*not* brown)

_____

4. *P*(*not* green)

_____

5 Refer to the table on air travel at selected airports. Suppose a flight that arrived at El Centro is selected at random. What is the probability that the flight did *not* arrive on time? Write the answer as a fraction, decimal, and percent. Explain your reasoning. (Example 4)

Air Travel	
Airport	**Arrivals (Percent on-time)**
El Centro (CA)	80
Baltimore (MD)	82

_____

_____

6. **(PS) Model with Mathematics** Refer to the graphic novel frame below. Jamar and Theresa decide to create a music mix and include an equal number of songs from each genre. What is the probability that any given song would be from the hip-hop genre? _____

CD-R WRITING...

Other surveys in cities like ours say there are five kinds of music that the kids like— country, classical, hip-hop, oldies, and alternative.

We gave surveys to 100 teens.

We want to make sure there are all five types on this mix CD for the school dance.

One jelly bean is picked, without looking, from the dish. Write a sentence that explains how likely it is for each event to happen.

7. black

_____

_____

_____

8. purple, red, or yellow

_____

_____

_____

 H.O.T. Problems Higher Order Thinking

9. (PS) **Persevere with Problems** The probability of landing in a certain section on a spinner can be found by considering the size of the angle formed by that section. On spinner shown, the angle formed by the yellow section is one-fourth of the angle formed by the entire circle. So, $P(\text{yellow}) = \frac{1}{4}$, 0.25, or 25%.

a. Determine $P(\text{green})$ and $P(\text{orange})$ for the spinner. Write the probabilities as fractions, decimals, and percents.

_____

b. Determine $P(not \text{ yellow})$.

_____

10. (PS) **Persevere with Problems** A bag contains 6 red, 4 blue, and 8 green marbles. How many marbles of each color should be added so that the total number of marbles is 27, but the probability of randomly selecting one marble of each color remains unchanged? _____

_____

_____

11. (PS) **Which One Doesn't Belong?** Circle the pair of probabilities that does not belong with the other three. Explain your reasoning.

| $0.625, \frac{3}{8}$ | $0.38, 62\%$ | $\frac{7}{8}, 0.125$ | $70\%, \frac{1}{3}$ |

_____

_____

Extra Practice

Ten cards numbered 1 through 10 are mixed together and then one card is drawn. Find the probability of each event. Write each answer as a fraction, percent, and decimal.

12. *P*(8)

$\frac{1}{10}$, 10%, or 0.1

Only 1 card has an 8. So,
P(8) is $\frac{1}{10}$, 10%, or 0.1.

13. *P*(7 or 9)

$\frac{1}{5}$, 20%, or 0.2

There is 1 card with a 7 and 1 card with a 9. So, *P*(7 or 9) is $\frac{1}{5}$, or 20%, or 0.2.

14. *P*(less than 5)

Homework Help

15. *P*(greater than 3)

16. *P*(odd)

17. *P*(even)

18. *P*(*not* a multiple of 4)

19. *P*(*not* 5, 6, 7, or 8)

20. *P*(divisible by 3)

21. Of the students at Grant Middle School, 63% are girls. The school newspaper is randomly selecting a student to be interviewed. Describe the complement of selecting a girl and find the probability of the complement. Write the answer as a fraction, decimal, and percent.

22. The table shows the number of dogs and cats at a groomer. If a pet is selected at random to be groomed, find the probability that Patches the cat will be selected. Then find the probability that a cat will be selected.

| Pets at the Groomer | |
Cats	Dogs
12	16

23. **PS Persevere with Problems** For a certain game, the probability of choosing a card with the number 13 is $\frac{8}{1,000}$. Find the probability of *not* choosing a card with the number 13. Then describe the likelihood of the event occurring.

24. The types of songs on Max's MP3 player are shown on the graph. Max will play one of the songs at random. Complete the model below to find P(country or R&B).

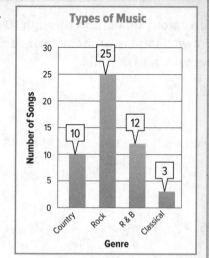

Types of Music

P(country or R&B) =

$$\frac{\boxed{} + \boxed{}}{\boxed{} + \boxed{} + \boxed{} + \boxed{}} = \boxed{}$$

25. Joel has a bowl containing the numbers of colored candies shown in the table. Which of the following probabilities are correct? Select all that apply.

☐ $P(\text{red}) = \frac{1}{4}$

☐ $P(\text{yellow}) = \frac{1}{10}$

☐ $P(\text{orange}) = \frac{1}{5}$

☐ $P(\text{green}) = \frac{2}{5}$

Color	Number
Red	5
Orange	3
Yellow	1
Green	6

Spiral Review

Compare each decimal using <, >, or =.

26. 0.2 ◯ 0.3

27. 0.75 ◯ 0.7

28. 5.89 ◯ 5.899

29. Dwayne misses 12% of his foul shots and Bryan misses 0.2 of his foul shots. Write 12% and 0.2 as fractions in simplest form. Then compare the fractions to determine who misses more foul shots.

Inquiry Lab

Relative Frequency

 Inquiry HOW is probability related to relative frequency?

Indiana Academic Standards
7.DSP.5, 7.DSP.7

PS Process Standards
1, 3

In a board game, you get an extra turn if you roll doubles or two of the same number.

You can conduct an experiment to find the relative frequency of rolling doubles using two number cubes. **Relative frequency** is the ratio of the number of experimental successes to the number of experimental attempts.

Hands-On Activity

Tools

Step 1 Complete the table to show all of the possible outcomes for rolling two number cubes. Shade all of the possible outcomes that are doubles.

The probability of rolling

doubles is _____ .

(1, 1)	(2, 1)				
(1, 2)	(2, 2)				
(1, 3)	(2, 3)				
(1, 4)					
(1, 5)					
(1, 6)					

How many times would you expect doubles to be rolled if you roll the

number cubes 50 times? Explain. _____

_____

Step 2 Roll two number cubes and record the number of doubles in the table. Repeat the experiment 50 times.

Number of Rolls	50
Number of Doubles	

Step 3 Find the relative frequency of rolling doubles. Use the

ratio $\dfrac{\text{number of times doubles were rolled}}{\text{number of rolls}}$. _____

Compare the ratios in Steps 1 and 3. What do you notice? Explain.

_____

_____

Suppose the number cubes are rolled 100 times. Would you expect the results to be the same? Explain why or why not.

_____

_____

Investigate

Work with a partner.

1. Place a paperclip around the tip of a pencil. Then place the tip on the center of the spinner. Spin the paperclip 40 times. Record the results in the table below.

Section	A	B	C	D
Frequency				
Relative Frequency				

The spinner above is spun once. Find the probability of each event.

2. $P(A)$ _____

3. $P(B)$ _____

4. $P(C)$ _____

5. $P(D)$ _____

Analyze and Reflect

6. Based on your results from the spinner experiment, are the outcomes of A, B, C, or D equally likely? _____

7. **PS Reason Inductively** What would you expect to happen to the long-run relative frequency of spinning an A as you increase the number of spins from 40 to 1,000? _____

_____

Create

8. **PS Justify Conclusions** If you rolled a number cube 600 times, approximate the relative frequency of rolling a 3 or 6. Explain your reasoning to a classmate. _____

9. **Inquiry** HOW is probability related to relative frequency?

_____

_____

Theoretical and Experimental Probability

 Real-World Link

 Watch

Carnival Games The prize wheels for a carnival game are shown. You receive a less expensive prize if you spin and win on wheel A. You receive a more expensive prize if you spin and win on wheel B.

Wheel A

Wheel B

Essential Question

HOW can you predict the outcome of future events?

Vocabulary

uniform probability model
theoretical probability
experimental probability

ⓘ **Indiana Academic Standards**
7.DSP.6

PS Process Standards
1, 3, 4

In a **uniform probability model**, each outcome has an equal probability of happening.

1. Which wheel has uniform probability? _____

2. Use a paperclip and the tip of your pencil to spin each wheel 4 times. Record your results.

Spin	Wheel A	Wheel B
1		
2		
3		
4		

3. Why do you think winners on wheel A receive a less expensive prize than winners on wheel B?

_____

_____

Which **PS Process Standards** did you use?
Shade the circle(s) that applies.

① Persevere with Problems   ⑤ Use Math Tools

② Reason Abstractly   ⑥ Attend to Precision

③ Construct an Argument   ⑦ Make Use of Structure

④ Model with Mathematics   ⑧ Use Repeated Reasoning

Experimental and Theoretical Probability

Theoretical probability is based on uniform probability — what *should* happen when conducting a probability experiment. **Experimental probability** is based on relative frequency — what *actually* occurrs during such an experiment.

The theoretical probability and the experimental probability of an event may or may not be the same. As the number of attempts increases, the theoretical probability and the experimental probability should become closer in value.

Real World

Examples

 Tools Tutor

1. **The graph shows the results of an experiment in which a spinner with 3 equal sections is spun sixty times. Find the experimental probability of spinning red for this experiment.**

   The graph indicates that the spinner landed on red 24 times, blue 15 times, and green 21 times.

   $$P(\text{red}) = \frac{\text{number of times red occurs}}{\text{total number of spins}}$$

   $$= \frac{24}{60} \text{ or } \frac{2}{5}$$

   The experimental probability of spinning red is $\frac{2}{5}$.

- -

2. **Compare the experimental probability you found in Example 1 to its theoretical probability.**

   The spinner has three equal sections: red, blue, and green. So, the theoretical probability of spinning red is $\frac{1}{3}$. Since $\frac{2}{5} \approx \frac{1}{3}$, the experimental probability is close to the theoretical probability.

 Show your work.

Got it? Do these problems to find out.

a. _____

b. _____

a. Refer to Example 1. If the spinner was spun 3 more times and landed on green each time, find the experimental probability of spinning green for this experiment.

b. Compare the experimental probability you found in Exercise **a** to its theoretical probability.

Examples

3. Two number cubes are rolled together 20 times. A sum of 9 is rolled 8 times. What is the experimental probability of rolling a sum of 9?

$P(9) = \dfrac{\text{number of times a sum of 9 occurs}}{\text{total number of rolls}}$

$\qquad = \dfrac{8}{20} \text{ or } \dfrac{2}{5}$

The experimental probability of rolling a sum of 9 is $\dfrac{2}{5}$.

. . . .

4. Compare the experimental probability you found in Example 3 to its theoretical probability. If the probabilities are not close, explain a possible reason for the discrepancy.

When rolling two number cubes, there are 36 possible outcomes.

The theoretical probability of rolling a sum of 9 is $\dfrac{4}{36}$ or $\dfrac{1}{9}$.

Rolls with Sum of 9	
First Cube	**Second Cube**
3	6
4	5
5	4
6	3

Since $\dfrac{1}{9}$ is not close to $\dfrac{2}{5}$, the experimental probability is *not* close to the theoretical probability. One possible explanation is that there were not enough trials.

> **Got it?** Do these problems to find out.

c. In Example 3, what is the experimental probability of rolling a sum that is *not* 9?

d. Two coins are tossed 10 times. Both coins land on heads 6 times. Compare the experimental probability to the theoretical probability. If the probabilities are not close, explain a possible reason for the discrepancy.

e. Suppose three coins are tossed 10 times. All three coins land on heads 1 time. Compare the experimental probability to the theoretical probability. If the probabilities are not close, explain a possible reason for the discrepancy.

Show your work.

c. _____

d. _____

e. _____

Predict Future Events

Theoretical and experimental probability can be used to make predictions about future events.

 Example

Tutor

5. Last year, a DVD store sold 670 action DVDs, 580 comedy DVDs, 450 drama DVDs, and 300 horror DVDs. A media buyer expects to sell 5,000 DVDs this year. Based on these results, how many comedy DVDs should she buy? Explain.

2,000 DVDs were sold and 580 were comedy. So, the probability is $\frac{580}{2,000}$ or $\frac{29}{100}$.

$\frac{29}{100} = \frac{x}{5,000}$ Write a proportion.

$29 \cdot 5,000 = 100 \cdot x$ Find the cross products.

$145,000 = 100x$ Multiply.

$1,450 = x$ Divide each side by 100.

She should buy about 1,450 comedy DVDs.

> **Solving Proportions**
> The cross products of any proportion are equal.
> $\frac{29}{100} \bowtie \frac{x}{5,000}$

Guided Practice

Check

1. A coin is tossed 50 times, and it lands on heads 28 times. Find the experimental probability and the theoretical probability of the coin landing on heads. Then, compare the experimental and theoretical probabilities. (Examples 1–4)

_____

_____

2. Yesterday, 50 bakery customers bought muffins and 11 of those customers bought banana muffins. If 100 customers buy muffins tomorrow, how many would you expect to buy a banana muffin? (Example 5)

_____

3. (Q) **Building on the Essential Question** How are experimental probability and theoretical probability alike?

_____

_____

Rate Yourself!

Are you ready to move on? Shade the section that applies.

I have a few questions. | I'm ready to move on.

I have a lot of questions.

For more help, go online to access a Personal Tutor.

Tutor

FOLDABLES Time to update your Foldable!

Independent Practice

Go online for Step-by-Step Solutions

1 A number cube is rolled 20 times and lands on 1 two times and on 5 four times. Find each experimental probability. Then compare the experimental probability to the theoretical probability. (Examples 1–4)

a. landing on 5

_____

_____

b. *not* landing on 1

_____

_____

2. The spinner at the right is spun 12 times. It lands on blue 1 time.
(Examples 1–4)

a. What is the experimental probability of the spinner landing on blue?

b. Compare the experimental and theoretical probabilities of the spinner landing on blue. If the probabilities are not close, explain a possible reason for the discrepancy.

_____

_____

3. The frequency table shows the results of a survey of 70 zoo visitors who were asked to name their favorite animal exhibit. (Example 5)

a. Suppose 540 people visit the zoo. Predict how many people will choose the monkey exhibit as their favorite. _____

b. Suppose 720 people visit the zoo. Predict how many people will choose the penguin exhibit as their favorite. _____

Exhibit	Tally	Frequency
Bears	|||||		6
Elephants	||||| ||||| ||||| ||	17
Monkeys	||||| ||||| ||||| |||||		21
Penguins	||||| ||||| |||	13
Snakes	||||| ||||| |||	13

What is your Favorite Animal Exhibit?

4. **PS Make a Conjecture** Cross out the part of the concept circle that does *not* belong. Then describe the relationship among the remaining parts.

_____

_____

a coin landing on tails 8 out of 10 times | results based on an experiment

outcomes that should happen | rolling a sum of 9 twice in 5 trials

5 **PS** **Multiple Representations** A spinner with three equal-sized sections marked A, B, and C is spun 100 times.

a. **Numbers** What is the theoretical probability of landing on A?

b. **Numbers** The results of the experiment are shown in the table. What is the experimental probability of landing on A? on C?

c. **Models** Make a drawing of what the spinner might look like based on its experimental probabilities. Explain.

Section	Frequency
A	24
B	50
C	26

Show your work.

H.O.T. Problems Higher Order Thinking

6. **PS** **Persevere with Problems** The experimental probability of a coin landing on heads is $\frac{7}{12}$. If the coin landed on tails 30 times, find the number of tosses.

7. **PS** **Reason Inductively** Twenty sharpened pencils are placed in a box containing an unknown number of unsharpened pencils. Suppose 15 pencils are removed at random and five of the removed pencils are sharpened. Based on this, is it reasonable to assume that the number of unsharpened pencils was 40? Explain your reasoning. _____

8. **PS** **Reason Inductively** The results of spinning a spinner with six equal sections are shown. Determine the minimum number of additional spins needed and their frequency of landing on each color so that the experimental probabilities will be equal to the theoretical probabilities.

Explain your reasoning. _____

Color	Frequency
Blue	8
Green	6
Orange	12
Purple	10
Red	8
Yellow	4

Extra Practice

For Exercises 9 and 10, find each experimental probability. Then compare the experimental probability to its theoretical probability. If the probabilities are not close, explain a possible reason for the discrepancy.

9. A coin is tossed 20 times. It lands on heads 9 times.

$$P(heads) = \frac{number\ of\ times\ heads\ occurs}{total\ number\ of\ coin\ tosses} = \frac{9}{20}$$

 The experimental probability of $\frac{9}{20}$ is close to

the theoretical probability of $\frac{1}{2}$.

10. A heart is randomly chosen 7 out of 12 times from the cards shown.

_____

_____

_____

_____

Solve.

11. Last month, customers at a gift shop bought 40 birthday cards, 19 congratulations cards, 20 holiday cards, and 21 thank you cards. Suppose 125 customers buy greeting cards next month. How many would you expect to buy a birthday card?

_____

12. Use the graph at the right.
    a. What is the probability that a mother received a gift of flowers or plants? Write the probability as a fraction in simplest form.

    _____

    b. Suppose 400 mothers will receive a gift. Predict how many will receive flowers or plants.

    _____

Most Popular Mother's Day Gifts

card 40%
flowers/plants 28%
dinner/brunch 8%
gardening items 8%
apparel 7%
jewelry 6%
home décor 3%

Percent 0 5 10 15 20 25 30 35 40 45

Example

Tutor

4. To win a carnival prize, you need to choose one of 3 doors labeled 1 through 3. Then you need to choose a red, yellow, or blue box behind each door. What is the probability that the prize is in the blue or yellow box behind door 2?

The table shows that there are 9 total outcomes. Two of the outcomes are favorable.

So, the probability that the prize is in a blue or yellow box behind door 2 is $\frac{2}{9}$.

Outcomes	
door 1	red box
door 1	yellow box
door 1	blue box
door 2	red box
door 2	yellow box
door 2	blue box
door 3	red box
door 3	yellow box
door 3	blue box

Guided Practice

Check

For each situation, find the sample space. (Examples 1–2)

1. A coin is tossed twice.

2. A pair of brown or black sandals are available in sizes 7, 8, or 9.

3. Gerardo spins a spinner with four equal sections, labeled A, B, C, and D, twice. If letter A is spun at least once, Gerardo wins. Otherwise, Odell wins. Use a list to find the sample space. Then find the probability that Odell wins. (Examples 3–4)

4. **Bulding on the Essential Question** How do tree diagrams, tables, and lists help you find the probability of a compound event?

Inquiry Lab
Fair and Unfair Games

 Inquiry HOW can you determine if a game is fair?

Indiana Academic Standards
7.DSP.6

PS Process Standards
1, 3

In a counter-toss game, players toss three two-color counters. The winner of each game is determined by how many counters land with either the red or yellow side facing up. Find out if this game is fair or unfair.

Mathematically speaking, a two-player game is **fair** if each player has an equal chance of winning. A game is **unfair** if there is not such a chance.

Hands-On Activity 1

Work in pairs to play the game described above.

Step 1   Player 1 tosses the counters. If 2 or 3 counters land red-side up, Player 1 wins. If 2 or 3 counters land yellow-side up, Player 2 wins. Record the results in the table below. Place a check in the winner's column for each game.

Game	Player 1	Player 2	Game	Player 1	Player 2
1			6		
2			7		
3			8		
4			9		
5			10		

Step 2   Player 2 then tosses the counters and the results are recorded.

Step 3   Continue alternating turns until the counters have been tossed 10 times.

Based on your results, do you think the game is fair or unfair? Circle your response below.

                     Fair   Unfair

Work with a partner.

1. Complete the organized list of all the possible outcomes resulting from one toss of the three counters described in Activity 1.

Counter 1	Counter 2	Counter 3	Outcome
red	red	red	red, red, red

2. In the outcome column of the table above, draw a circle around the outcomes that are a win for Player 1. Draw a box around the outcomes that are a win for Player 2.

3. Calculate the theoretical probability of each player winning. Write each probability as a fraction and as a percent. Is the game fair or unfair?

_____

4. Use your results from Activity 1 to calculate the experimental probability of each player winning.

_____

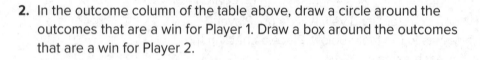

5. **PS Justify Conclusions** Compare the probabilities you found in Exercises 3 and 4. Explain any discrepancies. _____

6. **PS Reason Inductively** Predict the number of times Player 1 would win if the game were played 100 times. Explain your reasoning. _____

Analyze and Reflect

David and Lyn made up a game using a plastic cup. A cup is tossed.
If it lands right-side up or open-end down, David wins. If it lands on
its side, Lyn wins. Is this game fair?

Hands-On Activity 2

Work in pairs to play the game and determine if David and Lyn created a
fair game.

Step 1   Player 1 tosses the cup. If it lands right-side up or open-end down,
Player 1 gets a point. If the cup lands on its side, Player 2 gets a point.
Record your results in the table below.

Toss	Player 1	Player 2	Toss	Player 1	Player 2
1			6		
2			7		
3			8		
4			9		
5			10		

Step 2   Player 2 then tosses the cup and the results are recorded.

Step 3   Continue alternating turns until there is a total of 10 tosses.

Based on your results, do you think the game David and Lyn
created is fair or unfair? Circle your response below.

Fair   Unfair

There are three possible outcomes when tossing the cup and David wins if
two of those outcomes happen. It may appear that David has a better chance
of winning, however this is not necessarily true.

Explain why Lyn actually has a better chance at winning the game.

_____

_____

_____

What was the experimental probability for the cup landing right-side up or
open-end down?

_____

Investigate

Work with a partner.

7. A game involves rolling two number cubes. Player 1 wins the game if the total of the numbers rolled is 5 or if a 5 is shown on one or both number cubes. Otherwise, Player 2 wins. Fill in the table for all of the possible outcomes of rolling two number cubes.

	1	2	3	4	5	6
1	1 + 1 = 2	1 + 2 = 3	1 + 3 = 4	1 + 4 = 5	1 + 5 = 6	1 + 6 = 7
2	2 + 1 = 3					
3						
4						
5						
6						

8. Shade in the cells of the table in which Player 1 is a winner.

Analyze and Reflect

9. For the number cube game, calculate the theoretical probability of each player winning. Write each probability as a fraction and as a percent.

_____

_____

10. **PS Justify Conclusions** Is the number cube game fair? Explain.

_____

_____

Create

On Your Own

11. **PS Model with Mathematics** Design and describe a game in which the outcome is not fair. Then explain how you could change the game to

make it fair. _____

12. **inquiry** HOW can you determine if a game is fair? _____

_____

Probability of Compound Events

 ## Real-World Link

Travel Aimee wants to pack enough items to create 6 different outfits. She packs 1 jacket, 3 shirts, and 2 pairs of jeans. Can Aimee create 6 different outfits from her clothing items?

1. Complete the table below.

Outfit	Clothing Items
1	jacket, shirt 1, jeans 1
2	jacket, shirt 1, jeans 2
3	jacket, shirt 2, jeans 1
4	jacket, shirt 2,
5	jacket, shirt 3,
6	jacket,

2. The table is an example of an organized list. What is another way to show the different outfits that Aimee can create?

_____

3. Describe another situation for which you might want to list all of the possible outcomes.

_____

_____

 Essential Question

HOW can you predict the outcome of future events?

Vocabulary

sample space
tree diagram
compound event

Indiana Academic Standards
7.DSP.7

PS Process Standards
1, 3, 4, 5

Which PS **Process Standards** did you use?
Shade the circle(s) that applies.

① Persevere with Problems

② Reason Abstractly

③ Construct an Argument

④ Model with Mathematics

⑤ Use Math Tools

⑥ Attend to Precision

⑦ Make Use of Structure

⑧ Use Repeated Reasoning

Find a Sample Space

The set of all of the possible outcomes in a probability experiment is called the **sample space**. Organized lists, tables, and **tree diagrams** can be used to represent the sample space.

Examples

Tutor

1. The three students chosen to represent Mr. Balderick's class in a school assembly are shown. All three of them need to sit in a row on the stage. Use a list to find the sample space for the different ways they can sit in a row.

Students
Adrienne
Carlos
Greg

Use A for Adrienne, C for Carlos, and G for Greg. Use each letter exactly once.

ACG   AGC   CAG   CGA   GAC   GCA

So, the sample space consists of 6 outcomes.

2. A car can be purchased in blue, silver, red, or purple. It also comes as a convertible or hardtop. Use a table or a tree diagram to find the sample space for the different styles in which the car can be purchased.

Color	Top
blue	convertible
blue	hardtop
silver	convertible
silver	hardtop
red	convertible
red	hardtop
purple	convertible
purple	hardtop

Color	Top	Sample Space
Blue	Convertible	BC
	Hardtop	BH
Silver	Convertible	SC
	Hardtop	SH
Red	Convertible	RC
	Hardtop	RH
Purple	Convertible	PC
	Hardtop	PH

Using either method, the sample space consists of 8 outcomes.

Got it? Do this problem to find out.

a. _____

a. The table shows the sandwich choices for a picnic. Find the sample space using a list, table, or tree diagram for a sandwich consisting one type of meat and one type of bread.

Meat	Bread
ham turkey	rye sourdough white

Show your work.

Find Probability

A **compound event** consists of two or more simple events. The probability of a compound event, just as with simple events, is the fraction of outcomes in the sample space for which the compound event occurs.

Example

3. **Suppose you toss a quarter, a dime, and a nickel. Find the sample space. What is the probability of getting three tails?**

Make a tree diagram to show the sample space.

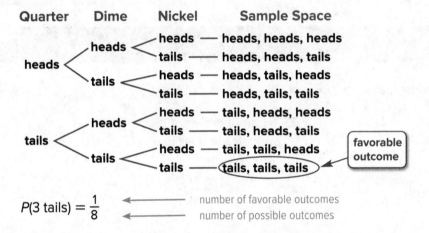

$P(3 \text{ tails}) = \dfrac{1}{8}$ ← number of favorable outcomes
                              ← number of possible outcomes

So, the probability of getting three tails is $\dfrac{1}{8}$.

Got it? **Do this problem to find out.**

b. The animal shelter has both male and female Labrador Retrievers in yellow, brown, or black. There is an equal number of each kind. What is the probability of choosing a female yellow Labrador Retriever? Show your work in the space below.

Random
When choosing an outcome, assume that each outcome is chosen randomly.

Example

Tutor

4. To win a carnival prize, you need to choose one of 3 doors labeled 1 through 3. Then you need to choose a red, yellow, or blue box behind each door. What is the probability that the prize is in the blue or yellow box behind door 2?

The table shows that there are 9 total outcomes. Two of the outcomes are favorable.

So, the probability that the prize is in a blue or yellow box behind door 2 is $\frac{2}{9}$.

Outcomes	
door 1	red box
door 1	yellow box
door 1	blue box
door 2	red box
door 2	yellow box
door 2	blue box
door 3	red box
door 3	yellow box
door 3	blue box

Guided Practice

Check ✓

For each situation, find the sample space. (Examples 1–2)

1. A coin is tossed twice.

2. A pair of brown or black sandals are available in sizes 7, 8, or 9.

3. Gerardo spins a spinner with four equal sections, labeled A, B, C, and D, twice. If letter A is spun at least once, Gerardo wins. Otherwise, Odell wins. Use a list to find the sample space. Then find the probability that Odell wins. (Examples 3–4)

_____

_____

4. @ **Bulding on the Essential Question** How do tree diagrams, tables, and lists help you find the probability of a compound event? _____

_____

_____

Rate Yourself!

☐ I understand how to show a sample space.

▶▶ Great! You're ready to move on!

☐ I still have questions about showing a sample space.

📘 No Problem! Go online to access a Personal Tutor. Tutor

Independent Practice

Go online for Step-by-Step Solutions

For each situation, find the sample space. (Examples 1–2)

1. tossing a coin and spinning the spinner at the right

2. picking a number from 1 to 5 and choosing the color red, white, or blue

3. choosing a purple, green, black, or silver bike having 10, 18, 21, or 24 speeds

4. choosing a letter from the word SPACE and choosing a consonant from the word MATH

For each game, find the sample space. Then find the indicated probability. (Examples 3–4)

5. Alana tosses 2 number cubes. She wins if she rolls double sixes.

   Find *P*(Alana wins). _____

6. Ming rolls a number cube, tosses a coin, and chooses a card from two cards marked A and B. If an even number and heads appears, Ming wins, no matter which card is chosen. Otherwise Lashonda wins.

   Find *P*(Ming wins). _____

6. **Model with Mathematics** Suppose a mouse is placed in the maze at the right. If each decision about direction is made at random, create a simulation to determine the probability that the mouse will find its way out before coming to a dead end or going out the In opening.

In _____ Out

_____

_____

_____

_____

H.O.T. Problems Higher Order Thinking

7. **Model with Mathematics** Describe a situation that could be represented by a simulation. What objects could be used in your simulation?

_____

_____

_____

8. **Persevere with Problems** A simulation uses cards numbered 0 through 9 to generate five 2-digit numbers. A card is selected for the tens digit and not replaced. Then a card for the ones digit is drawn and not replaced. The process is repeated until all the cards are used. If the simulation is performed 10 times, about how many times could you expect a 2-digit number to begin with a 5? Explain.

_____

_____

9. **Justify Conclusions** Determine whether the following statement is *sometimes*, *always*, or *never* true. Justify your answer.

   A spinner can be used to model equally likely outcomes.

_____

_____

10. **Justify Conclusions** Barton believes that the coin his teacher uses for an experiment gives an advantage to one team of students. His teacher has students toss the coin 50 times each and record their results. Based on the results in the table, do you think the coin is fair? Explain.

Student	Heads	Tails
1	17	33
2	22	28
3	28	22
4	21	29
5	13	37
6	20	30

_____

_____

Extra Practice

11. Three-course dinners can be made from the menu shown. Find the sample space for a dinner consisting of an appetizer, entrée, and dessert.

Appetizers	Entrees	Desserts
Soup	Steak	Carrot cake
Salad	Chicken	Apple pie

Appetizer   Entree   Dessert   Sample Space

Homework Help

S
   S
     C ——— SSC
     A ——— SSA
   C
     C ——— SCC
     A ——— SCA

Sa
   S
     C ——— SaSC
     A ——— SaSA
   C
     C ——— SaCC
     A ——— SaCA

12. Mr. and Mrs. Romero are expecting triplets. Suppose the chance of each child being a boy is 50% and of being a girl is 50%. Find the probability of each event.

   a. *P*(all three children will be boys) _____

   b. *P*(at least one boy and one girl) _____

   c. *P*(two boys and one girl) _____

   d. *P*(at least two girls) _____

Copy and Solve For Exercises 13 and 14, show your work on a separate piece of paper.

13. The University of Oregon's football team has many different uniforms. The coach can choose from four colors of jerseys and pants: green, yellow, white, and black. There are three helmet options: green, white, and yellow. Also, there are the same four colors of socks and two colors of shoes, black and yellow.

   a. How many jersey/pant combinations are there?

   b. If the coach picks a jersey/pant combination at random, what is the probability he will pick a yellow jersey with green pants?

   c. Use a tree diagram to find all of the possible shoe and sock combinations.

14. (PS) **Use Math Tools** Use the Internet or another source to find the top five best-selling animated movies. Then create a list of the possibilities for choosing a movie and choosing a wide-screen or full-screen version.

15. Mr. Skeels will choose one student from each of the two groups to present their history report to the class. Which of the following represent possible outcomes? Select all that apply.

☐ (Ava, Brooke)   ☐ (Greg, Brooke)

☐ (Antoine, Greg)   ☐ (Antoine, Mario)

Group 1	Group 2
Ava	Mario
Antoine	Brooke
Greg	

16. Campers choose one activity from each of the morning, afternoon, and evening activities shown below.

Morning	Afternoon	Evening
Hiking (H)	Archery (A)	Horseback Riding (R)
Canoeing (C)	Bird Watching (B)	Campfire Building (F)
		Navigating (N)

Make a list to show the sample space for the possible morning, afternoon, and evening activities.

What is the probability that a randomly selected camper will be horseback riding in the evening?

Spiral Review

Eight cards numbered 1–8 are shuffled together. A card is drawn at random. Find the probability of each event.

17. $P(8)$ _____

18. P(greater than 5) _____

19. P(even) _____

20. P(3 or 7) _____

21. What is the probability of rolling a number greater than 4 on a number cube? Explain.

_____

_____

Simulations

 Real-World Link

Music Downloads A new electronics store is opening at the mall. One out of six new customers will receive a free music download. The winners are chosen at random. On Monday, the store had 50 customers. You can act out or *simulate* 50 random customers by using the random number generator on a graphing calculator.

Type in the following keystrokes to set 1 as the lower bound and 6 as the upper bound for 50 trials.

Keystrokes: [MATH] [◄] 5 1 [,] 6 [,] 50 [)] [ENTER]

The screen should look similar to the screen shown below.

A set of 50 numbers ranging from 1 to 6 appears. Use the right arrow key to see the next number in the set.

1. Let the number 3 represent a customer who wins a free download. Write the experimental probability of winning a download.

   _____

2. Compare the experimental probabilities found in Exercise 1 to the theoretical probability of winning a download.

   _____

   _____

 Essential Question

HOW can you predict the outcome of future events?

 Vocab **Vocabulary**

simulation

🅘 **Indiana Academic Standards**
7.DSP.7

🅟🅢 **Process Standards**
1, 3, 4

Which 🅟🅢 **Process Standards** did you use?
Shade the circle(s) that applies.

① Persevere with Problems
② Reason Abstractly
③ Construct an Argument
④ Model with Mathematics

⑤ Use Math Tools
⑥ Attend to Precision
⑦ Make Use of Structure
⑧ Use Repeated Reasoning

Model Equally Likely Outcomes

A **simulation** is an experiment that is designed to model the action in a given situation. For example, you used a random number generator to simulate rolling a number cube. Simulations often use models to act out an event that would be impractical to perform.

 Example

1. A cereal company is placing one of eight different trading cards in its boxes of cereal. If each card is equally likely to appear in a box of cereal, describe a model that could be used to simulate the cards you would find in 15 boxes of cereal.

Choose a method that has 8 possible outcomes, such as tossing 3 coins. Let each outcome represent a different card.

For example, the outcome of all three coins landing heads up could simulate finding card 1.

Toss 3 coins to simulate the cards that might be in 15 boxes of cereal. Repeat 15 times.

Coin Toss Simulation			
Outcome	**Card**	**Outcome**	**Card**
HHH	1	TTT	5
HHT	2	TTH	6
HTH	3	THT	7
HTT	4	THH	8

 Show your work.

Got it? Do this problem to find out.

a. A restaurant is giving away 1 of 5 different toys with its children's meals. If the toys are given out randomly, describe a model that could be used to simulate which toys would be given with 6 children's meals.

a. _____

Example

2. Every student who volunteers at the concession stand during basketball games will receive a free school T-shirt. The T-shirts come in 3 different designs.

Design a simulation that could be used to model this situation. Use your simulation to find how many times a student must volunteer in order to get all 3 T-shirts.

Use a spinner divided into 3 equal sections. Assign each section one of the T-shirts. Spin the spinner until you land on each section.

first spin   **second spin**

third spin   **fourth spin**

Based on this simulation, a student should volunteer 4 times in order to get all 3 T-shirts.

Got it? Do this problem to find out.

b. Mr. Chen must wear a dress shirt and a tie to work. Each day he picks one of his 6 ties at random. Design a simulation that could be used to model this situation. Use your simulation to find how many days Mr. Chen must work in order to wear all of his ties.

b. _____

Model Unequally Likely Outcomes

Simulations can also be used to model events in which the outcomes are not equally likely.

Show your work.

c. _____

Example

 Tutor

3. There is a 60% chance of rain for each of the next two days. Describe a method you could use to find the experimental probability of having rain on both of the next two days.

Place 3 red and 2 blue marbles in a bag. Let 60% or $\frac{3}{5}$ of them represent rain. Let 40% or $\frac{2}{5}$ of them represent no rain.

Randomly pick one marble to simulate the first day. Replace the marble and pick again to simulate the second day. Find the probability of rain on both days.

Got it? Do this problem to find out.

c. During the regular season, Jason made 80% of his free throws. Describe an experiment to find the experimental probability of Jason making his next two free throws.

Guided Practice

 Check

1. An ice cream store offers waffle cones or sugar cones. Each is equally likely to be chosen. Describe a model that could be used to simulate this situation. Based on your simulation, how many people must order an ice cream cone in order to sell all possible combinations? (Examples 1 and 2)

_____

_____

2. An electronics store has determined that 45% of its customers buy a wide-screen television. Describe a model that you could use to find the experimental probability that the next three television-buying customers will buy a wide-screen television. (Example 3)

_____

_____

3. **Building on the Essential Question** Explain how using a simulation is related to experimental probability.

_____

_____

Independent Practice

Go online for Step-by-Step Solutions eHelp

1 The questions on a multiple-choice test each have 4 answer choices. Describe a model that you could use to simulate the outcome of guessing the correct answers to a 50-question test. (Example 1)

_____

_____

_____

2. A game requires drawing balls numbered 0 through 9 for each of four digits to determine the winning number. Describe a model that could be used to simulate the selection of the number. (Example 1)

_____

_____

_____

PS Model with Mathematics Describe a model you could use to simulate each event.

3 A jar of cookies contains 18 different types of cookies. Each type is equally likely to be chosen. Based on your simulation, how many times must a cookie be chosen in order to get each type? (Example 2)

_____

_____

_____

_____

4. A cooler contains 5 bottles of lemonade, 4 bottles of water, and 3 bottles of juice. Each type is equally likely to be chosen. Based on your simulation, how many times must a drink be chosen in order to get each type? (Example 3)

_____

_____

_____

5. Players at a carnival game win about 30% of the time. Based on your simulation, what is the experimental probability that the next four players will win. (Example 3)

_____

_____

_____

_____

6. **Model with Mathematics** Suppose a mouse is placed in the maze at the right. If each decision about direction is made at random, create a simulation to determine the probability that the mouse will find its way out before coming to a dead end or going out the In opening.

In

Out

🔥 H.O.T. Problems Higher Order Thinking

7. **PS Model with Mathematics** Describe a situation that could be represented by a simulation. What objects could be used in your simulation?

8. **PS Persevere with Problems** A simulation uses cards numbered 0 through 9 to generate five 2-digit numbers. A card is selected for the tens digit and not replaced. Then a card for the ones digit is drawn and not replaced. The process is repeated until all the cards are used. If the simulation is performed 10 times, about how many times could you expect a 2-digit number to begin with a 5? Explain.

9. **PS Justify Conclusions** Determine whether the following statement is *sometimes*, *always*, or *never* true. Justify your answer.

   A spinner can be used to model equally likely outcomes.

10. **PS Justify Conclusions** Barton believes that the coin his teacher uses for an experiment gives an advantage to one team of students. His teacher has students toss the coin 50 times each and record their results. Based on the results in the table, do you think the coin is fair? Explain.

Student	Heads	Tails
1	17	33
2	22	28
3	28	22
4	21	29
5	13	37
6	20	30

Extra Practice

11. A store employee randomly gives scratch-off discount cards to the first 50 customers. The cards offer discounts of 10%, 20%, 25%, 30%, or 40%. There is an equal chance of receiving any of the 5 cards. Describe a model that could be used to simulate the discount received by 4 customers.

> Homework Help
>
> Use a spinner with 5 equal sections to represent the 5 different discounts. Spin 4 times to simulate 4 customers receiving cards.

12. On average, 75% of the days in Henderson county are sunny, with little or no cloud cover. Describe a model that you could use to find the experimental probability of sunny days each day for a week in Henderson county.

_____

_____

_____

_____

PS **Model with Mathematics** Describe a model you could use to simulate each event.

13. Every student who participated in field day activities received a water bottle. The water bottles came in 2 different colors. Based on your simulation, how many students had to receive a water bottle in order to distribute water bottles in both colors?

_____

_____

_____

14. A field hockey team wins 80% of its games. Based on your simulation, what is the experimental probability of the team winning its next 3 games?

_____

_____

_____

15. There are 4 different magazines on Hannah's nightstand. Each evening, she randomly selects one magazine to read. Based on your simulation, how many days must she select a magazine in order to read all 4 magazines?

_____

_____

_____

16. The table shows the chance of rain this weekend. Select values to fill in the boxes in the model below to describe a method you could use to find the experimental probability of having rain on both days.

Day	Saturday	Sunday
Chance of Rain	30%	30%

Place 3 red and [   ] blue marbles in a bag. Let the [   ] marbles represent rain since [   ] % of the marbles are this color. Let the [   ] marbles represent no rain since [   ] % of the marbles are this color.

2	4	6	7	red
10	30	60	70	blue

Randomly pick one marble to simulate the first day. Replace the marble and pick again to simulate the second day. Find the experimental probability of rain on both days. Do you think it matters how many trials of the simulation you conduct? Will conducting more trials result in a better prediction? Explain your reasoning.

[   ]

17. At a restaurant, 1 out of every 6 kids' meals wins a prize. Determine which probability models could be used to simulate winning a prize. Select all that apply.

☐ Toss a coin. Let tossing heads represent winning a prize and let tossing tails represent not winning a prize.

☐ Spin a spinner with equal size spaces labeled A, B, C, D, E, and F. Let spinning A represent winning a prize and let spinning other letters represent not winning a prize.

☐ Roll a number cube. Let rolling a 1 represent winning a prize and let rolling a 2, 3, 4, 5, or 6 represent not winning a prize.

Spiral Review

18. A local video store has advertised that one out of every four customers will receive a free box of popcorn with their video rental. So far, 15 out of 75 customers have received popcorn. Compare the experimental and theoretical probabilities of receiving popcorn.

_____

_____

Inquiry Lab
Simulate Compound Events

 HOW do simulations help you understand the probability of events happening?

Indiana Academic Standards
7.DSP.7

PS Process Standards
1, 3

A local shop randomly gives coupons to 3 out of every 8 customers. Use a spinner to determine the probability that a customer will receive a coupon two days in a row.

Hands-On Activity 1

Step 1 A spinner with eight equal sections can be used to simulate the situation. Label three of the sections with the letter C to represent the people that receive a coupon. Label five of the sections with the letter D to represent the people that do not receive a coupon.

Step 2 Every two spins of the spinner represents one trial. Use a paperclip and the tip of your pencil to spin the spinner twice and record the results in the table. Perform a total of 15 trials.

Trial	Spin 1	Spin 2	Trial	Spin 1	Spin 2	Trial	Spin 1	Spin 2
1			6			11		
2			7			12		
3			8			13		
4			9			14		
5			10			15		

Based on your results, what is the experimental probability that a customer will receive a coupon two days in a row?

You can also use a random number table to simulate a compound event.

There is a 10% chance of rain for a city on Sunday and a 20% chance of rain on Monday. Use a random number table to find the probability that it will rain on both days.

Hands-On Activity 2

Step 1   A random number table has random digits in rows that can be grouped in different combinations as needed. These digits are arranged in groups of 5, but the grouping often does not matter. Since the situation we want to represent involves two days, continue drawing lines to separate the numbers into two-digit numbers.

48587	49460	89640	30270
19507	87835	99812	52353
11364	35645	90087	64254
87045	39769	77995	14316
69913	93449	68497	31270
81827	32901	82033	43714
33386	99637	25725	31900
41575	86692	40882	44123
77351	12790	62795	77307

Step 2   Using the digits 0 through 9, assign one digit in the tens place for rain on Sunday and assign two different digits in the ones place for rain on Monday. For example, the digit 1 in the tens place can represent rain occurring on Sunday and the digits 1 and 2 in the ones place can represent rain occurring on Monday.

Step 3   Find the numbers in the table that have a 1 in the tens place and either a 1 or 2 in the ones place. Those numbers are 11 and 12. Circle those numbers in the table.

Step 4   Find the probability using the numbers found in Step 3.

There were ☐ instances of the random numbers 11 and 12 occurring out of 90 random numbers.

So, the probability that it will rain on both days is $\frac{\Box}{90}$ or $3\frac{1}{3}$%.

Investigate

Collaborate

Work with a partner.

1. Luke plays goalie on his soccer team. He usually stops 2 out of every 6 penalty kicks. Label the sections of the spinner at the right. Then use the spinner to determine the experimental probability that Luke stops 2 penalty kicks in a row.

Trial	Spin 1	Spin 2	Trial	Spin 1	Spin 2	Trial	Spin 1	Spin 2
1			6			11		
2			7			12		
3			8			13		
4			9			14		
5			10			15		

The experimental probability is _____ .

2. Suppose 40% of customers who enter a pet store own a cat. What is the probability that it will take at least 4 customers before a cat owner enters the store? Use a random number table to simulate this compound event.

In the table below, separate the numbers into groups of 4. Then use the digits 0, 1, 2, and 3 to represent people who own cats. You are looking for groups of 4 numbers that do *not* contain a 0, 1, 2, or 3. Circle those groups.

18771	47374	36541	83454
97907	40978	34947	78482
26071	12644	94567	35467
02459	78467	06161	85897
44480	71716	13166	44096
72769	18974	24186	50866
35842	78478	45468	15441
58438	37487	16187	89892
83711	54631	19846	08483

In this case, the probability is $\dfrac{\boxed{}}{45}$ or 15.6%.

So, the experimental probability that it takes at least 4 customers before a cat owner enters the store is 15.6%.

3. In Exercise 1, what does spinning a Stop on your first spin, and spinning a Goal on your second spin represent in this situation?

_____

_____

_____

4. **(PS) Justify Conclusions** Explain how your results might change for Exercise 1 if you simulated 100 penalty kicks.

_____

_____

5. In Exercise 2, why were the numbers from the random number table separated into groups of four?

_____

_____

_____

6. In Exercise 2, you could have used any 4 numbers to represent cat owners. Complete the simulation four more times using the numbers in the table to represent the cat owners.

Numbers that Represent Cat Owners	Experimental Probability
4, 5, 6, 7	$\dfrac{\boxed{}}{45}$
0, 1, 8, 9	$\dfrac{\boxed{}}{45}$
3, 4, 5, 6	$\dfrac{\boxed{}}{45}$

Create

7. **(PS) Model with Mathematics** Design a simulation that could be used to predict the probability of taking a four question multiple-choice test with four answer choices and getting all four questions correct by guessing. Conduct 50 trials of the experiment. Then calculate the experimental probability of getting all four questions correct by guessing.

8. **Inquiry** HOW do simulations help you understand the probability of events happening?

_____

_____

_____

PS Problem-Solving Investigation
Act It Out

Indiana Academic Standards
7.DSP.6, 7.DSP.7

PS **Process Standards**
1, 3, 4

Case #1 Winning Serves

Edie has been practicing her volleyball serve every day after school. She hits a good serve an average of 3 out of 4 times.

What is the probability that Edie will hit two good serves in a row?

Understand *What are the facts?*

You know that Edie hits a good serve an average of 3 out of 4 times. Act it out with a spinner.

Plan *What is your strategy?*

Spin a spinner, numbered 1 to 4, two times. If the spinner lands on 1, 2, or 3, she hits a good serve. If the spinner lands on 4, she doesn't. Repeat the experiment 10 times.

Solve *How can you apply the strategy?*

Here are some possible results. Circle the columns that show two good serves. The first two are done for you.

Trials	1	2	3	4	5	6	7	8	9	10
First Spin	4	1	4	3	1	2	2	1	3	2
Second Spin	2	3	3	2	1	4	1	4	3	3

The circled columns show that six out of 10 trials resulted in two good serves in a row. So, the probability is _____ %.

Check *Does the answer make sense?*

Repeat the experiment several times to see whether the results agree.

Analyze the Strategy

PS **Reason Inductively** Describe an advantage of using the *act it out* strategy?

_____

_____

Case #2 Tests

James uses a spinner with four equal sections to answer a five-question multiple-choice quiz. Each question has choices A, B, C, and D.

Is this a good way to answer the quiz questions?

Understand

- **Read the problem. What are you being asked to find?**

  I need to find _____

  _____.

- **What information do you know?**

  The spinner has 4 equal parts. There are 5 multiple-choice questions.

  The answer choices are A, B, C, and D.

Plan

- **Choose a problem-solving strategy.**

  I will use the _____ strategy.

Solve

Use your problem-solving strategy to solve the problem.
Spin a spinner with four equal parts labeled A, B, C, and D five times.
Repeat the experiment two times. Make a table of the results.

Question	1	2	3	4	5
Trial 1					
Trial 2					

With each spin there is an equal chance of landing on any section. Since the

probability of an answer being A, B, C, or D is _____ likely, any answer
choice is possible.

Is using a spinner to answer a multiple-choice question a good idea? _____

Check

Use information from the problem to check your answer.
Repeat the experiment several times to see if the results agree.

**Work with a small group to solve the following cases.
Show your work on a separate piece of paper.**

Case #3 Chess

A chess tournament will be held and 32 students will participate.
If a player loses one match, he or she will be eliminated.

How many total games will be played in the
tournament?

_____

Case #4 Running

Six runners are entered in a race. Assume there are no ties.

In how many ways can first and second places be awarded?

_____

Case #5 Fair Games

Karla and Jason are playing a game with number cubes. Each number cube is
numbered 1 to 6. They roll both number cubes. If the product is a multiple of 3,
Jason wins. If the product is a multiple of 4, Karla wins.

Is this game fair or unfair? Justify your response.

_____

_____

_____

Use any
strategy!

Case #6 Algebra

The figure shown at the right is
known as Pascal's Triangle.
Make a conjecture for the
numbers in the 6th and
7th rows.

_____

Mid-Chapter Check

Vocabulary Check

1. Define *probability*. Give an example of the probability of a simple event. (Lesson 1)

_____

_____

2. Fill in the blank in the sentence below with the correct term. (Lesson 4)

A(n) _____ is an experiment that is designed to act out a given situation.

Skills Check and Problem Solving

The table shows the number of science fiction, action, and comedy movies Jason has in his collection. Suppose one movie is selected at random. Find each probability. Write as a fraction in simplest form. (Lesson 1)

Type of Movie	
Science Fiction	10
Action	7
Comedy	3

3. *P*(science fiction) _____

4. *P*(*not* action) _____

5. A coin is tossed 20 times. It lands heads 4 times. Compare the experimental probability to its theoretical probability. If the probabilities are not close, explain a possible reason for the discrepancy. (Lesson 2)

_____

_____

6. A weather forecaster predicts a 30% chance of rain for each of the next three days. Describe a way to simulate the chance that it will rain the next

three days. (Lesson 4) _____

_____

_____

_____

7. **PS Persevere with Problems** Without looking, Santiago took a handful of multi-colored candies from a bag and found that 20% of the candies were yellow and 15% were green. Suppose there were 480 candies in the bag. Based on Santiago's results, how many more yellow candies would you

expect there to be than green candies? (Lesson 1) _____

Fundamental Counting Principle

Real-World Link

Classes Tyler wants to take a class at the community center. The table shows the class options he is considering. All of the classes are offered only on Monday and Tuesday.

Class	Day
Drawing Martial Arts Dance	Monday Tuesday

1. According to the table, how many classes is he considering? _____

2. How many days are the classes offered?

_____

3. Complete the tree diagram to find the number of different class and day outcomes.

Class	Day	Sample Space
Drawing	**Monday**	**Drawing, Monday**
	Tuesday	**Drawing, Tuesday**
Martial Arts	_____	**Martial Arts, Monday**
	_____	_____
_____	_____	_____
	_____	_____

4. Find the product of the two numbers you found in Exercises 1 and 2. How does the number of outcomes compare to the product?

_____

 Essential Question

HOW can you predict the outcome of future events?

 Vocabulary

fundamental counting principle

Indiana Academic Standards
7.DSP.5

PS Process Standards
1, 3, 4

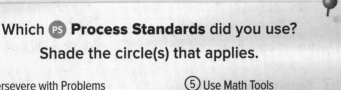

Which PS Process Standards did you use?
Shade the circle(s) that applies.

① Persevere with Problems
② Reason Abstractly
③ Construct an Argument
④ Model with Mathematics
⑤ Use Math Tools
⑥ Attend to Precision
⑦ Make Use of Structure
⑧ Use Repeated Reasoning

Fundamental Counting Principle

If event *M* has *m* possible outcomes and event *N* has *n* possible outcomes, then event *M* followed by event *N* has $m \times n$ possible outcomes.

You can use multiplication instead of making a tree diagram to find the number of possible outcomes in a sample space. This is called the **Fundamental Counting Principle**.

 Example

1. **Find the total number of outcomes when a coin is tossed and a number cube is rolled.**

A coin has 2 possible outcomes. A number cube has 6 possible outcomes. Multiply the possible outcomes of each event.

coin	number cube	total
↓	↓	↓

$$2 \quad \bullet \quad 6 \quad = \quad 12 \qquad \text{Fundamental Counting Principle}$$

There are 12 different outcomes.

Check Draw a tree diagram to show the sample space.

Coin	Number Cube	Sample Space
	1	heads, 1
	2	heads, 2
	3	heads, 3
heads	4	heads, 4
	5	heads, 5
	6	heads, 6
	1	tails, 1
	2	tails, 2
	3	tails, 3
tails	4	tails, 4
	5	tails, 5
	6	tails, 6

The tree diagram also shows that there are 12 outcomes. ✓

Got it? Do this problem to find out.

 Show your work.

a. Find the total number of outcomes when choosing from bike helmets that come in three colors and two styles.

a. _____

Find Probability

You can use the Fundamental Counting Principle to help find the probability of events.

 Examples

2. Find the total number of outcomes from rolling a number cube with sides labeled 1–6 and choosing a letter from the word NUMBERS. Then find the probability of rolling a 6 and choosing an M.

number cube	letters	total

$$6 \quad \bullet \quad 7 \quad = \quad 42$$ Fundamental Counting Principle

There are 42 different outcomes.

There is only one favorable outcome. So, the probability of rolling a 6 and choosing an M is $\frac{1}{42}$ or about 2%.

3. Find the number of different jeans available at The Jeans Shop. Then find the probability of randomly selecting a size 32 × 34 slim fit. Is it likely or unlikely that the jeans would be chosen?

The Jeans Shop		
Waist Size	Length (in.)	Style
30	30	slim fit
32	32	bootcut
34	34	loose fit
36		
38		

> **Jean Size**
> In men's jeans, the size is labeled waist × length. So, a 32 × 34 is a 32-inch waist with a 34-inch length.

size	length	style	total

$$5 \quad \bullet \quad 3 \quad \bullet \quad 3 \quad = \quad 45$$ Fundamental Counting Principle

There are 45 different types of jeans to choose. Out of the 45 possible outcomes, only one is favorable. So, the probability of randomly selecting a 32 × 34 slim fit is $\frac{1}{45}$ or about 2%.

It is very unlikely that the size would be chosen at random.

Got it? Do this problem to find out.

 Show your work.

b. Two number cubes are rolled. What is the probability that the sum of the numbers on the cubes is 12? How likely is it that the sum would be 12?

b. _____

Example

Tutor

4. A box of toy cars contains blue, orange, yellow, red, and black cars. A separate box contains a male and a female action figure. What is the probability of randomly choosing an orange car and a female action figure? Is it likely or unlikely that this combination is chosen?

First, find the number of possible outcomes.

There are 5 choices for the car and 2 choices for the action figure.

$5 \cdot 2 = 10$ Fundamental Counting Principal

There are 10 possible outcomes. There is one way to choose an orange car and a female action figure. It is very unlikely that this combination is chosen at random.

$P(\text{orange car, female action figure}) = \frac{1}{10}$ or 10%.

Guided Practice

Check ✓

1. Use the Fundamental Counting Principle to find the number of outcomes from tossing a quarter, a dime, and a nickel. (Example 1)

_____

_____

2. How many outcomes are possible when rolling a number cube and picking a cube from 4 different colored cubes? (Example 1)

3. Find the number of different outfits that can be made from 3 sweaters, 4 blouses, and 6 skirts. Then find the probability of randomly selecting a particular sweater-blouse-skirt outfit. Is the probability of this event likely or unlikely? (Examples 2–4)

_____

4. **Building on the Essential Question** Compare and contrast tree diagrams and the Fundamental Counting Principle.

_____

_____

_____

Rate Yourself!

How confident are you about using the Fundamental Counting Principle? Shade the ring on the target.

I'm on target.

I need help.

For more help, go online to access a Personal Tutor.

Tutor

Independent Practice

Go online for Step-by-Step Solutions

Use the Fundamental Counting Principle to find the total number of outcomes for each situation. (Example 1)

1 choosing a bagel with one type of cream cheese from the list shown in the table

_____

Bagels	Cream Cheese
Plain	Plain
Blueberry	Chive
Cinnamon raisin	Sun-dried tomato
Garlic	

2. choosing a sandwich and a side from the list shown in the table

_____

Sandwiches	Sides
Ham	Pasta Salad
Turkey	Fruit Cup
Roast Beef	Potato Chips
Tuna Salad	Side Salad
Vegetarian	

3. picking a month of the year and a day of

the week _____

4. choosing from a comedy, horror, or action movie each shown in four different theaters

_____

5. Find the number of possible routes from Eastland to Johnstown that pass through Harping. Then find the probability that State and Fairview will be used if a route is selected at random. State the probability as a fraction and percent. (Examples 2–3)

_____

6. Find the number of possible choices for a 2-digit number that is greater than 19. Then find the number of possible choices for a 4-digit Personal Identification Number (PIN) if the digits cannot be repeated. (Example 1)

_____

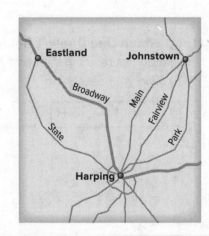

7. An electronics company makes educational apps for 5 subjects, including math. The app has 10 versions, with a different avatar in each version. One version has an avatar that looks similar to a lion. The company is randomly giving free apps to its customers. Find the probability of randomly receiving a math app with a lion avatar. How likely is the probability of receiving this app at random? (Examples 2–4)

_____

8. A sandwich shop offers 4 different meats and 2 different cheeses. Suppose the sandwich shop offers 24 different meat-cheese sandwiches. How many different breads does the sandwich shop use?

_____

9 **PS** **Justify Conclusions** A store offers 32 different T-shirt designs and 11 choices of color. Is the store's advertisement true? Explain.

_____

_____

A
T-shirt for
Every Day of the
Year!
32
designs! 11
colors!

H.O.T. Problems Higher Order Thinking

10. **PS** **Persevere with Problems** Determine the number of possible outcomes when tossing one coin, two coins, and three coins. Then determine the number of possible outcomes for tossing *n* coins. Describe the strategy you used.

_____

_____

_____

11. **PS** **Which One Doesn't Belong?** Identify the choices for events *M* and *N* that do not result in the same number of outcomes as the other two. Explain your reasoning.

9 drinks, 8 desserts		10 groups, 8 activities

_____

_____

12. **PS** **Justify Conclusions** Marcus has a choice of a white, gray, or black shirt to wear with a choice of tan, black, brown, or denim pants. Without calculating the number of possible outcomes, how many more outfits can he make if he buys a green shirt? Explain your reasoning to a classmate.

_____

_____

13. **PS** **Persevere with Problems** Write an algebraic expression to find the number of outcomes if a number cube is rolled *x* times.

_____

Extra Practice

Use the Fundamental Counting Principle to find the total number of outcomes for each situation.

14. rolling a number cube and spinning a spinner with eight equal sections _48____

$$6 \cdot 8 = 48$$

Homework Help

15. tossing a coin and selecting one letter from the word MATH _____

16. selecting one sweatshirt from a choice of five sweatshirts and one pair of pants from a choice of four pairs of pants _____

17. selecting one entrée from a choice of nine entrées and one dessert from a choice of three desserts _____

18. rolling a number cube and tossing two coins _____

19. choosing tea in regular, raspberry, lemon, or peach; sweetened or unsweetened; and in a glass or bottle _____

20. A cafeteria offers oranges, apples, or bananas as its fruit option. It offers peas, green beans, or carrots as the vegetable option. Find the number of fruit and vegetable options. If the fruit and the vegetable are chosen at random, what is the probability of getting an orange and carrots? Is it likely or unlikely that a customer would get an orange and carrots?

_____

21. **PS Justify Conclusions** The table shows cell phone options offered by a wireless phone company. If a phone with one payment plan and one accessory is given away at random, predict the probability that it will be Brand B and have a headset. Explain your reasoning.

Phone Brands	Payment Plans	Accessories
Brand A	Individual	Leather case
Brand B	Family	Car mount
Brand C	Business	Headset
	Government	Travel charger

_____

_____

_____

_____

22. A restaurant has 24 different lunch combinations. Which of the following could describe the lunch options? Select all that apply.

☐ 3 drink sizes, 4 main dishes, 2 side dishes

☐ 2 appetizers, 6 main dishes, 3 desserts

☐ 3 kinds of bread, 8 kinds of sandwiches

☐ 2 drink sizes, 7 appetizers, 2 main dishes

23. Hat Shack sells 9 different styles of hats in several different colors for 2 different sports teams. The company makes 108 kinds of hats in all. Select the correct values to complete the formula below to find the number of different color hats the Hat Shack makes.

Hat Shack		
Styles	**Colors**	**Teams**
9	?	2

$$\boxed{} = \boxed{} \times \boxed{} \times \boxed{}$$

How many different colors does the company use for hats?

$\boxed{}$

2
9
108
c

Spiral Review

Find each probability.

24. A coin is tossed and a spinner with 4 equal sections labeled W–Z is spun. Find P(heads and Z).

_____

25. A pizza shop offers a single item pizza with choice of pepperoni, green peppers, pineapple, sausage, or mushroom toppings. The pizza can be thick crust or thin crust. Find P(thick crust).

_____

Describe a model that could be used to simulate each situation.

26. There is a fifty percent chance of rain on Monday.

_____

27. A restaurant randomly gives away 1 of 6 toys. Determine the number of times a child needs to visit the restaurant to receive all 6 toys.

_____

_____

Real-World Link

Scheduling Colt is planning his Saturday. He wants to mow the grass, go swimming, and do his homework. How many different ways are there to arrange what he wants to do?

Fill in the blanks of the organized list below to find all of the possible arrangements of the activities.

 Essential Question

HOW can you predict the outcome of future events?

Vocab

 Vocabulary

permutation

Indiana Academic Standards
7.DSP.5

PS Process Standards
1, 3, 4

1: Mowing	2: Swimming	3: Homework
1: Mowing	2: Homework	3: _____
1: Swimming	2: Mowing	3: Homework
1: Swimming	2: Homework	3: _____
1: Homework	2: _____	3: _____
1: _____	2: _____	3: _____

1. How many choices does Colt have for his first activity?

   _____

2. Once the first activity is selected, how many choices does Colt have for the second activity?

   _____

3. Once the first and second activities are selected, how many choices does Colt have for the third activity?

   _____

Which PS **Process Standards** did you use?
Shade the circle(s) that applies.

1. Persevere with Problems
2. Reason Abstractly
3. Construct an Argument
4. Model with Mathematics
5. Use Math Tools
6. Attend to Precision
7. Make Use of Structure
8. Use Repeated Reasoning

Find a Permutation

A **permutation** is an arrangement, or listing, of objects in which order is important.

Mowing
Swimming
Homework

Swimming
Mowing
Homework

You can use the Fundamental Counting Principle to find the number of permutations.

Examples

 Tutor

1. Julia is scheduling her first three classes. Her choices are math, science, and language arts. Use the Fundamental Counting Principle to find the number of different ways Julia can schedule her first three classes.

There are **3** choices for the first class.

There are **2** choices that remain for the second class.

There is **1** choice that remains for the third class.

$$3 \cdot 2 \cdot 1 = 6 \longleftarrow \text{the number of permutations of 3 classes}$$

There are 6 possible arrangements, or permutations, of the 3 classes.

2. An ice cream shop has 31 flavors. Carlos wants to buy a three-scoop cone with three different flavors. How many cones could he buy if the order of the flavors is important?

There are 31 choices for the first scoop, 30 choices for the second scoop, and 29 choices for the third scoop.

Use the Fundamental Counting Principle.

$31 \cdot 30 \cdot 29 = 26{,}970$

Carlos could buy 26,970 different cones.

 Show your work.

Got it? Do these problems to find out.

a. _____

a. In how many ways can the starting six players of a volleyball team stand in a row for a picture?

b. _____

b. In a race with 7 runners, in how many ways can the runners end up in first, second, and third place?

The symbol $P(31, 3)$ represents the number of permutations of 31 things taken 3 at a time.

Start with 31.

$$P(31, 3) \;=\; 31 \cdot 30 \cdot 29$$

Use three factors.

Example

Tutor

3. Find $P(8, 3)$.

$P(8, 3) = 8 \cdot 7 \cdot 6$ or 336   8 things taken 3 at a time

Got it? Do these problems to find out.

c. $P(12, 2)$ d. $P(4, 4)$ e. $P(10, 5)$

c. _____

d. _____

Show your work

e. _____

Find Probabililty

Permutations can be used when finding probabilities of real-world situations.

Examples

Tutor

4. Ashley's MP3 player has a setting that allows the songs to play in a random order. She has a playlist that contains 10 songs. What is the probability that the MP3 player will randomly play the first three songs in order?

First find the permutation of ten things taken three at a time or $P(10, 3)$.

10 songs · Choose 3

$P(10, 3) = 10 \cdot 9 \cdot 8$ 10 choices for the 1st song

$= 720$ 9 choices for the 2nd song

8 choices for the 3rd song

So, there are 720 different ways to play the first 3 songs. Since you want the first three songs in order, there is only 1 out of the 720 ways to do this.

So, the probability that the first 3 songs will play in order is $\frac{1}{720}$.

Notation

In Example 4, the notation $P(10, 3)$ indicates a permutation while the notation P(playing the first three songs in order) indicates probability.

5. A swimming event features 8 swimmers. If each swimmer has an equally likely chance of finishing in the top two, what is the probability that Yumii will be in first place and Paquita in second place?

Swimmers	
Octavia	Eden
Natasha	Paquita
Calista	Samantha
Yumii	Lorena

First find the permutation of 8 things taken two at a time or $P(8, 2)$.

$$P(8, 2) = 8 \cdot 7$$
$$= 56$$

There are 56 possible arrangements, or permutations, of the two places. Since there is only one way of having Yumii come in first and Paquita second, the probability of this event is $\frac{1}{56}$.

Reasonable Answers

A possible probability of $\frac{1}{56}$ indicates that it is very unlikely that Yumii will finish first and Paquita will finish second.

Show your work.

Got it? Do this problem to find out.

f. Two different letters are randomly selected from the letters in the word *math*. What is the probability that the first letter selected is *m* and the second letter is *h*?

f. _____

Guided Practice

1. In how many ways can a president, vice president, and secretary be randomly selected from a class of 25 students?
(Examples 1 and 2) _____

2. Find the value of $P(5, 3)$. (Example 3)
_____

3. Adrianne, Julián, and two of their friends will sit in a row at a baseball game. If each friend is equally likely to sit in any seat, what is the probability that Adrianne will sit in the first seat and Julián will sit in the second seat? (Examples 4 and 5)
_____

4. 🅠 **Building on the Essential Question** HOW can you find the number of permutations of a set of objects?
_____
_____
_____

Independent Practice

Go online for Step-by-Step Solutions

eHelp

1 In the Battle of the Bands contest, in how many ways can the four participating bands perform? (Examples 1 and 2)

_____

2. A garage door code has 5 digits. If no digit is repeated, how many codes are possible?

_____

Find each value. Use a calculator if needed. (Example 3)

3. P(7, 4) _____

4. P(12, 5) _____

5. P(8, 8) _____

6. You have five seasons of your favorite TV show on DVD. If you randomly select two of them from a shelf, what is the probability that you will select season one first and season two second? (Examples 4 and 5)

_____

7. (PS) **Model with Mathematics** The graphic novel frame below explains how the survey has students rank their favorite kinds of music. In how

many ways can the survey be answered? _____

8. A certain number of friends are waiting in line to board a new roller coaster. They can board the ride in 5,040 different ways. How many friends are in line?

_____

9 The Coughlin family discovered they can stand in a row for their family portrait in 720 different ways. How many members are in the Coughlin

family? _____

10. Howland Middle School assigns a four-digit identification number to each student. The number is made from the digits 1, 2, 3, and 4, and no digit is repeated. If assigned randomly, what is the probability that an ID

number will end with a 3? _____

H.O.T. Problems Higher Order Thinking

11. PS **Model with Mathematics** Describe a real-world situation that has 6 permutations.

_____

_____

12. PS **Persevere with Problems** There are 1,320 ways for three students to win first, second, and third place during a debate match. How many students are there on the debate team? Explain your reasoning.

_____

_____

13. PS **Persevere with Problems** A *combination* is an arrangement where order is *not* important. You can find the number of combinations of items by dividing the number of permutations by the number of ways the smaller set can be arranged. The combination at the right shows the number of combinations if you choose 2 flavors of ice cream out of 5 flavors. Use this method to find each value.

From 5 flavors take 2 at a time.

$$C(5, 2) = \frac{5 \cdot 4}{2 \cdot 1} \text{ or } 10$$

There are $2 \cdot 1$ ways to order 2 flavors.

a. $C(6, 4)$ _____

b. $C(10, 3)$ _____

c. $C(5, 3)$ _____

d. $C(8, 6)$ _____

Extra Practice

14. How many permutations are possible of the letters in the word FRIEND? _720_

Homework Help ➡ $6 \cdot 5 \cdot 4 \cdot 3 \cdot 2 \cdot 1 = 720$

15. How many different 3-digit numbers can be formed using the digits 9, 3, 4, 7, and 6? Assume no number can be used more than once. _____

Find each value. Use a calculator if needed.

16. $P(9, 2)$ _____

17. $P(5, 5)$ _____

18. $P(7, 7)$ _____

19. The members of the Evergreen Junior High Quiz Bowl team are listed in the table. If a captain and an assistant captain are chosen at random, what is the probability that Walter is selected as captain and Mi-Ling as co-captain? _____

Evergreen Junior High Quiz Bowl Team	
Jamil	Luanda
Savannah	Mi-Ling
Tucker	Booker
Ferdinand	Nina
Walter	Meghan

20. Alex, Aiden, Dexter, and Dion are playing a video game. If they each have an equally likely chance of getting the highest score, what is the probability that Dion will get the highest score and Alex the second highest? _____

21. A child has wooden blocks with the letters shown. Find the probability that the child randomly arranges the letters in the order TIGER. _____

Power Up! Test Practice

22. The schools listed in the table are finalists in a science competition. First through third places will win a prize. Each school is equally likely to win the competition. Select values to complete the model below to find the probability that Lincoln wins first place, River Valley wins second place, and Glenwood wins third place.

Finalists
Chester Middle School
Glenwood Middle School
Lincoln Middle School
River Valley Middle School
South Middle School

Find the number of ways the schools can finish in first, second, and third place:

$P\left(\boxed{}, \boxed{}\right) = \boxed{}$

The number of ways that Lincoln can finish first, River Valley second, and Glenwood third is equal to $\boxed{}$.

1	2	3	4	5
10	20	30	60	90

$P(\text{Lincoln first, River Valley second, Glenwood third}) = \dfrac{\boxed{}}{\boxed{}}$

23. The five finalists in a writing contest are Cesar, Teresa, Sean, Nikita, and Alfonso. There will be a first place award and a second place award. Each finalist is equally likely to win an award. Determine if each statement is true or false.

a. There are 10 permutations of 5 finalists taken 2 at a time. ☐ True ☐ False

b. There is only 1 way that Teresa can earn first place and Sean can earn second place. ☐ True ☐ False

c. The probability that Teresa earns first place and Sean earns second place is 0.05. ☐ True ☐ False

Spiral Review

A card is pulled from a stack of 30 cards labeled 1–30. Find each probability. Write as a fraction in simplest form.

24. $P(\text{greater than 5})$ _____

25. $P(not\ 1)$ _____

26. $P(\text{an even number})$ _____

27. A cross country athlete has a white, a red, and a gray sweatshirt. She has black and gray running pants. Make a list to show the possible combinations of training outfits. _____

Inquiry Lab

Independent and Dependent Events

 Inquiry HOW can one event impact a second event in a probability experiment?

Indiana Academic Standards
7.DSP.5

PS Process Standards
1, 3

Jeanie wants to go to the movies and Kate wants to go skating. They decide by doing a simulation. They place two red counters in a bag to represent going to the movies and two white counters to represent going skating. If they draw or remove two red counters, they will go to the movies. If they draw two white counters they will go skating. If they draw a red and a white counter, they will stay home.

You can simulate this activity using counters.

Hands-On Activity

Step 1 Place two red counters and two white counters in a paper bag.

Step 2 Without looking, draw a counter from the bag and record its color in the table below. Place the counter back in the bag.

Step 3 Without looking, draw a second counter and record its color in the table. The two colors are one trial. Place the counter back in the bag.

Step 4 Repeat until you have 18 trials.

Trial	1st Color	2nd Color	Trial	1st Color	2nd Color	Trial	1st Color	2nd Color
1			7.			13		
2			8			14		
3			9			15		
4			10			16		
5			11			17		
6			12			18		

What is the experimental probability that the girls will go to the movies?

Investigate

Work with a partner.

1. Complete the same experiment from the Activity. Except do not replace the counter after the first draw for each trial. Record your results.

Trial	1st Color	2nd Color	Trial	1st Color	2nd Color	Trial	1st Color	2nd Color
1			7			13		
2			8			14		
3			9			15		
4			10			16		
5			11			17		
6			12			18		

What is the experimental probability that the girls will go to the movies?

Analyze and Reflect

The tree diagrams below represent the possible outcomes for the Activity and for Exercise 1. Use the diagrams to answer Exercises 2–3.

Investigation

1st Draw	2nd Draw	Outcome
R	R	RR
	R	RR
	W	RW
	W	RW
W	R	WR
	R	WR
	W	WW
	W	WW

Exercise 1

1st Draw	2nd Draw	Outcome
R	R	RR
	W	RW
	W	RW
W	R	WR
	R	WR
	W	WW

2. What is the theoretical probability of drawing two reds in the Investigation? In Exercise 1? _____

3. **PS** **Reason Inductively** Is there a better chance that the girls will go to the movies if the counters are replaced after the first draw? Explain.

Create

4. **Inquiry** HOW can one event impact a second event in a probability experiment?

21ST CENTURY CAREER
in Medicine

Pediatricians

Do you have compassion, a sense of humor, and the ability to analyze data? You might want to consider a career in medicine. Pediatricians care for the health of infants, children, and teenagers. They diagnose illnesses, interpret diagnostic tests, and prescribe and administer treatment.

College & Career
R E A D I N E S S

Is This the Career for You?

Are you interested in a career as a pediatrician? Take some of the following courses in high school.

◆ Algebra
◆ Biology
◆ Calculus
◆ Chemistry
◆ Psychology

Find out how math relates to a career in Medicine.

Probability of Independent Events

Words The probability of two independent events can be found by multiplying the probability of the first event by the probability of the second event.

Symbols $P(A \text{ and } B) = P(A) \cdot P(B)$

You can use organized lists, tables, tree diagrams, or multiplication to find the probability of compound events.

Examples

Tools Tutor

1. One letter tile is selected and the spinner is spun. What is the probability that both will be a vowel?

Method 1 Make a Tree Diagram

Tile	Spinner	Sample Space
G	A	G, A
	B	G, B
	C	G, C
B	A	B, A
	B	B, B
	C	B, C
E	A	E, A
	B	E, B
	C	E, C
A	A	A, A
	B	A, B
	C	A, C

There are 12 outcomes. Two outcomes contain only vowels. The probability that both will be a vowel is $\frac{2}{12}$ or $\frac{1}{6}$.

Method 2 Use Multiplication

$P(\text{selecting a vowel}) = \frac{2}{4}$ or $\frac{1}{2}$. $P(\text{spinning a vowel}) = \frac{1}{3}$.

$P(\text{both vowels}) = \frac{1}{2} \cdot \frac{1}{3}$ or $\frac{1}{6}$.   Multiply the probabilities.

So, using either method the probability is $\frac{1}{6}$.

2. The spinner and number cube shown are used in a game. What is the probability of a player *not* spinning blue and then rolling a 3 or 4?

You are asked to find the probability of the spinner *not* landing on blue and rolling a 3 or 4 on a number cube. The events are independent because spinning the spinner does not affect the outcome of rolling a number cube.

First, find the probability of each event.

$P(not \text{ blue}) = \dfrac{4}{5}$ ⟵⟵ $\dfrac{\text{number of ways not to spin blue}}{\text{number of possible outcomes}}$

$P(3 \text{ or } 4) = \dfrac{2}{6} \text{ or } \dfrac{1}{3}$ ⟵⟵ $\dfrac{\text{number of ways to roll 3 or 4}}{\text{number of possible outcomes}}$

Then, find the probability of both events occurring.

$P(not \text{ blue and 3 or 4}) = \dfrac{4}{5} \cdot \dfrac{1}{3}$ $P(A \text{ and } B) = P(A) \cdot P(B)$

$\qquad\qquad\qquad\qquad\quad = \dfrac{4}{15}$ Multiply.

The probability is $\dfrac{4}{15}$.

Check   Make an organized list, table, or a tree diagram to show the sample space.

Got it?   **Do this problem to find out.**

Show your work.

a. A game requires players to roll two number cubes to move the game pieces. The faces of the cubes are labeled 1 through 6. What is the probability of rolling a 2 or 4 on the first number cube and then rolling a 5 on the second?

a. _____

Probability of Dependent Events

Key Concept

Words	If two events *A* and *B* are dependent, then the probability of both events occurring is the product of the probability of *A* and the probability of *B* after *A* occurs.
Symbols	$P(A \text{ and } B) = P(A) \cdot P(B \text{ following } A)$

If the outcome of one event affects the outcome of another event, the events are called **dependent events**. For example, you have a bag with blue and green marbles. You pick one marble, do not replace it, and pick another one.

Example

3. There are 4 oranges, 7 bananas, and 5 apples in a fruit basket. Ignacio selects a piece of fruit at random and then Terrance selects a piece of fruit at random. Find the probability that two apples are chosen.

Since the first piece of fruit is not replaced, the first event affects the second event. These are dependent events.

$P(\text{first piece is an apple}) = \dfrac{5}{16}$ ⟵ number of apples ⟵ total pieces of fruit

$P(\text{second piece is an apple}) = \dfrac{4}{15}$ ⟵ number of apples left ⟵ total pieces of fruit left

$P(\text{two apples}) = \dfrac{\overset{1}{\cancel{5}}}{\underset{4}{\cancel{16}}} \cdot \dfrac{\overset{1}{\cancel{4}}}{\underset{3}{\cancel{15}}} \text{ or } \dfrac{1}{12}.$

The probability that two apples are chosen is $\dfrac{1}{12}$.

Show your work.

b. _____

c. _____

Got it? Do these problems to find out.

Refer to the situation above. Find each probability.

    b. $P(\text{two bananas})$ **c.** $P(\text{orange then apple})$

Guided Practice

A penny is tossed and a number cube is rolled. Find each probability. (Examples 1–2)

1. $P(\text{tails and 3})$ _____

2. $P(\text{heads and odd})$ _____

3. Cards labeled 5, 6, 7, 8, and 9 are in a stack. A card is drawn and not replaced. Then, a second card is drawn at random. Find the probability of drawing two even numbers.

(Example 3) _____

4. **Building on the Essential Question** Explain the difference between independent events and dependent events.

_____

_____

_____

_____

Rate Yourself!

Are you ready to move on?
Shade the section that applies.

I have a few questions.

I'm ready to move on.

I have a lot of questions.

For more help, go online to access a Personal Tutor.

Tutor

Independent Practice

Go online for Step-by-Step Solutions

A number cube is rolled and a marble is selected at random from the bag at the right. Find each probability. Show your work. (Example 1)

1. P(1 and red) _____

2. P(3 and purple) _____

3. P(even and yellow) _____

4. P(odd and *not* green) _____

5. A carnival game wheel has 12 equal sections. One of the sections contains a star. To win a prize, players must land on the section with the star on two consecutive spins. What is the probability of a player winning?

(Example 2) _____

6. A standard set of dominoes contains 28 tiles, with each tile having two sides of dots from 0 to 6. Of these tiles, 7 have the same number of dots on each side. If four players each randomly choose a tile, without replacement, what is the probability that each chooses a tile with the

same number of dots on each side? (Example 3) _____

Mrs. Ameldo's class has 5 students with blue eyes, 7 with brown eyes, 4 with hazel eyes, and 4 with green eyes. Two students are selected at random. Find each probability. (Example 3)

7. P(green then brown) _____

8. P(two blue) _____

9. P(hazel then blue) _____

10. P(brown then blue) _____

11. **Reason Inductively** You and a friend plan to see 2 movies over the weekend. You can choose from 6 comedy, 2 drama, 4 romance, 1 science fiction, or 3 action movies. You write the movie titles on pieces of paper, place them in a bag, and each randomly select a movie. What is the probability that neither of you selects a comedy? Is this a dependent or independent event? Explain.

_____

_____

H.O.T. Problems Higher Order Thinking

12. **PS Model with Mathematics** There are 9 marbles representing 3 different colors. Write a problem where 2 marbles are selected at random without replacement and the probability is $\frac{1}{6}$.

_____

_____

13. **PS Find the Error** A spinner with equal sections numbered from 1 to 5 is spun twice. Raul is finding the probability that both spins will result in an even number. Find his mistake and correct it.

_____

_____

$$\frac{2}{5} \cdot \frac{1}{4} = \frac{2}{20}$$

14. **PS Justify Conclusions** Determine whether the following statement is *true* or *false*. If false, provide a counterexample.
If two events are independent, then the probability of both events is less than 1. _____

_____

_____

15. **PS Persevere with Problems** A company has determined that 2% of the pudding cups it produces are defective in some way. The pudding cups are sold in packages of two.

a. What is the probability that both pudding cups in a package are defective?

_____

b. The company produces 1,000,000 packages each year. Predict the number of packages in which both cups are defective.

_____

Extra Practice

A number cube is rolled and a letter is selected from the word AMERICA. Find each probability. Show your work.

16. P(less than 4 and vowel) $\dfrac{1}{7}$

 Homework Help

$P(\text{less than 4}) = \dfrac{1}{2}$

$P(\text{vowel}) = \dfrac{4}{7}$

$\dfrac{1}{2} \cdot \dfrac{4}{7} = \dfrac{4}{14} \text{ or } \dfrac{1}{7}$

17. P(greater than 1 and a consonant) _____

18. A number cube is rolled and a coin is tossed. What is the probability of the cube landing on 5 or 6 and the coin landing on heads?

19. A laundry basket contains 18 blue socks and 24 black socks. What is the probability of randomly picking 2 black socks, without replacement, from the basket?

20. **PS Persevere with Problems** Corbin is playing a board game that requires rolling two number cubes to move a game piece. He needs to roll a sum of 6 on his first turn and then a sum of 10 on his second turn to land on the next two bonus spaces. What is the probability that Corbin will roll a sum of 6 and then a sum of 10 on his next two turns? _____

Copy and Solve Solve Exercises 21–28 on a separate sheet of paper. **A card is pulled from a stack of 15 cards labeled 1–15 and the spinner shown is spun. Find each probability.**

21. P(less than 10 and red)

22. P(odd and red or blue)

23. P(even and blue)

24. P(prime number and blue)

Maddie is packing for a trip. In her closet, there are 3 red, 4 black, 2 green, and 2 yellow blouses. She randomly selects 2 blouses. Find each probability.

25. P(red and red)

26. P(black and yellow)

27. P(red and black)

28. P(green and green)

29. A bag contains letter tiles. There are 6 vowels in the bag and 14 consonants. On Michael's next turn, he will select a letter tile at random from the bag. Without replacing the first tile, he will then select a second letter tile. Determine if each of the following probabilities is true or false.

a. $P(\text{vowel then vowel}) = \frac{3}{38}$ ☐ True   ☐ False

b. $P(\text{vowel then consonant}) = \frac{21}{95}$ ☐ True   ☐ False

c. $P(\text{consonant then consonant}) = \frac{49}{100}$ ☐ True   ☐ False

30. The spinners are each spun once.

Do the two spins represent independent or dependent events? ☐

Select the correct values to complete the model below to find $P(2 \text{ and white})$.

$P(2 \text{ and white}) = \dfrac{\square}{\square} \times \dfrac{\square}{\square} = \dfrac{\square}{\square}$

1	6
2	8
3	12
4	16

Spiral Review

Solve each proportion.

31. $\frac{1}{4} = \frac{x}{72}$ $x = $ _____

32. $\frac{8}{n} = \frac{0.5}{0.9}$ $n = $ _____

33. $\frac{1}{3} = \frac{m}{153}$ $m = $ _____

34. $\frac{0.2}{a} = \frac{1.8}{18}$ $a = $ _____

35. 9 is 15% of what number? Write an equation. Then solve.

_____

36. A school librarian surveyed students about their favorite type of novel. The results are shown in the table at the right. What percent of students chose science fiction as their favorite type of novel? Round to the nearest whole percent.

_____

Type of Novel	Number of Students
mystery	18
romance	10
science fiction	26
other	4

21ST CENTURY CAREER
in Medicine

Pediatricians

Do you have compassion, a sense of humor, and the ability to analyze data? You might want to consider a career in medicine. Pediatricians care for the health of infants, children, and teenagers. They diagnose illnesses, interpret diagnostic tests, and prescribe and administer treatment.

College & Career
R E A D I N E S S

Explore college and careers at ccr.mcgraw-hill.com

Is This the Career for You?

Are you interested in a career as a pediatrician? Take some of the following courses in high school.

◆ Algebra
◆ Biology
◆ Calculus
◆ Chemistry
◆ Psychology

Find out how math relates to a career in Medicine.

ⓅⓈ On Call for Kids

Use the information in the table below to solve each problem. Write each answer as a percent rounded to the nearest whole number.

1. What is the probability that one of the patients tested has strep throat? _____

2. If a patient has strep throat, what is the probability that they have a positive test?

   _____

3. What is the probability that a patient with the disease has a negative test? _____

4. If a patient does not have the disease, what is the probability that they have a positive test? _____

5. What is the probability that a patient that does *not* have strep throat tested negative for the disease? _____

6. The *positive predictive value*, or *PPV*, is the probability that a patient with a positive test result will have the disease. What is the PPV? _____

7. The *negative predictive value*, or *NPV*, is the probability that a patient with a negative test result will not have the disease. What is the NPV? _____

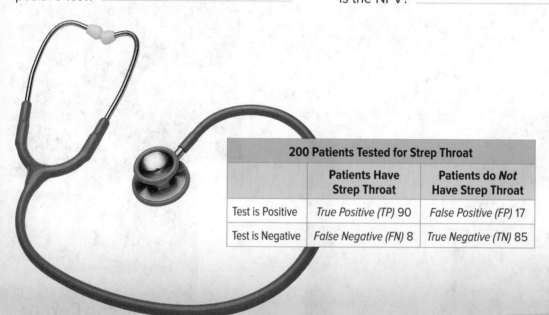

200 Patients Tested for Strep Throat		
	Patients Have Strep Throat	Patients do *Not* Have Strep Throat
Test is Positive	True Positive (TP) 90	False Positive (FP) 17
Test is Negative	False Negative (FN) 8	True Negative (TN) 85

ⓅⓈ Career Project

It's time to update your career portfolio! Interview your pediatrician. Be sure to ask what he or she enjoys most about being a pediatrician and what is most challenging. Include all the interview questions and answers in your portfolio.

_____

_____

_____

_____

_____

What are some short term goals you need to achieve to become a pediatrician?

• _____

• _____

• _____

• _____

• _____

Chapter Review

Vocabulary Check

Unscramble each of the clue words. After unscrambling all of the terms, use the numbered letters to find a sentence assoicated with probability.

HELATCORTEI

☐☐☐☐☐☐☐☐☐☐☐☐
           8   5

PORTUNMETAI

☐☐☐☐☐☐☐☐☐☐☐
             2   9

LEAPMS ECPAS

☐☐☐☐☐☐   ☐☐☐☐☐
4   3   6

COAPELMERTMYN

☐☐☐☐☐☐☐☐☐☐☐☐☐
 7   1

☐☐☐☐   ☐   ☐☐☐☐
1 2 3 4   5   6 7 8 9

Complete each sentence using one of the unscrambled words above.

1. The _____ is the set of all of the possible outcomes of a probability experiment.

2. A _____ is an arrangement, or listing, of objects in which order is important.

3. The _____ probability is based on what should happen when conducting a probability experiment.

4. Two events in which one or the other must happen, but they cannot

   happen at the same time are _____.

Use Your FOLDABLES

Use your Foldable to help review the chapter.

Tape here

Probability

Example

Picture

Example

Picture

Got it?

Match each term or phrase on the left with the words on the right.

1. Based on what actually occurred in a probability experiment

2. The outcome of one event affects the outcome of a separate event

3. Consists of two or more simple events

4. Can be used to find the sample space

a. compound event

b. experimental probability

c. Fundamental Counting Principle

d. dependent event

e. tree diagrams

f. organized lists

Power Up! Performance Task

Carnival Prizes

Kelli is in charge of a game booth at the school carnival. The game has two simple rules.

- Randomly pick one blue card and one red card.
- If the product of the two numbers is greater than or equal to 45, you win a prize.

Write your answers on another piece of paper. Show all of your work to receive full credit.

Part A

Create a sample space and find the product of each combination. What is the probability that a person wins the game? Express your answer as a fraction in lowest terms and as a percent rounded to the nearest whole number.

Part B

The sponsor of the booth determines that they are giving away too many prizes. Recommend a minimum winning number that lowers the chance of winning to 25%. Explain your reasoning.

Part C

Participants achieving a winning score of 70 or higher in four consecutive attempts will receive a large stuffed animal. What is the probability of this occurring?

Part D

After changing the game rules, patrons and onlookers are disappointed when the first five games yield products of 12, 21, 32, 35, and 12. Recommend a statement that the sponsor can use to reassure customers that the game is fair.

Reflect

 Answering the Essential Question

Use what you learned about probability to complete the graphic organizer.

Theoretical Probability

Experimental Probability

Essential Question

HOW can you predict the outcome
of future events?

Sample Space

Simulation

Answer the Essential Question. HOW can you predict the outcome of
future events?

Chapter 10
Statistics

Essential Question

HOW do you know which type of graph to use when displaying data?

Indiana Academic Standards
7.DSP.1, 7.DSP.2, 7.DSP.3, 7.DSP.4

PS Process Standards
1, 3, 4, 5, 6,

Math in the Real World

Surveys are used to collect information. Survey results can be shown in graphs.

The results of a survey of 50 middle school students are shown in the table. On the circle graph, write the percent of students who preferred each activity.

Activity	Number of Students
Gaming	22
Social Networking	18
Viewing Movies	6
Other	4

Favorite Online Activity

Viewing Movies ___%

Other

Social Networking ___%

Gaming ___%

FOLDABLES
Study Organizer

1 Cut out the Foldable on page FL13 of this book.

2 Place your Foldable on page 850.

3 Use the Foldable throughout this chapter to help you learn about statistics.

789

Vocabulary

biased sample	population	survey
convenience sample	sample	systematic random sample
double box plot	simple random sample	unbiased sample
double dot plot	statistics	voluntary response sample

Study Skill: Writing Math

Describe Data When you *describe* something, you represent it in words.

The table shows the prices for takeout orders at Lombardo's Restaurant.

Takeout	Price ($)
Main Dish	8.00
Side Dish	2.50
Dessert	4.00

Use the table to complete the following statements.

1. The price of a dessert is _____ .

2. The price of a main dish is twice the price of

   _____ .

3. A _____ is the least expensive item.

Write two other statements that describe the data.

4. _____

   _____

   _____

5. _____

   _____

   _____

Read each statement. Decide whether you agree (A) or disagree (D). Place a checkmark in the appropriate column and then justify your reasoning.

Statistics			
Statement	A	D	Why?
Statistics deal with collecting, organizing, and interpreting data.			
A sample is the same thing as the entire population.			
A biased sample accurately represents the entire population.			
Graphs are sometimes made to influence conclusions by misrepresenting the data.			
A double box plot consists of two box plots that are drawn on the same number line.			
Any type of display can be used to represent data.			

When Will You Use This?

Here are a few examples of how statistics are used in the real world.

Activity 1 Find the average monthly high and low temperatures for the city where you live. Then find the average monthly high and low temperatures for another city. How do these temperatures compare to the temperatures for your city?

Blake, Hannah, and Jamar in **Record Highs**

For our report we decided to compare record temperatures for 2 of the hottest places in the U.S.

Let's find the U.S. city that is closest to the equator.

Activity 2 Go online at **connectED.mcgraw-hill.com** to read the graphic novel **Record Highs**. Blake, Hannah, and Jamar need to compare the record high temperatures for two different cities.

What cities do they use? _____

Are You Ready?

Try the Quick Check below.
Or, take the Online Readiness Quiz.

Quick Review

Example 1

Which players averaged more than 10 points per game?

Nick, Walter, and Marreese averaged more than 10 points per game.

Example 2

Use the circle graph. Suppose 300 people were surveyed. How many people have two accounts?

Find 61% of 300.

61% of $300 = 61\% \times 300$
$= 0.61 \times 300$ or 183

So, 183 people have two accounts.

Quick Check

Graphs The bar graph at the right shows the number of items each student obtained during a scavenger hunt.

1. Who obtained the most items?

   _____

2. Who obtained the least items?

   _____

3. Refer to the circle graph in Example 2. Suppose 300 people were surveyed. How many people have 1 account?

   _____

How Did You Do?

Which problems did you answer correctly in the Quick Check?
Shade those exercise numbers below.

1   2   3

Make Predictions

Vocabulary Start-Up

Statistics deal with collecting, organizing, and interpreting data. A **survey** is a method of collecting information. The group being studied is the **population**. Sometimes the population is very large. To save time and money, part of the group, called a **sample**, is surveyed.

For each survey topic, determine which set represents the population and which represents a sample of the population. Write *population* or *sample*.

	Survey Topic	Set A	Set B
1.	dress code changes	the students in a middle school	the seventh graders in the middle school
2.	favorite flavors of ice cream	the customers at an ice cream shop in the town	the residents of a town

Real-World Link

Logan wants to survey students in his school about their favorite and least favorite zoo exhibit. Describe a possible sample Logan could survey instead of surveying the entire school.

Which **PS Process Standards** did you use?
Shade the circle(s) that applies.

① Persevere with Problems   ⑤ Use Math Tools

② Reason Abstractly   ⑥ Attend to Precision

③ Construct an Argument   ⑦ Make Use of Structure

④ Model with Mathematics   ⑧ Use Repeated Reasoning

Make Predictions Using Ratios

You can use the results of a survey or past actions to predict the actions of a larger group. Since the ratios of the responses of a good sample are often the same as the ratios of the responses of the population.

 Examples

The students in Mr. Blackwell's class brought photos from their summer break. The table shows how many students brought each type of photo.

Summer Break Photos	
Location	**Students**
beach	6
campground	4
home	7
theme park	11

1. What is the probability that a student brought a photo taken at a theme park?

$$P(\text{theme park}) = \frac{\text{number of theme park photos}}{\text{number of students with a photo}} = \frac{11}{28}$$

So, the probability of a theme park photo is $\frac{11}{28}$.

- -

2. There are 560 students at the school where Mr. Blackwell teaches. Predict how many students would bring in a photo taken at a theme park.

Let s represent the number of theme park photos.

$\frac{11}{28} = \frac{s}{560}$ Write an equivalent ratio.

$\overset{\times 20}{\frac{11}{28} = \frac{s}{560}}$ Since 28 × 20 = 560, multiply 11 by 20 to find s.

$\frac{11}{28} = \frac{220}{560}$ $s = 220$

Of the 560 students, you can expect about 220 to bring a photo from a theme park.

Got it? Do these problems to find out.

A survey found that 6 out of every 10 students have a blog.

   a. What is the probability that a student at the school has a blog?

   b. Suppose there are about 250 students at the school. About how many have a blog?

a. _____

b. _____

Make Predictions Using Equations

You can also use the percent equation to make predictions.

  Examples

3. A survey found that 85% of people use emoticons on their instant messengers. Predict how many of the 2,450 students at Washington Middle School use emoticons.

Words	What number of students is 85% of 2,450 students?
Variable	Let n represent the number of students.
Equation	n = 0.85 • 2,450

$n = 0.85 \cdot 2{,}450$ Write the percent equation.

$n = 2{,}082.5$ Multiply.

About 2,083 of the students use emoticons.

- - - - - - - - - - - - - - - - - -

4. The circle graph shows the results of a survey in which children ages 8 to 12 were asked whether they have a television in their bedroom. Predict how many out of 1,725 students would not have a television in their bedroom.

TV's in the Bedroom

54% No TV's in Bedroom

46% TV's in Bedroom

You can use the percent equation and the survey results to predict what part p of the 1,725 students have no TV in their bedroom.

part = percent • whole

$p = 0.54 \cdot 1{,}725$ Survey results: 54%

$p = 931.5$ Multiply.

About 932 students do not have a television in their bedroom.

Got it? Do this problem to find out.

c. Refer to Example 4. Predict how many out of 1,370 students have a television in their bedroom.

STOP and **Reflect**

What proportion could you use to solve Example 4? Write your answer below.

Show your work.

c. _____

The table shows the results of a survey of Hamilton Middle School seventh graders. Use the table to find the following probabilities. (Examples 1 and 2)

Career Field	Students
Entertainment	17
Education	14
Medicine	11
Public service	6
Sports	2

1. the probability of choosing a career in public service

Show your work.

_____

2. the probability of choosing a career in education

_____

3. the probability of choosing a career in sports

_____

4. Predict how many students out of 400 will enter the education field.

_____

5. Predict how many students out of 500 will enter the medical field.

_____

6. Use the circle graph that shows the results of a poll to which 60,000 teens responded. Predict how many of the approximately 28 million teens in the United States would buy a music CD if they were given $20. (Examples 3 and 4)

_____

How Would You Spend a Gift of $20?

Other 9%
Go to movie 5%
Save it 33%
Clothing/jewelry 21%
Music CD 32%

7. 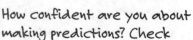 **Building on the Essential Question** When can statistics be used to gain information about a population from a sample?

_____

_____

_____

_____

Independent Practice

Go online for Step-by-Step Solutions

The table shows the results of a survey of 150 students. Use the table to find the probability of a student participating in each sport. (Example 1)

Sport	Students
Baseball/softball	36
Basketball	30
Football	45
Gymnastics	12
Tennis	18
Volleyball	9

Show your work.

1. football

_____

2. tennis

_____

3 gymnastics

_____

4. volleyball

_____

5 Three out of every 10 students ages 6–14 have a magazine subscription. Suppose there are 30 students in Annabelle's class. About how many will have a magazine subscription? (Example 2)

_____

6. Use the graph that shows the percent of cat owners who train their cats in each category. (Examples 3 and 4)

   a. Out of 255 cat owners, predict how many owners trained their cat not to climb on furniture.

   _____

   b. Out of 316 cat owners, predict how many cat owners trained their cat not to claw on furniture.

   _____

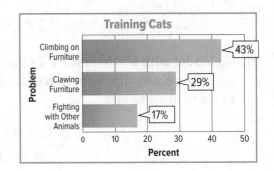

7. **PS Make a Prediction** The school librarian recorded the types of books students checked out on a typical day. Suppose there are 605 students enrolled at the school. Predict the number of students that prefer humor books. Compare this to the number of students at the school who prefer nonfiction.

_____

_____

_____

H.O.T. Problems Higher Order Thinking

8. (PS) **Find the Error** A survey of a seventh-grade class showed that 4 out of every 10 students are taking a trip during spring break. There are 150 students in the seventh grade. Caitlyn is trying to determine how many of the seventh-grade students can be expected to take a trip during spring break. Find her mistake and correct it.

$$\frac{4}{10} = \frac{150}{x}$$

$$\frac{4}{10} = \frac{150}{375}$$

$$x = 375 \text{ students}$$

_____

_____

9. (PS) **Persevere with Problems** One letter tile is drawn from the bag and replaced 300 times. Predict how many times a consonant will *not* be picked.

_____

10. (PS) **Persevere with Problems** A survey found that 80% of teens enjoy going to the movies in their free time. Out of 5,200 teens, predict how many said that they do not enjoy going to the movies in their free time.

_____

11. (PS) **Model with Mathematics** Explain how to use a sample to predict what a group of people prefer. Then give an example of a situation in which it makes sense to use a sample.

_____

_____

_____

12. (PS) **Model with Mathematics** Design a survey to give to your classmates. Construct a bar graph in the space below to represent your data. Then write and solve a problem that involves a prediction based on the data you collected.

_____

Show your work.

Extra Practice

Solve.

13. Luther won 12 of the last 20 video games he played. Find the probability of Luther winning the next game he

plays. $\frac{3}{5}$, 0.6, or 60%

$$P(winning) = \frac{number\ of\ games\ won}{number\ of\ games\ played}$$

$$= \frac{12}{20}\ or\ \frac{3}{5}$$

14. Refer to Exercise 13. Suppose Luther plays a total of 60 games with his friends over the next month. Predict how many of these games Luther will win. _____

15. Use the graph that shows the number of times teens volunteer.

  a. About 300,000 teens ages 12–14 live in Virginia. Predict the number of teens in this age group who volunteer a few times a year.

  _____

  b. Tennessee has about 250,000 teens ages 12–14. Predict the number of teens in this age group who volunteer once a week.

  _____

  c. About 240,000 teens ages 12–14 live in Missouri. Predict the number of teens in this age group who volunteer once a year.

  _____

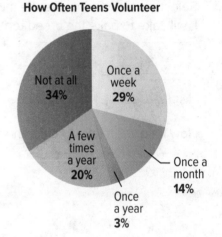

How Often Teens Volunteer

Not at all 34%
Once a week 29%
A few times a year 20%
Once a month 14%
Once a year 3%

16. **PS Make a Prediction** The probability of Jaden making a free throw is 15%. Predict the number of free throws that he can expect to make if he attempts 40 free throws.

_____

Draw a line to match each situation with the appropriate equation or proportion.

17. 27 MP3s is what percent of 238 MP3s?

18. 238% of 27 is what number?

19. 27% of MP3 owners download music weekly. Predict how many MP3 owners out of 238 owners download music weekly.

a. $n = 27 \cdot 2.38$

b. $\frac{27}{100} = \frac{p}{238}$

c. $\frac{27}{238} = \frac{n}{100}$

20. There were 515 students surveyed on how they spend time with their families. Which of the following estimates are accurate? Select all that apply.

☐ About 175 students spend time with their family eating dinner.

☐ About 72 students spend time with their family playing sports.

☐ About 50 students spend time with their family watching TV.

☐ About 38 students spend time with their family taking walks.

How Students Spend Time with Family	
Eating Dinner	34%
Watching TV	20%
Talking	14%
Playing Sports	14%
Talking Walks	4%
Other	14%

21. Yesterday a bakery baked 54 loaves of bread in 20 minutes. Today the bakery needs to bake 405 loaves of bread at the same rate. Select values to complete the model below to predict how long it will take to bake the bread today.

$$\frac{\boxed{}}{\boxed{}} = \frac{\boxed{}}{\boxed{}}$$

20
54
405
x

How long will it take to bake the bread today?

$\boxed{}$

Spiral Review

22. A magazine rack contains 5 sports magazines, 7 news magazines, and 10 fashion magazines. After a magazine is chosen, it is *not* replaced. Find the probability of randomly choosing two fashion magazines.

_____

23. Each week, Ryan's mother has him randomly choose a chore that he must complete from the list shown. The first week, he chose washing the dishes. What is the probability that Ryan will choose washing the dishes two more weeks in a row?

Weekly Chores

Collecting the trash
Folding the laundry
Cleaning the house
Washing the dishes
Cutting the grass

24. In how many different orders can a person watch 3 different movies? Use a list to show the sample space.

_____

_____

_____

Unbiased and Biased Samples

Entertainment A T.V. programming manager wants to conduct a survey to determine which reality television show is the favorite of viewers in a certain viewing area. He is considering the three samples shown. Draw an X through the two samples that would not fairly represent all of the people in the viewing area.

Sample 1
100 people that are trying out for a reality show

Sample 2
100 students at your middle school

Sample 3
Every 100th person at a shopping mall

Explain why the two samples that you crossed out do *not* fairly represent all of the people in the viewing area? Explain.

_____

_____

_____

Essential Question

HOW do you know which type of graph to use when displaying data?

 Vocabulary

unbiased sample
simple random sample
systematic random sample
biased sample
convenience sample
voluntary response sample

Indiana Academic Standards
7.DSP.1, 7.DSP.2

PS Process Standards
1, 3, 4, 5

 Which **PS Process Standards** did you use?
Shade the circle(s) that applies.

① Persevere with Problems   ⑤ Use Math Tools

② Reason Abstractly   ⑥ Attend to Precision

③ Construct an Argument   ⑦ Make Use of Structure

④ Model with Mathematics   ⑧ Use Repeated Reasoning

Biased and Unbiased Samples

To get valid results, a sample must be chosen very carefully. An **unbiased sample** is selected so that it accurately represents the entire population. Two ways to pick an unbiased sample are listed below.

Unbiased Samples		
Type	**Description**	**Example**
Simple Random Sample	Each item or person in the population is as likely to be chosen as any other.	Each student's name is written on a piece of paper. The names are placed in a bowl, and names are picked without looking.
Systematic Random Sample	The items or people are selected according to a specific time or item interval.	Every 20th person is chosen from an alphabetical list of all students attending a school.

In a **biased sample**, one or more parts of the population are favored over others. Two ways to pick a biased sample are listed below.

Biased Samples		
Type	**Description**	**Example**
Convenience Sample	A convenience sample consists of members of a population that are easily accessed.	To represent all the students attending a school, the principal surveys the students in one math class.
Voluntary Response Sample	A voluntary response sample involves only those who want to participate in the sampling.	Students at a school who wish to express their opinions complete an online survey.

Everyday Use
Bias is a tendency or prejudice
Math Use
Bias is an error introduced by selecting or encouraging a specific outcome

Examples

Determine whether the conclusion is valid. Justify your answer.

1. A random sample of students at a middle school shows that 10 students prefer listening to rock, 15 students prefer listening to hip hop, and 25 students prefer no music while they exercise. It can be concluded that half the students prefer no music while they exercise.

This is a simple random sample. So, the sample is unbiased and the conclusion is valid.

Determine whether each conclusion is valid. Justify your answer.

2. Every tenth person who walks into a department store is surveyed to determine his or her music preference. Out of 150 customers, 70 stated that they prefer rock music. The manager concludes that about half of all customers prefer rock music.

Since the population is every tenth customer of a department store, the sample is an unbiased, systematic random sample. The conclusion is valid.

3. The customers of a music store are surveyed to determine their favorite leisure time activity. The results are shown in the graph. The store manager concludes that most people prefer to listen to music in their leisure time.

Leisure Time Activities

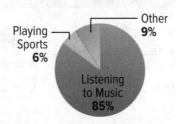

Playing Sports 6%

Other 9%

Listening to Music 85%

The customers of a music store probably like to listen to music in their leisure time. The sample is a biased, convenience sample since all of the people surveyed are in one specific location. The conclusion is not valid.

Got it? Do this problem to find out.

Show your work.

a. A radio station asks its listeners to indicate their preference for one of two candidates in an upcoming election. Seventy-two percent of the listeners who responded preferred candidate A, so the radio station announced that candidate A would win the election. Is the conclusion valid? Justify your answer.

a. _____

Use Sampling to Predict

A valid sampling method uses unbiased samples. If a sampling method is valid, you can make generalizations about the population.

Example

4. A store sells 3 types of pants: jeans, capris, and cargos. The store workers survey 50 customers at random about their favorite type of pants. The survey responses are indicated at the right. If 450 pairs of pants are ordered, how many should be jeans?

Type	Number
Jeans	25
Capris	15
Cargos	10

First, determine whether the sample method is valid. The sample is a simple random sample since customers were randomly selected. Thus, the sample method is valid.

$\frac{25}{50}$ or 50% of the customers prefer jeans. So, find 50% of 450.

$0.5 \times 450 = 225$, so about 225 pairs of jeans should be ordered.

Guided Practice

1. Zach is trying to decide which of three golf courses is the best. He randomly surveyed people at a sports store and recorded the results in the table. Is the sample method valid? If so, suppose Zach surveyed 150 more people. How many people would be expected to vote for Rolling Meadows? (Example 4)

Course	Number
Whispering Trail	10
Tall Pines	8
Rolling Meadows	7

_____

_____

2. To find how much money the average American family spends to cool their home, 100 Alaskan families are surveyed at random. Of the families, 85 said that they spend less than $75 per month on cooling. The researcher concluded that the average American family spends less than $75 on cooling per month. Is the conclusion valid? Explain. (Examples 1–3)

_____

_____

_____

_____

3. **Building on the Essential Question** How is using a survey one way to determine experimental probability?

_____

_____

_____

Rate Yourself!

Are you ready to move on? Shade the section that applies.

YES   ?   NO

For more help, go online to access a Personal Tutor.

FOLDABLES Time to update your Foldable!

Independent Practice

Go online for Step-by-Step Solutions

Determine whether each conclusion is valid. Justify your answer.
(Examples 1–3)

1. To evaluate the quality of their product, a manufacturer of cell phones checks every 50th phone off the assembly line. Out of 200 phones tested, 4 are defective. The manager concludes that about 2% of the cell phones produced will be defective.

Show your work.

_____

_____

2. To determine whether the students will attend an arts festival at the school, Oliver surveys his friends in the art club. All of Oliver's friends plan to attend. So, Oliver assumes that all the students at his school will also attend.

_____

_____

3. A random sample of people at a mall shows that 22 prefer to take a family trip by car, 18 prefer to travel by plane, and 4 prefer to travel by bus. Is the sample method valid? If so, how many people out of 500 would you expect to say they prefer to travel by plane? (Example 4)

_____

_____

Preferred Ways to Travel

Bus 9%
Plane 41%
Car 50%

4. **PS** **Use Math Tools** Use the organizer to determine whether the conclusion is valid.

Step 1:
Read the situation.

Marcus wants to predict the next student council president. He polls every fourth person from each grade level as they exit the cafeteria. In his poll, 65% chose Sophia. So, Marcus predicts Sophia will win the election.

Step 2:
Determine the type of sample taken.

_____

_____

Step 3:
Determine if the conclusion is valid.

_____

_____

5. **PS Persevere with Problems** How could the wording of a question or the tone of voice of the interviewer affect a survey? Provide an example.

PS **Justify Conculsions** Determine whether each statement is *sometimes*, *always*, or *never* true. Explain your reasoning to a classmate.

6. A biased sample is valid.

7. A simple random sample is valid.

8. A voluntary response sample is valid.

9. **PS Find the Error** Marisol wants to determine how many students plan to attend the girls' varsity basketball game. Find her mistake and correct it.

> I will survey students at the boys' varsity basketball game.

10. **PS Model with Mathematics** Give an example of a data set from a random sample. Then make an inference about the population represented by the sample.

Extra Practice

Determine whether each conclusion is valid. Justify your answer.

11. To determine what people in California think about a proposed law, 5,000 people from the state are randomly surveyed. Of the people surveyed, 58% are against the law. The legislature concludes that the law should not be passed.

This is an unbiased, simple random sample because randomly selected

Californians were surveyed. So, the conclusion is valid.

12. A magazine asks its readers to complete and return a questionnaire about popular television actors. The majority of those who replied liked one actor the most, so the magazine decides to write more articles about that actor.

_____

_____

13. The Student Council advisor asked every tenth student in the lunch line how they preferred to be contacted with school news. The results are shown in the table. Is this a random sample? If yes, suppose there are 684 students at the school. How many can be expected to prefer E-mail?

_____

Method	Number
E-mail	16
Newsletter	12
Announcement	5
Telephone	3

PS **Justify Conclusions** Each of the following surveys results in a biased sample. For each situation, explain why the survey is biased. Then explain how you would change the survey to obtain an unbiased sample.

14. A store manager sends an E-mail survey to customers who have registered at the store's Web site.

_____

_____

_____

_____

15. A school district surveys the family of every tenth student to determine if they would vote in favor of the construction of a new school building.

_____

_____

_____

_____

16. Maci surveyed all the members of her softball team about their favorite sport. Based on these results, Maci concludes that softball is the favorite sport among all her classmates. Explain why Maci's conclusion might *not* be valid. How could she change the survey to achieve a more valid conclusion?

Sport	Number of Members
Softball	12
Basketball	5
Soccer	3
Volleyball	8

17. Ms. Hernandez determined that 60% of the students in her classes brought an umbrella to school when the weather forecast predicted rain. She has a total of 150 students in her classes. Determine if each statement represents a valid or invalid conclusion.

a. On days when rain is forecasted, less than $\frac{2}{5}$ of her students bring an umbrella to school.   ☐ Valid   ☐ Invalid

b. On days when rain is forecasted, about 90 of her students bring an umbrella to school.   ☐ Valid   ☐ Invalid

c. On days when rain is forecasted, more than $\frac{1}{2}$ of her students bring an umbrella to school.   ☐ Valid   ☐ Invalid

Spiral Review

For Exercises 18 and 19, use the table that shows Alana's first six math test scores.

Test	1	2	3	4	5	6
Score	88%	92%	70%	96%	84%	96%

18. Find the mean, median, and mode of Alana's test scores. Round to the nearest tenth if necessary.

mean: _____   median: _____   mode: _____

19. Determine which measure of center best represents Alana's performance. Justify your reasoning.

_____

_____

Inquiry Lab
Multiple Samples of Data

 WHY is it important to analyze multiple samples of data before making predictions?

Indiana Academic Standards
7.DSP.2

PS Process Standards
1, 3, 4, 5

A hostess at a restaurant randomly hands out crayons to young children. There are three different color crayons: green (G), red (R), and blue (B). The server gives out the green crayon 40% of the time, the red crayon 40% of the time, and the blue crayon 20% of the time.

Hands-On Activity 1

When you draw a conclusion about a population from a sample of data, you are making *inferences* about that population. Sometimes, making inferences about a population from only one sample is not as accurate as using multiple samples of data.

Use a spinner to simulate the situation above.

Step 1 Create a spinner with five equal sections. Label two sections G. Label another two sections R and label one section B.

Step 2 Each spin of the spinner represents a young child receiving a crayon. Spin the spinner 20 times. Record the number of times each color of crayon was received in the column labeled Sample 1 in the table below. Repeat two more times. Record the results in the columns labeled Sample 2 and Sample 3 in the table.

Color	Sample 1 Frequency	Sample 2 Frequency	Sample 3 Frequency
Green			
Red			
Blue			

Compare the results of the 3 samples. Do you notice any differences?

The most commonly used keyboard is the QWERTY keyboard. However, there is another type of keyboard called the Dvorak keyboard that is based on letter frequency. Complete the Activity below about letter frequencies.

Hands-On Activity 2

The table at the right contains fifteen randomly selected words from the English language dictionary.

Sample 1		
airport	juggle	sewer
blueberry	lemon	standard
costume	mileage	thread
doorstop	percentage	vacuum
instrument	print	whale

Step 1 Find the frequency of each letter. Record the frequencies in the Sample 1 rows of the tables below.

Letter	a	b	c	d	e	f	g	h	i	j	k	l	m
Sample 1 Frequency													
Sample 2 Frequency													
Sample 3 Frequency													

Letter	n	o	p	q	r	s	t	u	v	w	x	y	z
Sample 1 Frequency													
Sample 2 Frequency													
Sample 3 Frequency													

Step 2 Randomly select another 15 words from a dictionary. Record the frequency of the letters in the rows labeled Sample 2 in the tables above.

Step 3 Repeat Step 2. Record the frequency of the letters in the rows labeled Sample 3.

Investigate

Collaborate

Work with a partner to collect multiple samples based on the following situation.

Janet and Masao are making centerpieces for their school's fall dance. They randomly select a ribbon to use in each centerpiece. There are four different colors of ribbon to choose from: brown (B), green (G), orange (O), and yellow (Y).

1. **PS Model with Mathematics** Design a method to simulate how many times each ribbon will be selected. Describe your simulation.

show your work.

_____

_____

2. Use the method you described in Exercise 1 to simulate the ribbon selection 20 times. Record the frequency of each color selection in the Sample 1 Frequency column of the table below.

Color	Sample 1 Frequency	Sample 2 Frequency	Sample 3 Frequency
Brown			
Green			
Orange			
Yellow			

3. Repeat the process described in Exercise 2 two more times. Record the frequencies of each color selection in the Sample 2 and Sample 3 columns.

4. Make an inference to determine which color was selected the most often in each sample.

_____

5. The *relative frequency* of a color being selected is the ratio of the number of times the color was selected to the total number of selections. Find the relative frequency of an orange ribbon being selected for each sample.

Sample 1: _____   Sample 2: _____   Sample 3: _____

6. Masao predicts that 5 out of 10 centerpieces will have an orange ribbon. How far off is Masao's prediction? Explain.

_____

_____

Work with a partner to answer the following questions. Refer to Activity 2.

7. What is the relative frequency for the letter *e* for each sample? Round to the nearest hundredth.

   Sample 1: _____   Sample 2: _____   Sample 3: _____

8. What is the mean relative frequency of the letter *e* for the three samples? the median relative frequency? Round to the nearest tenth if necessary.

   mean relative frequency: _____   median relative frequency: _____

9. (PS) **Use Math Tools** Research on the Internet to find the actual relative frequency of the letter *e* for words in the English language. How do your sample results compare to the actual relative frequency?

   _____

   _____

10. (PS) **Reason Inductively** Write a few sentences describing the inferences you can make about the frequency of letters in the words in the English language using your three samples.

    _____

    _____

    _____

On Your Own
Create

11. (PS) **Justify Conclusions** Research on the Internet to find the relative frequency of other letters in words in the English language. Write how your sample results compare to the actual frequencies. Note any differences.

    _____

    _____

    _____

12. (Inquiry) WHY is it important to analyze multiple samples of data before making predictions?

    _____

    _____

Misleading Graphs and Statistics

 Real-World Link

Essential Question

HOW do you know which type of graph to use when displaying data?

 Indiana Academic Standards
Extension of 7.DSP.1

PS **Process Standards**
1, 3, 4

Hockey The Stanley Cup is awarded annually to the champion team in the National Hockey League. The graph shows the total number of points scored in Stanley Cup playoff games by three players during their careers.

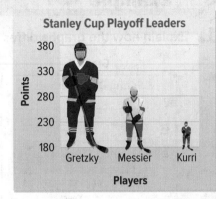

Stanley Cup Playoff Leaders

Points: 380, 330, 280, 230, 180

Players: Gretzky, Messier, Kurri

1. According to the size of the players, how many times more points does Messier appear to have than Kurri?

_____

_____

_____

2. Do you think this is representative of the players' number of points? Explain.

_____

_____

_____

3. What reason could someone have for intentionally creating a misleading Stanley Cup graph?

_____

_____

_____

Which **PS** **Process Standards** did you use?
Shade the circle(s) that applies.

① Persevere with Problems
② Reason Abstractly
③ Construct an Argument
④ Model with Mathematics

⑤ Use Math Tools
⑥ Attend to Precision
⑦ Make Use of Structure
⑧ Use Repeated Reasoning

Identify a Misleading Graph

Graphs let readers analyze data easily, but are sometimes made to influence conclusions by misrepresenting the data.

 Real World

Example Tutor

1. Explain how the graphs differ.

Graph A — Spring Dance Tickets

Graph B — Spring Dance Tickets

The graphs show the same data. However, the graphs differ in that Graph A uses an interval of 4, and Graph B uses an interval of 2.

Which graph appears to show a sharper increase in price?
Graph B makes it appear that the prices increased more rapidly even though the price increase is the same.

Which graph might the Student Council use to show that while ticket prices have risen, the increase is not significant? Why?
They might use Graph A. The scale used on the vertical axis of this graph makes the increase appear less significant.

Got it? Do this problem to find out.

a. The line graphs show monthly profits of a company from October to March. Which graph suggests that the business is extremely profitable? Is this a valid conclusion? Explain.

Graph A

Graph B

Changing Scales

To emphasize a change over time, reduce the scale interval on the vertical axis.

Show your work.

a. _____

Misleading Statistics

Statistics can also be used to influence conclusions.

Example

Tutor

2. **An amusement park boasts that the average height of their roller coasters is 170 feet. Explain how this might be misleading.**

Park Roller Coaster Heights	
Coaster	**Height (ft)**
Viper	109
Monster	135
Red Zip	115
Tornado	365
Riptide	126

Mean

$$\frac{109 + 135 + 115 + 365 + 126}{5} = \frac{850}{5}$$

$$= 170$$

Median   109, 115, 126, 135, 365

Mode   none

The average used by the park was the mean. This measure is much greater than most of the heights listed because of the coaster that is 365 feet. So, it is misleading to use this measure to attract visitors.

A more appropriate measure to describe the data is the median, 126 feet, which is closer to the height of most of the coasters.

> **Mode**
> The mode is the number or numbers that appear most often in a set of data.

Got it? Do this problem to find out.

b. Find the mean, median, and mode of the sofa prices shown in the table. Which measurement might be misleading in describing the average cost of a sofa? Explain.

Sofa Prices	
Sofa Style	**Cost**
leather	$1,700
reclining	$1,400
DIY assembly	$350
sectional	$1,600
micro-fiber	$1,400

Show your work.

b. _____

1. The graph suggests that Cy Young had three times as many wins as Jim Galvin. Is this a valid conclusion? Explain. (Example 1)

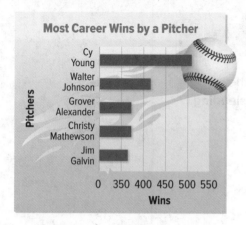

Most Career Wins by a Pitcher

Pitchers: Cy Young, Walter Johnson, Grover Alexander, Christy Mathewson, Jim Galvin

Wins: 0 350 400 450 500 550

_____

2. The graph at the right shows the results of a survey to determine students' favorite pets. Why is the graph misleading? (Example 1)

_____

Favorite Pet

Number of Students: 0 1 2 4 6 8

Type of Pet: Dog Cat Hamster Fish

3. The table lists the five largest land vehicle tunnels in the United States. Write a convincing argument for which measure of center you would use to emphasize the average length of the tunnels. (Example 2)

U.S. Vehicle Tunnels	Length (ft)
Anton Anderson Memorial	13,300
E. Johnson Memorial	8,959
Eisenhower Memorial	8,941
Allegheny	6,072
Liberty Tubes	5,920

_____

4. **Building on the Essential Question** Describe at least two ways in which the display of data can influence the conclusions reached.

_____

Rate Yourself!

How well do you understand misleading graphs and statistics? Circle the image that applies.

Clear   Somewhat Clear   Not So Clear

For more help, go online to access a Personal Tutor.

Tutor

Independent Practice

Go online for Step-by-Step Solutions

1 Which graph could be used to indicate a greater increase in monthly gas prices? Explain. (Example 1)

_____

_____

_____

_____

Graph A

Graph B

For Exercises 2 and 3, use the table. (Example 2)

2. Find the mean, median, and mode of the data. Which measure might be misleading in describing the average annual number of visitors who visit these sights? Explain.

_____

_____

_____

Annual Sight-Seeing Visitors	
Sight	**Visitors**
Cape Cod	4,600,000
Grand Canyon	4,500,000
Lincoln Memorial	4,000,000
Castle Clinton	4,600,000
Smoky Mountains	10,200,000

3 Which measure would be best if you wanted a value close to the most number of visitors? Explain.

_____

_____

4. **PS** **Model with Mathematics** Refer to the graphic novel frame below. Which measure of center should the students use? _____

_____

_____

For Exercises 5 and 6, create a display that would support each argument. The monthly costs to rent an apartment for the last five years are $500, $525, $560, $585, and $605.

5. Rent has remained fairly stable.

Show your work.

6. Rent has increased dramatically.

H.O.T. Problems Higher Order Thinking

7. **PS Reason Inductively** How could the graph you created in Exercise 5 help influence someone's decision to rent the apartment?

_____

_____

_____

8. **PS Persevere with Problems** Does adding values that are much greater or much less than the other values in a set of data affect the median of the set? Give an example to support your answer.

_____

_____

_____

9. **PS Reason Inductively** The circle graph shows the results of a survey. In what way is this graph misleading? Explain.

_____

_____

_____

Favorite Time of Year

26% Winter
16% Spring
16% Fall
42% Summer

Extra Practice

10. To determine how often his students are tardy, Mr. Kessler considered the attendance record for his first period class. Why is this graph misleading?

There are not equal intervals on the horizontal axis. So, the height of the bars is not representative of the sample.

11. The graph shows the height of a plant after 9 weeks of growth. Why is the graph misleading?

_____

_____

12. (PS) **Justify Conclusions** Each of the graphs below show the distance Romerio travels on his bike. Romerio wants to impress his friends with the distance he travels. Which graph should he show his friends? Explain.

_____

_____

_____

13. The scores Emily received on her math tests were 80, 90, 85, 100, 100, and 84. Why might it be misleading for Emily to say that most of the time she receives a score of 100?

_____

_____

14. Phones For All uses the display shown at the right to compare the number of minutes that they offer per month versus their competitor.

Cell Phone Minutes

Phones for All
750 min

Phonetastic
525 min

a. How many more minutes per month does Phones For All offer than its competitor? ☐

b. Why might the display be misleading?

15. The graph shows the average number of hours each week that certain students spend on extracurricular activities after school. Which of the following describe reasons why the graph may be misleading? Select all that apply.

☐ The graph does not show the number of hours each student spent on extracurricular activities.

☐ The intervals on the vertical scale are inconsistent.

☐ The graph's title is misleading.

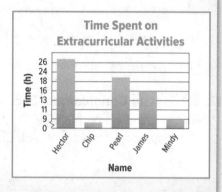

Time Spent on Extracurricular Activities

Spiral Review

Draw a histogram to represent the set of data.

16.

Test Scores		
Percent	**Tally**	**Frequency**
50–59	|	1
60–69	||	2
70–79	||||	4
80–89	ⅢⅢ Ⅲ	11
90–99	Ⅲ |||	8

Show your work.

Problem-Solving Investigation

Use a Graph

Case #1 Fishy Waters

Tess recently purchased a saltwater aquarium. She needs to add 1 tablespoon of sea salt for every 5 gallons of water.

Sea Salt Requirements						
Tablespoons of Sea Salt	1	2	3	4	5	6
Capacity of Tank (gallons)	5	10	15	20	25	30

How can she use a graph to show the number of tablespoons of salt required for a 50-gallon saltwater fish tank?

Indiana Academic Standards
7.DSP.1

PS Process Standards
1, 3, 4

 Understand *What are the facts?*

You know the number of gallons of the tank. You need to show the number of tablespoons of sea salt.

 Plan *What is your strategy to solve this problem?*

Organize the rest of the data in a graph so you can easily see any trends.

 Solve *How can you apply the strategy?*

Continue the graph until you align horizontally with 50 gallons. Graph a point. What value of sea salt corresponds with the point?

Graph: Tank Capacity (gal) on y-axis vs Sea Salt (tbsp) on x-axis, with points (1, 5), (2, 10), (3, 15).

 Check *Does the answer make sense?*

Find the unit rate of tablespoons of sea salt per gallon of water. Multiply the unit rate by the number of gallons to find the number of tablespoons of sea salt.

$$\frac{0.2 \text{ tbsp salt}}{1 \text{ gal water}} \times \frac{50 \text{ gal water}}{1} = \boxed{} \text{ tbsp salt } \checkmark$$

Analyze the Strategy [Tutor]

PS Make a Prediction Suppose the tank holds 32 gallons. Predict how much sea salt is required.

Case #2 Calories

The table shows the average number of Calories burned while sleeping for various numbers of hours. Assume the trend continues.

Calories Burned While Sleeping	
Hours	Calories
6	386
7	450
8	514
9	579

Make a graph to determine the approximate number of Calories that are burned by sleeping for 10 hours.

Understand

Read the problem. What are you being asked to find?

I need to find _____.

What information do you know?

There is an average of _____ Calories burned while sleeping for

6 hours and 514 Calories burned while sleeping for _____ hours.

Plan

Choose a problem-solving strategy.

I will use the _____ strategy.

Solve

Use your problem-solving strategy to solve the problem.

Continue the graph until it is aligned vertically with 10 hours. Graph a point.

Find what value of Calories corresponds with the point. So, about _____

Calories are burned while sleeping for 10 hours.

Check

Review the data in the table.

$450 - 386 = 64; 514 - 450 = 64; 579 - 514 = 65. 645 - 579 = 66.$

So, the answer seems reasonable.

Collaborate

Work with a small group to solve the following cases. Show your work on a separate piece of paper.

Case #3 Postage

The table shows the postage stamp rate from 1999 to 2009.

Make a graph of the data. Predict the year the postage rate will reach $0.52.

Postage Stamp Rates	
Year	Cost ($)
1999	0.33
2001	0.34
2002	0.37
2006	0.39
2007	0.41
2008	0.42
2009	0.44

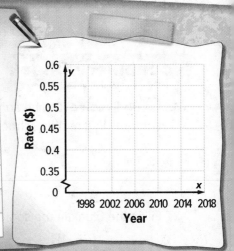

Case #4 Trains

The lengths of various train rides are 4, 1, 2, 3, 6, 2, 3, 2, 5, 8, and 4 hours.

Draw a box plot for the data set. What percent of the train rides are longer than 3 hours?

Case #5 Advertising

A local newspaper charges $14.50 for every three lines of a classified ad plus a 7% sales tax.

What is the cost of a 7-line ad? Round to the nearest hundredth.

Use any strategy!

Case #6 Anatomy

Each human hand has 27 bones. There are 6 more bones in the fingers than in the wrist. There are 3 fewer bones in the palm than in the wrist.

How many bones are in each part of the hand?

Mid-Chapter Check

Vocabulary Check

1. **PS Be Precise** Define *sample*. Give an example of a sample of the students in a middle school. (Lesson 1)

   _____

   _____

2. Fill in the blank in the sentence below with the correct terms. (Lesson 2)

   _____ and _____ are two types of unbiased samples.

Skills Check and Problem-Solving

3. A travel agent surveyed her customers to determine their favorite vacation locations. Use the table to find the probability of choosing a beach vacation. (Lesson 1)

   _____

Vacation Locations	
Location	**Customers**
amusement park	2
beach	11
campground	8
national park	4

4. Refer to the table. Suppose 120 customers are planning vacations. Predict how many will plan a national park vacation. (Lesson 1)

   _____

5. The number of points Emerson scored in 5 basketball games is 10, 8, 9, 8, and 30. Why might it be misleading for Emerson to say that she averages 13 points per game? (Lesson 3)

   _____

   _____

6. **PS Persevere with Problems** An online gaming site conducted a survey to determine the types of games people play online. The results are shown in the circle graph. If 1,500 people participated in the study, how many more would play card games than arcade games?

   (Lesson 1) _____

   Games People Play Online

   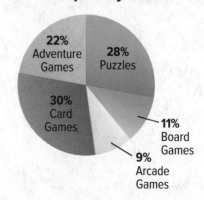

7. An owner of a restaurant wants to conduct a survey about possible menu changes. Give an example of a sampling method that would produce a valid sample. (Lesson 2)

   _____

Inquiry Lab

Collect Data

Indiana Academic Standards
7.DSP.3

PS **Process Standards**
1, 3, 4

 HOW can you use the measures of center and the range to compare two populations?

Studies show that teens need around 9 hours of sleep each night to stay healthy.

Hands-On Activity

Step 1 The results of a survey that asked 24 teens how many hours they slept last night are shown below. The teens were split into two populations, male and female.

Males	7	7	6	8	6	8	7	6	7	6	8	6
Females	8	8	7	6	8	7	6	6	7	8	9	7

Step 2 Graph the data for each population on a single line plot.

Number of Hours of Sleep

```
        m
   m         f       f
        f    m
   f    m    f
   m    m    m
   f    f    f
   m    m    m
   f    f    f
   m    m    m    f
  +--+----+----+----+--
   5    6    7    8    9
```

m	male
f	female

Step 3 Find the measures of center and range for each population.

	Mean	Median	Mode	Range
Males	6.83̄			
Females				

Are the data for males more or less varied than females?

_____

Which measure most accurately represents the data of the whole class?

Explain. _____

_____

_____

1. Work with a partner to design your own survey that meets the following guidelines.

- Create a survey question that involves two populations. For example, you might want to know about how many hours of sleep per night male students get in your school versus female students. Write your survey question below.

- Survey a random sample that is representative of your school's population. Survey at least 25 people. Collect the data and record your results in a table on a separate piece of paper.

- Create a display of your data. Be sure that the display shows the two populations.

Analyze and Reflect

Collaborate

Work with a partner to complete the exercises below based on the data you collected above.

2. Determine the measures of center (mean, median, and mode) and the range for each population's set of data.

3. **PS Reason Inductively** Compare the two populations. Are the data for one population more or less varied than the data for the other population? Justify your response.

4. Describe any other comparative inferences, or conclusions, you can make about differences in the two populations.

Create

On Your Own

5. **Inquiry** HOW can you use the measures of center and the range to compare two populations?

Compare Populations

 Real-World Link

 Essential Question

HOW do you know which type of graph to use when displaying data?

Vocab **Vocabulary**

double box plot
double dot plot

Indiana Academic Standards
7.DSP.3

PS **Process Standards**
1, 3, 4, 6

Exercise Mr. Singh surveyed the students in his first period gym class to find out how many times they exercised this month. The box plot below shows the results.

How Many Times Have You Exercised This Month?

0   5   10   15   20   25   30

1. Find the following values.

   Minimum: ☐   First Quartile: ☐

   Maximum: ☐   Third Quartile: ☐

   Range: ☐   Interquartile Range: ☐

2. What is the median? What does the median represent?

   _____

   _____

   _____

3. Write a conclusion that you can make from the box plot.

   _____

   _____

Which PS **Process Standards** did you use?
Shade the circle(s) that applies.

① Persevere with Problems   ⑤ Use Math Tools

② Reason Abstractly   ⑥ Attend to Precision

③ Construct an Argument   ⑦ Make Use of Structure

④ Model with Mathematics   ⑧ Use Repeated Reasoning

Compare Two Populations

A **double box plot** consists of two box plots graphed on the same number line. A **double dot plot** consists of two dot plots that are drawn on the same number line. You can draw inferences about two populations in a double box plot or double dot plot by comparing their centers and variations. The centers and variations to use are shown.

	Most Appropriate Measures		
	Both sets of data are symmetric.	**Neither set of data is symmetric.**	**Only one set of data is symmetric.**
Measure of Center	mean	median	median
Measure of Variation	mean absolute deviation	interquartile range	interquartile range

Example

1. Kacey surveyed a different group of students in her science and math classes. The double box plot shows the results for both classes. Compare their centers and variations. Write an inference you can draw about the two populations.

How Many Times Have You Posted A Blog This Month?

Neither box plot is symmetric. Use the median to compare the centers and the interquartile range to compare the variations.

	Math Class	**Science Class**
Median	10	20
Interquartile Range	20 − 5, or 15	25 − 15, or 10

Overall, the science students posted more blogs than the math students. The median for the science class is twice the median for the math class. There is a greater spread of data around the median for the math class than the science class.

Got it? Do this problem to find out.

a. The double box plot shows the costs of MP3 players at two different stores. Compare the centers and variations of the two populations. Write an inference you can draw about the two populations.

Cost of MP3 Players ($)

a. _____

Example

Tutor

2. The double dot plot below shows the daily high temperatures for two cities for thirteen days. Compare the centers and variations of the two populations. Write an inference you can draw about the two populations.

Daily High Temperatures (°F)

Both dot plots are symmetric. Use the mean to compare the centers and use the mean absolute deviation, rounded to the nearest tenth, to compare the variations.

	Springfield	Lake City
Mean	81	84
Mean Absolute Deviation	1.4	1.4

While both cities have the same variation, or spread of data about each of their means, Lake City has a greater mean temperature than Springfield.

Mean Absolute Deviation

To find the mean absolute deviation, find the absolute values of the differences between each value and the mean. Then find the average of those differences.

Got it? Do this problem to find out.

b. _____

b. The double dot plot shows the number of new E-mails in each of Pedro's and Annika's inboxes for sixteen days. Compare the centers and variations of the two populations. Write an inference you can draw about the two populations.

Number of E-mails in Inbox

Pedro

Annika

28 29 30 31 32 33 34 35 36 37 38

Examples

Tutor

3. The double box plot shows the daily participants for two zip line companies for one month. Compare the centers and variations of the two populations. Which company has the greater number of daily participants?

Number of Daily Participants

Treetop Tours

Zip Adventures

20 30 40 50 60 70 80 90 100 110 120 130

The distribution for Zip Adventures is symmetric, while the distribution for Treetop Tours is not symmetric. Use the median and the interquartile range to compare the populations.

	Treetop Tours	**Zip Adventures**
Median	70	50
Interquartile Range	30	20

Overall, Treetop Tours has a greater number of daily participants. However, Treetop Tours also has a greater variation, so it is more difficult to predict how many participants they may have each day. Zip Adventures has a greater consistency in their distribution.

STOP and **Reflect**

What can you tell about the set of data for Zip Adventures by looking at its box plot? Write your answer in the space below.

4. The double dot plot shows Jada's and Angel's number of hours worked in two weeks at their part-time jobs. Compare the centers and variations of the two populations. Who typically works the greater number of hours in a week?

Hours Worked

The distribution for Jada's number of hours is symmetric, while the distribution for Angel's number of hours is not symmetric. Use the median and interquartile range to compare the populations.

	Jada	Angel
Median	8	8
Interquartile Range	2	2

The median and interquartile range for both sets of data are the same. However, the interquartile range for Angel's number of hours worked is the difference of 10 and 8, while the interquartile range for Jada's number of hours is the difference of 9 and 7. So, Angel typically works more per week.

Got it? Do this problem to find out.

c. The double dot plot shows Kareem's and Martin's race times for a three-mile race. Compare the centers and variations of the two populations. Which runner is more likely to run a faster race?

Race Times (min)

c. _____

1. The double dot plot at the right shows the quiz scores out of 20 points for two different class periods. Compare the centers and variations of the two populations. Round to the nearest tenth. Write an inference you can draw about the two populations. (Examples 1 and 2)

Quiz Scores (points)

Second Period

Fifth Period

Show your work.

_____

_____

_____

_____

_____

2. The double box plot shows the speeds of cars recorded on two different roads in Hamilton County. Compare the centers and variations of the two populations. On which road are the speeds greater?
(Examples 3 and 4)

Speed of Cars (mph)

Hayes Road

Jefferson Road

_____

_____

_____

_____

_____

_____

3. **Building on the Essential Question** Marcia recorded the daily temperatures for two cities for 30 days. The two populations have similar centers, but City A has a greater variation than City B. For which city can you more accurately predict the daily temperature? Explain.

_____

_____

_____

_____

Rate Yourself!

Are you ready to move on?
Shade the section that applies.

YES ? NO

For more help, go online to access a Personal Tutor.

Tutor

Independent Practice

Go online for Step-by-Step Solutions

1 Jordan randomly asked customers at two different restaurants how long they waited for a table before they were seated. The double box plot shows the results. Compare their centers and variations. Write an inference you can draw about the two populations. (Examples 1 and 2)

Average Wait Times (min)

Lucy's Steakhouse

Gary's Grill

0 5 10 15 20 25 30 35 40 45

_____

_____

_____

_____

2. The double dot plot shows the times, in hours, for flights of two different airlines flying out of the same airport. Compare the centers and variations of the two populations. Which airline's flights had shorter flight times? (Examples 3 and 4)

Flight Times (h)

Airjet Express

Cross Country Airlines

1 2 3 4 5 6 7 8 9 10

_____

_____

_____

_____

Copy and Solve Write your answers for Exercise 3 on a separate piece of paper.

3. **PS** **Multiple Representations** For a science project, Mackenzie is measuring the growth of two plants.

Weekly Plant Growth (cm)							
	Week 1	Week 2	Week 3	Week 4	Week 5	Week 6	Week 7	Week 8
Plant A	2	3	2	2.5	3.4	3	2.5	3
Plant B	3	2.5	3	3.4	3.2	3.8	3.5	2.5

a. Numbers Find the median and interquartile range for both plants.

b. Graphs Graph the data using a double box plot.

c. Words Write an inference you can draw about the two populations.

4. The median and interquartile range of a set of data is shown. Write a set of data consisting of seven values for the pair of measures.

Median: 6   Interquartile Range: 5

H.O.T. Problems Higher Order Thinking

5. **PS** **Persevere with Problems** The histograms below show the number of tall buildings for two cities. Explain why you cannot describe the specific location of the centers and spreads of the histograms.

 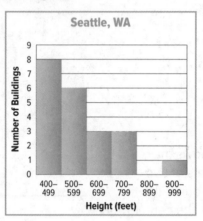

6. **PS** **Model with Mathematics** Refer to Exercise 1. What is a specific question you could ask about the two populations? _____

7. **PS** **Model with Mathematics** Two hockey teams, the Warriors and the Bulldogs, played 15 games each during a month. Both scored a minimum of 0 goals and a maximum of 8 goals. The Bulldogs generally scored fewer goals than the Warriors. Draw a double box plot that could represent the situation.

Extra Practice

8. The double dot plot shows the heights in inches for the girls and boys in Franklin's math class. Compare the centers and variations of the two populations. Round to the nearest tenth. Write an inference you can draw about the two populations.

Heights (in.)

Girls

Boys

62 63 64 65 66 67 68 69 70 71 72

Homework Help → Both plots are symmetric. The girls' heights have a

mean of 65 inches with a mean absolute deviation of

about 0.8 inch. The boys' heights have a mean of 69 inches with a mean

absolute deviation of about 1.4 inches. Overall, the girls' heights are lower

than the boys' heights and are also more consistently grouped together.

9. The double box plot shows the number of points scored by the football team for two seasons. Compare the centers and variations of the two populations. During which season was the team's performance more consistent?

Points Scored

Last Season

This Season

0 5 10 15 20 25 30 35 40 45 50

_____

_____

_____

_____

10. The double box plot shows the number of daily visitors to two different parks. Compare the centers and variations of the two populations. In general, which park has more daily visitors?

Number of Daily Visitors

Summer Lake

Canyon Overlook

20 30 40 50 60 70 80 90 100 110 120 130

_____

_____

_____

_____

11. **PS Be Precise** The median and interquartile range of a set of data is shown. Write a set of data consisting of seven values for the pair of measures.

Median: 5   Interquartile Range: 5

_____

12. The double box plot shows the top speeds reached by wood and steel roller coasters.

Speed (miles per hour) of Roller Coasters

Which of the following is not true about the double box plot? Select all that apply.

☐ The data for steel coasters is symmetric.

☐ The data for wood coasters is symmetric.

☐ The top speed of the fastest steel coaster is 135 miles per hour.

☐ The top speed of the slowest wooden coaster is 60 miles per hour.

13. The double dot plot shows the daily low temperatures of two cities in January over a two week period. Determine if each statement is true or false

Daily Low Temperatures (°F)

a. The medians are the same.   ☐ True   ☐ False

b. The interquartile ranges are the same.   ☐ True   ☐ False

c. The temperatures for City B are more consistent.   ☐ True   ☐ False

Spiral Review

Find the mean absolute deviation of each set of data. Round to the nearest hundredth if necessary.

14. _____

Maximum Speeds of Boats (mph)			
40	48	58	60
66	72	80	88

15. _____

Populations of Largest U.S. Cities (millions)			
1.3	3.8	1.5	8.4
0.9	1.4	2.3	1.3

16. Refer to the graph in Exercise 2. Describe the shape of the distribution of the data for Airjet Express.

_____

_____

_____

17. Refer to the graph in Exercise 10. Describe the shape of the distribution of the data for Canyon Overlook.

_____

_____

_____

Inquiry Lab

Visual Overlap of Data Distributions

 WHAT does the ratio $\dfrac{\text{difference in means}}{\text{mean absolute deviation}}$ tell you about how much visual overlap there is between two distributions with similar variation?

Indiana Academic Standards
7.DSP.4

PS Process Standards
1, 3

A survey was done. The tables below show the number of text messages sent and received daily for two different age groups.

Text Messages Ages 12–15			
70	90	80	90
85	75	85	80
90	80	75	95
100	85	95	85

Text Messages Ages 16–19			
85	75	80	70
75	80	65	75
85	70	90	80
70	75	60	65

Hands-On Activity

You can compare two numerical data sets by comparing the shape of their distributions. The **visual overlap** of two distributions with similar variation is a visual demonstration that compares their centers to their variation, or spread.

Step 1 Use a double dot plot to display the data in each table.

Text Messages Sent and Received

Ages 12–15

Ages 16–19

60 65 70 75 80 85 90 95 100

Step 2 Find the mean number of text messages for each age group.

Ages 12–15 mean = ☐   Ages 16–19 mean = ☐

Step 3 A red dotted line has been drawn through both dot plots that corresponds to the mean for the age group, 12–15 years. Draw a vertical dotted line through both dot plots that corresponds to the mean for the age group, 16–19 years. The dotted lines show the visual overlap between the centers.

Work with a partner.
The double dot plot
compares the number of
text messages sent and
received by a third age
group to the age group,
12–15 years.

Text Messages Sent and Received

Ages 12–15

Ages 24–27

50 55 60 65 70 75 80 85 90 95 100

1. What is the mean number of texts for the age group, 24–27 years?

_____

2. In the graph above, draw a vertical dotted line through both dot plots that
   corresponds to the mean for the age group, 24–27 years.

 Analyze and Reflect
Collaborate

Work with a partner.

3. What is the difference between the means of the distributions for the Activity?
   for Exercise 1?

_____

4. The mean absolute deviation of each distribution is 6.25 texts. For the Activity
   and Exercise 1, write the difference between the means and the mean
   absolute deviation as a ratio. Express the ratio as a decimal.

_____

5. **PS Reason Inductively** Compare the ratios you wrote in Exercise 4.

_____

_____

 Create
On Your Own

6. **Inquiry** What does the ratio $\dfrac{\text{difference in means}}{\text{mean absolute deviation}}$ tell you about how much
   visual overlap there is between two distributions with similar variation?

_____

_____

_____

Appropriate Measures

 ## Real-World Link Watch ▶

Recycling The green committee had a recycling drive where they collected aluminum cans, plastic bottles, newspapers, and batteries. The weights collected on the first day are shown.

Essential Question

HOW are the mean, median, and mode helpful in describing data?

Indiana Academic Standards
7.DSP.4

PS Process Standards
1, 3, 4

| 12.2 lb | 11 lb | 19.5 lb | 13 lb |

1. Find the mean weight collected. _____

2. If the newspapers are not included, find the mean weight rounded to the nearest hundredth. _____

3. How does the weight of the newspapers affect the mean?

_____

_____

4. What is the median for the data set? How does the median differ if the newspapers are not included?

_____

_____

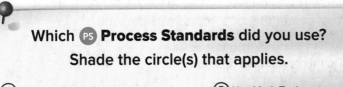

Which PS **Process Standards** did you use?
Shade the circle(s) that applies.

① Persevere with Problems   ⑤ Use Math Tools

② Reason Abstractly   ⑥ Attend to Precision

③ Construct an Argument   ⑦ Make Use of Structure

④ Model with Mathematics   ⑧ Use Repeated Reasoning

Using Mean, Median, and Mode

Measure	Most appropriate when...
mean	• the data have no extreme values.
median	• the data have extreme values. • there are no big gaps in the middle of the data.
mode	• data have many repeated numbers.

Sometimes, one measure is more appropriate than others to use to summarize a data set.

Examples

Tutor

1. The table shows the number of medals won by the U.S. Which measure of center best represents the data? Then find the measure of center.

Year	1992	1996	2000	2004	2008
Number of Medals	112	101	97	103	110

Since the set of data has no extreme values or numbers that are repeated, the mean would best represent the data.

Mean $\dfrac{112 + 101 + 97 + 103 + 110}{5} = \dfrac{523}{5}$ or $104\dfrac{3}{5}$

The mean number of medals won is $104\dfrac{3}{5}$ medals.

· ·

2. The table shows the water temperature over several days. Which measure of center best represents the data? Then find the measure of center.

Water Temperature (°F)			
82	85	82	81
	82	82	78

In the set of data, there are no extreme values. There is a temperature repeated four times, so the mode 82° is the measure of center that best represents the data.

Show your work.

Got it? Do this problem to find out.

a. _____

a. The prices of several DVDs are $22.50, $21.95, $25.00, $21.95, $19.95, $21.95, and $21.50. Which measure of center best represents the data? Justify your selection. Then find the measure of center.

Outliers and Appropriate Measure

Sometimes data sets contain outliers. Outliers are deviations from the majority of the data set. The outlier may affect the measures of center.

Examples

The table shows average life spans of some animals.

3. **Identify the outlier in the data set.**

Compared to the other values, 200 years is extremely high. So, it is an outlier.

Average Life Span	
Animal	**Life Span (years)**
African elephant	35
Bottlenose dolphin	30
Chimpanzee	50
Galapagos tortoise	200
Gorilla	30
Gray whale	70
Horse	20

4. **Determine how the outlier affects the mean, median, and mode of the data.**

Find the mean, median, and mode with and without the outlier.

With the outlier

Mean $\dfrac{35 + 30 + 50 + 200 + 30 + 70 + 20}{7} \approx 62$

Median   35

Mode   30

Without the outlier

Mean $\dfrac{35 + 30 + 50 + 30 + 70 + 20}{6} \approx 39$

Median   32.5

Mode   30

The mean life span decreased by 62 − 39 or 23 years. The median life span decreased by 35 − 32.5 or 2.5 years. The mode did not change.

5. **Which measure of center best describes the data with and without the outlier? Justify your selection.**

The mean was affected the most with the outlier. The median life span changed very little with and without the outlier, so it best describes the data in both cases. The mode does not describe the data very well since there were only two repeated numbers.

Outliers

In Example 3, 200 is an outlier.

IQR = 40

40 · 1.5 = 60

70 + 60 = 130

200 > 130

So, 200 is an outlier.

STOP and Reflect

If a data set has an outlier, why might you use the median instead of the mean?

Show your work.

Got it? Do these problems to find out.

The prices of some new athletic shoes are shown in the table.

Price of Athletic Shoes			
$51.95	$47.50	$46.50	$48.50
	$52.95	$78.95	$39.95

b. Identify the outlier in the data set.

b. _____

c. Determine how the outlier affects the mean, median, and mode of the data. _____

_____

_____

d. Tell which measure of center best describes the data with and without the outlier. _____

_____

_____

1. The table shows the required temperatures for different recipes. (Examples 1–5)

Cooking Temperature (°F)			
175	325	325	350
350	350	400	450

a. Identify the outlier in the data set. _____

b. Determine how the outlier affects the mean, median, and mode of the data. _____

_____

_____

c. Tell which measure of center best describes the data with and without the outlier. Justify your selection.

_____

_____

_____

2. **Building on the Essential Question** How does an outlier affect the mean, median, and mode of a data set?

_____

_____

_____

Rate Yourself!

How well do you understand choosing the appropriate measure of center for a data set? Circle the image that applies.

Clear   Somewhat   Not So
          Clear   Clear

For more help, go online to access a Personal Tutor.

Tutor

Independent Practice

Go online for Step-by-Step Solutions

1 The number of minutes spent studying are: 60, 70, 45, 60, 80, 35, and 45. Find the measure of center that best represents the data. Justify your selection and then find the measure of center. (Examples 1 and 2)

_____

_____

2. The table shows monthly rainfall in inches for five months. Identify the outlier in the data set. Determine how the outlier affects the mean, median, and mode of the data. Then tell which measure of center best describes the data with and without the outlier. Round to the nearest hundredth. Justify your selection. (Examples 3–5)

Month	June	July	Aug.	Sept.	Oct.	Nov.
Rainfall (in.)	6.14	7.19	8.63	8.38	6.47	2.43

_____

_____

_____

_____

3 The table shows the average depth of several lakes.

Lake	Depth (ft)
Crater Lake	1,148
East Okoboji	10
Lake Gilead	43
Lake Erie	62
Great Salt Lake	14
Medicine Lake	24

a. Identify the outlier in the data set. _____

b. Determine how the outlier affects the mean, median, mode, and

range of the data. _____

_____

_____

c. Tell which measure of center best describes the data with and without

the outlier. _____

_____

4. **PS** **Construct an Argument** Fill in the graphic organizer below.

Measure of Center	How can an outlier affect it?
mean	
median	
mode	

5. **PS Find the Error** Pilar is determining which measure of center best describes the data set {12, 18, 16, 44, 15, 15}. Find her mistake and correct it.

$$\frac{12 + 18 + 16 + 15 + 15}{5} = 15.2$$

6. **PS Justify Conclusions** Determine whether the following statement is *true* or *false*. If true, explain your reasoning. If false, give a counterexample.

   Of mean, median, and mode, the median will always be most affected by outliers.

7. **PS Persevere with Problems** Add three data values to the following data set so the mean increases by 10 and the median does not change.

   42, 37, 32, 29, 20

8. **PS Model with Mathematics** Use the Internet to find some real-world data. Record your data in the space below.

   a. Find the mean, median, and mode of your data set.

   b. Are there any outliers? If so, how do they affect the measures of center?

   c. Which measure of center best describes the data with and without the outlier?

Extra Practice

9. The number of songs downloaded per month by a group of friends were 8, 12, 6, 4, 2, 0, and 10. Find the measure of center that best represents the data. Justify your selection then find the measure of center. _Since the set of_
data has no extreme values or numbers that are identical, the mean or
median, 6 songs, would best represent the data.

There are no extreme values and no repeated numbers.

mean: $\dfrac{0 + 2 + 4 + 6 + 8 + 10 + 12}{7} = 6$

median: 0, 2, 4, ⑥, 8, 10, 12

10. The ages of participants in a relay race are 12, 15, 14, 13, 15, 12, 22, 16, and 11. Identify the outlier in the data set. Determine how the outlier affects the mean, median, and mode of the data. Then tell which measure of center best describes the data with and without the outlier. _____

_____

_____

_____

_____

11. **PS Justify Conclusions** The table shows the high temperatures during one week. Round to the nearest hundredth if necessary.

High Temperatures			
29°	27°	29°	25°
28°	29°	62°	

a. Identify the outlier in the data set. _____

b. Determine how the outlier affects the mean, median, mode, and range of the data. _____

_____

_____

c. Tell which measure of center best describes the data with and without the outlier. Explain your reasoning to a classmate. _____

_____

_____

_____

Power Up! Test Practice

12. The table shows the number of points scored by a basketball team during their first 6 games. Determine if each statement is true or false.

Points Scored		
79	83	79
85	41	77

a. The median or mode is the best measure of center to represent the data. ☐ True ☐ False

b. The range is affected by the outlier. ☐ True ☐ False

c. The mean is the measure of center least affected by the outlier. ☐ True ☐ False

13. For each data set, select the most appropriate measure of center.

a. mp3 player prices: $45, $249, $77, $55, $24, $36, $60 ▭

b. years of teaching experience: 19, 5, 7, 24, 20, 3, 28, 2, 16 ▭

c. forecast high temperatures: 72°, 74°, 73°, 74°, 74°, 75°, 74° ▭

mean
median
mode

Spiral Review

Find the total of each set of numbers.

14. {19, 16, 24, 22, 18} _____

15. {54, 48, 52, 57, 49} _____

16. {9, 5, 6, 7, 4, 11, 7} _____

17. {31, 36, 28, 34, 25} _____

18. Graph the numbers 15, 18, 22, 19, and 16 on the number line.

19. The table shows the number of tickets sold to the school musical on three days. How many total tickets were sold?

_____

Day	Number of Tickets Sold
Wednesday	56
Thursday	79
Friday	68

21ST CENTURY CAREER
in Market Research

Market Research Analyst

Do you think that gathering and analyzing information about people's opinions, tastes, likes, and dislikes sounds interesting? If so, then you should consider a career in market research. Market research analysts help companies understand what types of products and services consumers want. They design Internet, telephone, or mail response surveys and then analyze the data, identify trends, and present their conclusions and recommendations. Market research analysts must be analytical, creative problem-solvers, have strong backgrounds in mathematics, and have good written and verbal communication skills.

 College & Career
R E A D I N E S S

Is This the Career for You?

Are you interested in a career as a market research analyst? Take some of the following courses in high school.

◆ Algebra
◆ Calculus
◆ Computer Science
◆ English
◆ Statistics

Find out how math relates to a career in Market Research.

Select an Appropriate Display

Type of Display	Best Used to...
Bar Graph	show the number of items in specific categories
Box Plot	show measures of variation for a set of data; also useful for very large sets of data
Circle Graph	compare parts of the data to the whole
Double Bar Graph	compare two sets of categorical data
Histogram	show frequency of data divided into equal intervals
Line Graph	show change over a period of time
Line Plot	show frequency of data with a number line

Data Displays

Many situations have more than one appropriate display.

When deciding what type of display to use, ask these questions.

- What type of information is given?
- What do you want the display to show?
- How will the display be analyzed?

Example

Tutor

1. **Select an appropriate display to show the number of boys of different age ranges that participate in athletics.**

   Since the display will show an interval, a histogram like the one below would be an appropriate display to represent this data.

Show your work.

Got it? Do this problem to find out.

a. Select an appropriate display for the percent of students in each grade at a middle school.

a. _____

Example

Tutor

2. Select an appropriate type of display to compare the percent of ethanol production by state. Justify your reasoning. Then construct the display. What can you conclude from your display?

Ethanol Production by State Per Year						
State	Iowa	Nebraska	Illinois	Minnesota	Indiana	Other
Gallons (millions)	3,534	1,665	1,135	1,102	1,074	5,098

You are asked to compare parts to a whole. A circle graph would be an appropriate display.

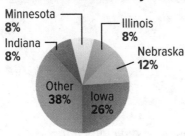

Indiana, Minnesota, and Illinois produce about the same amount of ethanol.

Got it? Do this problem to find out.

b. The table lists the ticket prices for school musicals during recent years. Select an appropriate display to predict the price of a ticket in 2013. Justify your reasoning. Then construct the display. What can you conclude from your display?

Show your work.

Ticket Prices	
Year	Price ($)
2009	5.00
2010	5.50
2011	6.50
2012	7.00

Select an appropriate display for each situation. Justify your reasoning.
(Example 1)

1. the number of people who have different kinds of pets

_____

_____

2. the percent of different ways electricity is generated

_____

_____

3. The prices of sandwiches at a restaurant are $4.50, $5.59, $3.99, $2.50, $4.99, $3.75, $2.99, $3.29, and $4.19. Select an appropriate display to determine how many sandwiches range from $3.00 to $3.99. Justify your reasoning. Then construct the display. What can you conclude from your display? (Example 2)

_____

_____

_____

4. A survey asked teens which subject they felt was most difficult. Of those who responded, 25 said English, 39 said social studies, 17 said science, and 19 said other. Construct an appropriate display of the data. Justify your reasoning. Then name one thing you can conclude from the display. (Example 2)

_____

_____

5. **(Q) Building on the Essential Question** What are some of the factors to consider when selecting an appropriate display for a set of data?

_____

_____

Rate Yourself!

How confident are you about selecting an appropriate display? Shade the ring on the target.

I'm on target.

I need help.

For more help, go online to access a Personal Tutor.

Tutor

Independent Practice

Go online for Step-by-Step Solutions

Select an appropriate display for each situation. Justify your reasoning.
(Example 1)

1 the median age of members in a community band

_____

_____

2. the number of students that favor chocolate or vanilla as a frosting

_____

_____

3. Select an appropriate display for the data. Justify your reasoning. Then construct the display. What can you conclude from your display? (Example 2)

Number of Push-ups			
45	35	42	37
44	40	36	42
45	40	42	39
44	43	36	39

_____

_____

_____

4. **PS Model with Mathematics** Refer to the graphic novel frame below. What is the best type of display to use for this data? Explain.

_____

_____

5. Refer to the situations described below.

Situation A	Situation B
the number of customers ages 12–19 compared to all age groups	the number of customers ages 12, 13, 14, 15, and 16 who made a purchase

a. Which situation involves data that is best displayed in a bar graph?

Explain your reasoning. _____

_____

_____

b. Refer to the situation you selected in part **a.** Could you display the data using another type of display? If so, which display? Explain.

_____

_____

H.O.T. Problems Higher Order Thinking

6. (PS) **Model with Mathematics** Give an example of a data set that would

be best represented in a line graph. _____

_____

7. (PS) **Reason Inductively** Determine if the following statement is *always, sometimes,* or *never* true. Justify your response.

　　　A circle graph can be used to display data from a bar graph.

_____

_____

_____

8. (PS) **Persevere with Problems** Determine if the following statement is *true* or *false.* Explain your reasoning.

　　　A line plot can be used to display data from a histogram.

_____

_____

9. (PS) **Reason Inductively** Compare and contrast bar graphs and histograms. Explain when it is appropriate to use a histogram rather than a bar graph.

_____

_____

_____

_____

_____

Extra Practice

PS Justify Conclusions Select an appropriate display for each situation. Justify your reasoning.

10. the resale value of a person's car over time

line graph; A line graph compares change over time.

11. the percent of people that drink 0, 1, 2, 3, or more than 3 glasses of water a day

_____

12. the number of different colored cars at a car dealership

_____

13. The circle graph shows the approximate percent of the total volume of each Great Lake.

   a. Display the data using another type of display.

Volume of the Great Lakes

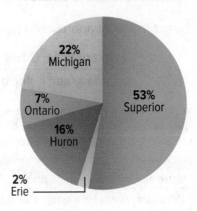

   b. Write a convincing argument telling which display is more appropriate.

   _____

   _____

   _____

Copy and Solve Select an appropriate display for each situation. Then justify your reasoning and construct the display on a separate sheet of paper. What can you conclude from your display?

14.

Favorite Movies	
Type of Movie	Number of People
Comedy	48
Action	17
Drama	5
Horror	2

15.

Age Group	Number of Texts per Day
11–15	25
16–20	23
21–25	17
26–30	10

16. The number of home runs hit by each player of a professional baseball team is shown in the table.

Home Runs					
10	15	5	10	12	5
12	12	4	5	10	7

Determine if each statement is true or false.

a. A line plot would be most appropriate for showing the frequency of the data on a number line. ☐ True ☐ False

b. A histogram would be most appropriate for showing the frequency of the data in equal intervals. ☐ True ☐ False

c. A circle graph would be most appropriate for showing how the number of home runs changes over time. ☐ True ☐ False

17. Select the most appropriate type of display for each situation.

| bar graph | histogram | line plot |
| circle graph | line graph |

Situation	Type of Graph
Mr. Reynolds measured the amount of rain that had fallen every 15 minutes during a storm. He wants to show how the amount of rain fallen changed over time during the storm.	
Alexandria recorded how many hours of her free time she spent playing sports, watching TV, talking with her friends, or playing video games. She wants to compare the percentages of her free time that she spends on each activity.	
Rachel collected data on how many of her classmates ride the bus, get a ride, or walk to school. She wants to compare how many students are in each category.	

Spiral Review

Use the graph to answer Exercises 18–20. The graph shows the number of male and the number of female students that chose certain occupations to research.

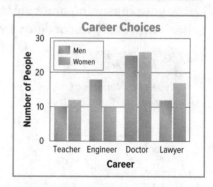

18. About how many people are represented in the graph? _____

19. About how many men and how many women are represented in the graph? _____

20. How many more women chose to research law? _____

21ST CENTURY CAREER
in Market Research

Market Research Analyst

Do you think that gathering and analyzing information about people's opinions, tastes, likes, and dislikes sounds interesting? If so, then you should consider a career in market research. Market research analysts help companies understand what types of products and services consumers want. They design Internet, telephone, or mail response surveys and then analyze the data, identify trends, and present their conclusions and recommendations. Market research analysts must be analytical, creative problem-solvers, have strong backgrounds in mathematics, and have good written and verbal communication skills.

College & Career
R E A D I N E S S

Explore college and careers at ccr.mcgraw-hill.com

Is This the Career for You?

Are you interested in a career as a market research analyst? Take some of the following courses in high school.

- ◆ Algebra
- ◆ Calculus
- ◆ Computer Science
- ◆ English
- ◆ Statistics

Find out how math relates to a career in Market Research.

Ⓟ Keeping Your Eye on the Target Market!

Use the results of the survey in the table below to solve each problem.

1. At Hastings Middle School, 560 of the students use social networking sites. Predict how many of them use the sites to make plans with friends. _____

2. Suppose 17.9 million teens use online social networks. Predict how many will be using the sites to make new friends.

   _____

3. According to the survey, what percent of a teen's networking site friends are people they regularly see? _____

4. Landon randomly selects a friend from his social networking site. What is the probability that it is someone he never sees in person? Write as a percent. _____

5. Paris wants to leave a message on 8 of her friends' social networking sites. In how many ways can she leave a message on her friends' sites? _____

Survey Results: Teens and Social Networking	
Reason to Use Social Networks	**Percent of Respondents**
Stay in touch with friends	91%
Make plans with friends	72%
Make new friends	49%
Friends on Social Networking Sites	**Average Number**
People who are regularly seen	43
People who are occasionally seen	23
People who are never seen in person	33
Total	99

Ⓟ Career Project

It's time to update your career portfolio! Use the Internet or another source to research a career as a market research analyst. Write a paragraph that summarizes your findings.

_____

_____

_____

_____

_____

_____

What skills would you need to improve to succeed in this career?

- _____
- _____
- _____
- _____
- _____

Chapter Review

Vocabulary Check

Complete the crossword puzzle using the vocabulary list at the beginning of the chapter.

Across

2. sample involving only those who want to participate (two words)

5. the group being studied

8. sample in which members of a population are easily accessed

9. part of a group

10. sample in which one or more parts of the population are favored over other parts

Down

1. random sample in which items are selected according to a specific time or interval

3. random sample in which each item is as likely to be chosen as any other item

4. a method of collecting information

6. two box plots on the same number line

7. sample that represents the entire population

Use Your FOLDABLES

Use your Foldable to help review the chapter.

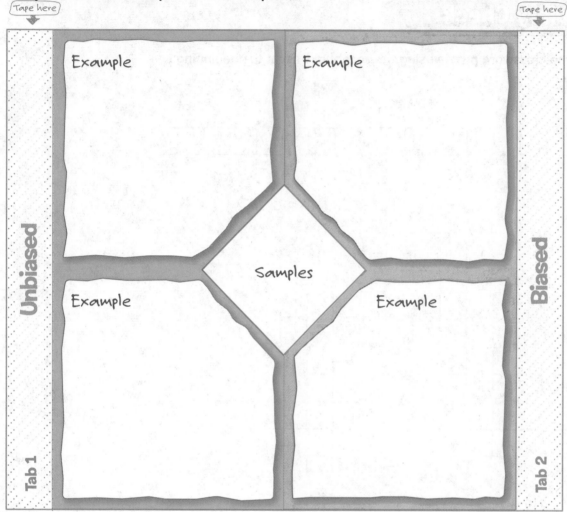

Got it?

Match each phrase with the correct term.

1. a method of collecting information

2. the group being studied

3. when one or more parts of the population is favored

4. a sample that involves only those who want to participate

a. voluntary response sample

b. biased sample

c. survey

d. population

e. convenience sample

Power Up! Performance Task

Class Evaluation

Mr. Fuentes is analyzing his student's grades over the last three years. He has had approximately 65 students each year. To simplify his analysis, he has decided to use a random sample of data from only ten students from 2012 and 2013. He had no records of the grades from 2014, so he asked students to bring in transcripts. He used the first few transcripts he received for his 2014 data.

	Student Grades									
2012	?	58	86	78	82	79	84	83	82	72
2013	83	85	85	85	87	87	88	90	91	91
2014	79	83	84	88	88	90	93	93	94	95

Write your answers on another piece of paper. Show all of your work to receive full credit.

Part A
Is the above information likely to be a legitimate representation of all the students of each respective year? Is the 2012 data biased or unbiased? Explain your answers.

Part B
In the year 2012, one of the grades is missing. If the mean was 80.1, what is the missing grade?

Part C
Considering the years 2013 and 2014, in which year were the grades the most consistent? Which of the two years had the better scores? What type of display would best show the data? Justify your responses.

Part D
Mr. Fuentes wants to submit the data from one year for a Teacher of the Year award. Choose a year. Could the data be seen as misleading? Explain.

Reflect

 Answering the Essential Question

Use what you learned about statistics to complete the graphic organizer.

Bar Graph

Line Graph

Essential Question

HOW do you know which type of graph to use when displaying data?

Double Dot Plot

Double Box Plot

Answer the Essential Question. HOW do you know which type of graph to use when displaying data?

_____

_____

UNIT PROJECT

Watch ▶ **Math Genes** A Punnett Square is a graphical way to predict the genetic traits of offspring. In this project you will:

- **Collaborate** with your classmates as you research genetics and the Punnet Square.
- **Share** the results of your research in a creative way.
- **ⓔ Reflect** on why learning mathematics is important.

Complete the activities below and discover the fun you can have with genetics.

Collaborate

Collaborate

ⓤ Go Online Work with your group to research and complete each activity. You will use your results in the Share section on the following page.

1. Use the Internet to research Punnett Squares and their role in genetics. Write a paragraph describing your findings.

2. Create sample genes for pet traits. Then create a Punnett Square using those traits. Describe what each outcome represents. Include a graph with your explanation.

3. Refer to Exercise 2. How many different genetic outcomes are possible according to your Punnett Square? What is the probability of each outcome occurring?

4. Create three word problems that involve using probability and the Punnett Squares to help answer the questions.

5. Collect two or more genetic-related information samples about students in your class. For example, you can collect data on attached/unattached earlobes. Analyze the data and make a prediction about the genetics of the entire school. Draw an appropriate graph of your results.

Share

Collaborate

With your group, decide on a way to share what you have learned about genetics and Punnett Squares. Some suggestions are listed below, but you can also think of other creative ways to your present your information. Remember to show how you used mathematics to complete each of the activities in this project.

- Create a digital presentation of the facts you learned about genetics.
- Act as a genetic scientist. Write a journal entry that explains your current research on predicting traits passed down from generations.

Check out the note on the right to connect this project with other subjects.

connect with Health

Health Literacy Select a health condition or disease and research how genetics may play a part in the disease. Write 1-2 paragraphs explaining how genetics may influence someone's risk of getting the disease and steps that can be taken to reduce the risk factors.

Reflect

On Your Own

6. (e) **Answer the Essential Question** Why is learning mathematics important?

   a. How did what you learned about probability help you to understand why learning mathematics is important?

   _____

   _____

   _____

   b. How did what you learned about statistics help you to understand why learning mathematics is important?

   _____

   _____

   _____

The eGlossary contains words and definitions in the following 13 languages:

Arabic	Cantonese	Hmong	Spanish	Urdu
Bengali	English	Korean	Tagalog	Vietnamese
Brazilian Portuguese	Haitian Creole	Russian		

English / Español

Aa

absolute value The distance the number is from zero on a number line.

acute angle An angle with a measure greater than 0° and less than 90°.

acute triangle A triangle having three acute angles.

Addition Property of Equality If you add the same number to each side of an equation, the two sides remain equal.

Addition Property of Inequality If you add the same number to each side of an inequality, the inequality remains true.

Additive Identity Property The sum of any number and zero is the number.

additive inverse Two integers that are opposites. The sum of an integer and its additive inverse is zero.

adjacent angles Angles that have the same vertex, share a common side, and do not overlap.

algebra A branch of mathematics that involves expressions with variables.

algebraic expression A combination of variables, numbers, and at least one operation.

---

valor absoluto Distancia a la que se encuentra un número de cero en la recta numérica.

ángulo agudo Ángulo que mide más de 0° y menos de 90°.

triángulo acutángulo Triángulo con tres ángulos agudos.

propiedad de adición de la igualdad Si sumas el mismo número a ambos lados de una ecuación, los dos lados permanecen iguales.

propiedad de desigualdad en la suma Si se suma el mismo número a cada lado de una desigualdad, la desigualdad sigue siendo verdadera.

propiedad de identidad de la suma La suma de cualquier número y cero es el mismo número.

inverso aditivo Dos enteros opuestos.

ángulos adyacentes Ángulos que comparten el mismo vértice y un común lado, pero no se sobreponen.

álgebra Rama de las matemáticas que trata de las expresiones con variables.

expresión algebraica Combinación de variables, números y por lo menos una operación.

alternate exterior angles   Angles that are on opposite sides of the transversal and outside the parallel lines.

ángulos alternos externos   Ángulos en lados opuestos de la trasversal y afuera de las rectas paralelas.

alternate interior angles   Angles that are on opposite sides of the transversal and inside the parallel lines.

ángulos alternos internos   Ángulos en lados opuestos de la trasversal y dentro de las rectas paralelas.

angle   Two rays with a common endpoint form an angle. The rays and vertex are used to name the angle.

∠ABC, ∠CBA, or ∠B

ángulo   Dos rayos con un extremo común forman un ángulo. Los rayos y el vértice se usan para nombrar el ángulo.

∠ABC, ∠CBA o ∠B

arithmetic sequence   A sequence in which the difference between any two consecutive terms is the same.

sucesión aritmética   Sucesión en la cual la diferencia entre dos términos consecutivos es constante.

Associative Property   The way in which numbers are grouped does not change their sum or product.

propiedad asociativa   La forma en que se agrupan números al sumarlos o multiplicarlos no altera su suma o producto.

Bb

bar notation   In repeating decimals, the line or bar placed over the digits that repeat. For example, $2.\overline{63}$ indicates that the digits 63 repeat.

notación de barra   Línea o barra que se coloca sobre los dígitos que se repiten en decimales periódicos. Por ejemplo, $2.\overline{63}$ indica que los dígitos 63 se repiten.

base   In a power, the number used as a factor. In 10^3, the base is 10. That is, $10^3 = 10 \times 10 \times 10$.

base   En una potencia, el número usado como factor. En 10^3, la base es 10. Es decir, $10^3 = 10 \times 10 \times 10$.

base   One of the two parallel congruent faces of a prism.

base   Una de las dos caras paralelas congruentes de un prisma.

biased sample A sample drawn in such a way that one or more parts of the population are favored over others.

muestra sesgada Muestra en que se favorece una o más partes de una población.

box plot A method of visually displaying a distribution of data values by using the median, quartiles, and extremes of the data set. A box shows the middle 50% of the data.

diagrama de caja Un método de mostrar visualmente una distribución de valores usando la mediana, cuartiles y extremos del conjunto de datos. Una caja muestra el 50% del medio de los datos.

center The point from which all points on circle are the same distance.

centro El punto desde el cual todos los puntos en una circunferencia están a la misma distancia.

circle The set of all points in a plane that are the same distance from a given point called the center.

círculo Conjunto de todos los puntos de un plano que están a la misma distancia de un punto dado denominado "centro".

circle graph A graph that shows data as parts of a whole. In a circle graph, the percents add up to 100.

gráfica circular Gráfica que muestra los datos como partes de un todo. En una gráfica circular los porcentajes suman 100.

Area of Oceans

Atlantic 22.9%
Pacific 46.4%
Indian 20.4%
Southern 6.1%
Arctic 4.2%

Área de superficie de los océanos

Atlántico 22.9%
Pacífico 46.4%
Índico 20.4%
Mar del Sur 6.1%
Ártico 4.2%

circumference The distance around a circle.

circunferencia Distancia en torno a un círculo.

circumference

circunferencia

coefficient The numerical factor of a term that contains a variable.

coeficiente El factor numérico de un término que contiene una variable.

common denominator A common multiple of the denominators of two or more fractions. 24 is a common denominator for $\frac{1}{3}$, $\frac{5}{8}$, and $\frac{3}{4}$ because 24 is the LCM of 3, 8, and 4.

común denominador El múltiplo común de los denominadores de dos o más fracciones. 24 es un denominador común para $\frac{1}{3}$, $\frac{5}{8}$ y $\frac{3}{4}$ porque 24 es el mcm de 3, 8 y 4.

Commutative Property The order in which two numbers are added or multiplied does not change their sum or product.

propiedad conmutativa El orden en que se suman o multiplican dos números no altera el resultado.

complementary angles Two angles are complementary if the sum of their measures is 90°.

∠1 and ∠2 are complementary angles.

ángulos complementarios Dos ángulos son complementarios si la suma de sus medidas es 90°.

∠1 y ∠2 son complementarios.

complementary events The events of one outcome happening and that outcome not happening. The sum of the probabilities of an event and its complement is 1 or 100%. In symbols, $P(A) + P(not A) = 1$.

eventos complementarios Los eventos de un resultado que ocurre y ese resultado que no ocurre. La suma de las probabilidades de un evento y su complemento es 1 ó 100. En símbolos $P(A) + P(no A) = 1$.

complex fraction A fraction $\frac{A}{B}$ where A or B are fractions and B does not equal zero.

fracción compleja Una fracción $\frac{A}{B}$ en la cual A o B son fracciones y B no es igual a cero.

composite figure A figure that is made up of two or more three-dimensional figures.

figura compuesta Figura formada por dos o más figuras tridimensionales.

compound event An event consisting of two or more simple events.

evento compuesto Un evento que consiste en dos o más eventos simples.

cone A three-dimensional figure with one circular base connected by a curved surface to a single vertex.

cono Una figura tridimensional con una base circular conectada por una superficie curva para un solo vértice.

congruent Having the same measure.

congruente Que tiene la misma medida.

congruent angles Angles that have the same measure.

ángulos congruentes Ángulos que tienen la misma medida.

∠1 and ∠2 are congruent angles.

∠1 y ∠2 son congruentes.

congruent figures Figures that have the same size and same shape and corresponding sides and angles with equal measure.

figuras congruentes Figuras que tienen el mismo tamaño y la misma forma y los lados y los ángulos correspondientes tienen igual medida.

congruent segments Sides with the same length.

segmentos congruentes Lados con la misma longitud.

Side $\overline{AB}$ is congruent to side $\overline{BC}$.

$\overline{AB}$ es congruente a $\overline{BC}$.

constant   A term that does not contain a variable.

constante   Término que no contiene ninguna variable.

constant of proportionality   A constant ratio or unit rate of two variable quantities. It is also called the constant of variation.

constante de proporcionalidad   Una razón constante o tasa por unidad de dos cantidades variables. También se llama constante de variación.

constant of variation   The constant ratio in a direct variation. It is also called the constant of proportionality.

constante de variación   Una razón constante o tasa por unidad de dos cantidades variables. También se llama constante de proporcionalidad.

constant rate of change   The rate of change in a linear relationship.

razón constante de cambio   Tasa de cambio en una relación lineal.

continuous data   Data that take on any real number value. It can be determined by considering what numbers are reasonable as part of the domain.

datos continuos   Datos que asumen cualquier valor numérico real. Se pueden determinar al considerar qué números son razonables como parte del dominio.

convenience sample   A sample which consists of members of a population that are easily accessed.

muestra de conveniencia   Muestra que incluye miembros de una población fácilmente accesibles.

coordinate plane   A plane in which a horizontal number line and a vertical number line intersect at their zero points. Also called a coordinate grid.

plano de coordenadas   Plano en el cual se han trazado dos rectas numéricas, una horizontal y una vertical, que se intersecan en sus puntos cero. También conocido como sistema de coordenadas.

coplanar   Lines or points that lie in the same plane.

coplanar   Líneas o puntos situados en el mismo plano.

corresponding angles   Angles in the same position on parallel lines in relation to a transversal.

ángulos correspondientes   Ángulos que están en la misma posición sobre rectas paralelas en relación con la transversal.

corresponding sides   The sides of similar figures that are in the same relative position.

lados correspondientes   Lados de figuras semejantes que estan en la misma posición.

counterexample   A specific case which proves a statement false.

contraejemplo   Caso específico que demuestra la falsedad de un enunciado.

cross product   The product of the numerator of one ratio and the denominator of the other ratio. The cross products of any proportion are equal.

producto cruzado   Producto del numerador de una razón por el denominador de la otra razón. Los productos cruzados de cualquier proporción son iguales.

cross section   The cross section of a solid and a plane.

sección transversal   Intersección de un sólido con un plano.

cube root One of three equal factors of a number. If $a^3 = b$, then a is the cube root of b. The cube root of 125 is 5 since $5^3 = 125$.

raíz cúbica Uno de tres factores iguales de un número. Si $a^3 = b$, entonces a es la raíz cúbica de b. La raíz cúbica de 125 es 5, dado que $5^3 = 125$.

cubed The product in which a number is a factor three times. Two cubed is 8 because $2 \times 2 \times 2 = 8$.

al cubo El producto de un número por sí mismo, tres veces. Dos al cubo es 8 porque $2 \times 2 \times 2 = 8$.

cylinder A three-dimensional figure with two parallel congruent circular bases connected by a curved surface.

cilindro Una figura tridimensional con dos paralelas congruentes circulares bases conectados por una superficie curva.

decagon A polygon having ten sides.

decágono Un polígono con diez lados.

defining a variable Choosing a variable and a quantity for the variable to represent in an expression or equation.

definir una variable El eligir una variable y una cantidad que esté representada por la variable en una expresión o en una ecuacion.

degrees The most common unit of measure for angles. If a circle were divided into 360 equal-sized parts, each part would have an angle measure of 1 degree.

grados La unidad más común para medir ángulos. Si un círculo se divide en 360 partes iguales, cada parte tiene una medida angular de 1 grado.

dependent events Two or more events in which the outcome of one event affects the outcome of the other event(s).

eventos dependientes Dos o más eventos en que el resultado de un evento afecta el resultado de otro u otros eventos.

dependent variable The variable in a relation with a value that depends on the value of the independent variable.

variable dependiente La variable en una relación cuyo valor depende del valor de la variable independiente.

derived unit A unit that is derived from a measurement system base unit, such as length, mass, or time.

unidad derivada Unidad que se deriva de una unidad básica de un sistema de medidas, como la longitud, la masa o el tiempo.

diagonal A line segment that connects two nonconsecutive vertices.

diagonal Segmento de recta que une dos vértices no consecutivos de un polígono.

diameter The distance across a circle through its center.

diámetro Segmento que pasa por el centro de un círculo y lo divide en dos partes iguales.

diameter

diámetro

dimensional analysis   The process of including units of measurement when you compute.

análisis dimensional   Proceso que incluye las unidades de medida al hacer cálculos.

direct variation   The relationship between two variable quantities that have a constant ratio.

variación directa   Relación entre las cantidades de dos variables que tienen una tasa constante.

discount   The amount by which the regular price of an item is reduced.

descuento   Cantidad que se le rebaja al precio regular de un artículo.

discrete data   When solutions of a function are only integer values. It can be determined by considering what numbers are reasonable as part of the domain.

datos discretos   Cuando las soluciones de una función son solo valores enteros. Se pueden determinar considerando qué números son razonables como parte del dominio.

disjoint events   Events that cannot happen at the same time.

eventos disjuntos   Eventos que no pueden ocurrir al mismo tiempo.

Distributive Property   To multiply a sum by a number, multiply each addend of the sum by the number outside the parentheses. For any numbers a, b, and c, $a(b + c) = ab + ac$ and $a(b - c) = ab - ac$.
Example: $2(5 + 3) = (2 \times 5) + (2 \times 3)$ and $2(5 - 3) = (2 \times 5) - (2 \times 3)$

propiedad distributiva   Para multiplicar una suma por un número, multiplíquese cada sumando de la suma por el número que está fuera del paréntesis. Sean cuales fuere los números a, b, y c, $a(b + c) = ab + ac$ y $a(b - c) = ab - ac$.
Ejemplo: $2(5 + 3) = (2 \cdot 5) + (2 \cdot 3)$ y $2(5 - 3) = (2 \cdot 5) - (2 \cdot 3)$

Division Property of Equality   If you divide each side of an equation by the same nonzero number, the two sides remain equal.

propiedad de igualdad de la división   Si divides ambos lados de una ecuación entre el mismo número no nulo, los lados permanecen iguales.

Division Property of Inequality   When you divide each side of an inequality by a negative number, the inequality symbol must be reversed for the inequality to remain true.

propiedad de desigualdad en la división   Cuando se divide cada lado de una desigualdad entre un número negativo, el símbolo de desigualdad debe invertirse para que la desigualdad siga siendo verdadera.

domain   The set of input values for a function.

dominio   El conjunto de valores de entrada de una función.

double box plot   Two box plots graphed on the same number line.

doble diagrama de caja   Dos diagramas de caja sobre la misma recta numérica.

double dot plot   A method of visually displaying a distribution of two sets of data values where each value is shown as a dot above a number line.

doble diagrama de puntos   Un método de mostrar visualmente una distribución de dos conjuntos de valores donde cada valor se muestra como un punto arriba de una recta numérica.

Ee

edge   The line segment where two faces of a polyhedron intersect.

borde   El segmento de línea donde se cruzan dos caras de un poliedro.

enlargement   An image larger than the original.

ampliación   Imagen más grande que la original.

equation   A mathematical sentence that contains an equals sign, =, stating that two quantities are equal.

ecuación   Enunciado matemático que contiene el signo de igualdad = indicando que dos cantidades son iguales.

equiangular   In a polygon, all of the angles are congruent.

equilateral   In a polygon, all of the sides are congruent.

equilateral triangle   A triangle having three congruent sides.

equivalent equations   Two or more equations with the same solution.

equivalent expressions   Expressions that have the same value.

equivalent ratios   Two ratios that have the same value.

evaluate   To find the value of an expression.

experimental probability   An estimated probability based on the relative frequency of positive outcomes occurring during an experiment. It is based on what *actually* occurred during such an experiment.

exponent   In a power, the number that tells how many times the base is used as a factor. In 5^3, the exponent is 3. That is, $5^3 = 5 \times 5 \times 5$.

exponential form   Numbers written with exponents.

equiangular   En un polígono, todos los ángulos son congruentes.

equilátero   En un polígono, todos los lados son congruentes.

triángulo equilátero   Triángulo con tres lados congruentes.

ecuaciones equivalentes   Dos o más ecuaciones con la misma solución.

expresiones equivalentes   Expresiones que tienen el mismo valor.

razones equivalentes   Dos razones que tienen el mismo valor.

evaluar   Calcular el valor de una expresión.

probabilidad experimental   Probabilidad estimada que se basa en la frecuencia relativa de los resultados positivos que ocurren durante un experimento. Se basa en lo que *en realidad* ocurre durante dicho experimento.

exponente   En una potencia, el número que indica las veces que la base se usa como factor. En 5^3, el exponente es 3. Es decir, $5^3 = 5 \times 5 \times 5$.

forma exponencial   Números escritos usando exponentes.

face   A flat surface of a polyhedron.

factor   To write a number as a product of its factors.

factored form   An expression expressed as the product of its factors.

factors   Two or more numbers that are multiplied together to form a product.

cara   Una superficie plana de un poliedro.

factorizar   Escribir un número como el producto de sus factores.

forma factorizada   Una expresión expresada como el producto de sus factores.

factores   Dos o más números que se multiplican entre sí para formar un producto.

fair game   A game where each player has an equally likely chance of winning.

juego justo   Juego donde cada jugador tiene igual posibilidad de ganar.

first quartile   For a data set with median M, the first quartile is the median of the data values less than M.

primer cuartil   Para un conjunto de datos con la mediana M, el primer cuartil es la mediana de los valores menores que M.

formula   An equation that shows the relationship among certain quantities.

fórmula   Ecuación que muestra la relación entre ciertas cantidades.

function   A relationship which assigns exactly one output value for each input value.

función   Relación que asigna exactamente un valor de salida a cada valor de entrada.

function rule   The operation performed on the input of a function.

regla de función   Operación que se efectúa en el valor de entrada.

function table   A table used to organize the input numbers, output numbers, and the function rule.

tabla de funciones   Tabla que organiza las entradas, la regla y las salidas de una función.

Fundamental Counting Principle   Uses multiplication of the number of ways each event in an experiment can occur to find the number of possible outcomes in a sample space.

Principio Fundamental de Contar   Este principio usa la multiplicación del número de veces que puede ocurrir cada evento en un experimento para calcular el número de posibles resultados en un espacio muestral.

Gg

gram   A unit of mass in the metric system equivalent to 0.001 kilogram. The amount of matter an object can hold.

gramo   Unidad de masa en el sistema métrico que equivale a 0.001 de kilogramo. La cantidad de materia que puede contener un objeto.

graph   The process of placing a point on a number line or on a coordinate plane at its proper location.

graficar   Proceso de dibujar o trazar un punto en una recta numérica o en un plano de coordenadas en su ubicación correcta.

gratuity   Also known as a tip. It is a small amount of money in return for a service.

gratificación   También conocida como propina. Es una cantidad pequeña de dinero en retribución por un servicio.

Hh

heptagon   A polygon having seven sides.

heptágono   Polígono con siete lados.

hexagon   A polygon having six sides.

hexágono   Polígono con seis lados.

histogram   A type of bar graph used to display numerical data that have been organized into equal intervals.

Grade 6 Math Test

histograma   Tipo de gráfica de barras que se usa para exhibir datos que se han organizado en intervalos iguales.

Examen de matemáticas de 6°grado

Ii

Identity Property of Zero   The sum of an addend and zero is the addend. Example: $5 + 0 = 5$

independent events   Two or more events in which the outcome of one event does not affect the outcome of the other event(s).

independent variable   The variable in a function with a value that is subject to choice.

indirect measurement   Finding a measurement using similar figures to find the length, width, or height of objects that are too difficult to measure directly.

inequality   An open sentence that uses $<$, $>$, $\neq$, $\leq$, or $\geq$ to compare two quantities.

integer   Any number from the set $\{..., -4, -3, -2, -1, 0, 1, 2, 3, 4, ...\}$, where ... means continues without end.

interquartile range   A measure of variation in a set of numerical data. It is the distance between first and third quartiles of the data set.

inverse variation   A relationship where the product of x and y is a constant k. As x increases in value, y decreases in value, or as y decreases in value, x increases in value.

irrational number   A number that cannot be expressed as the ratio of two integers.

isosceles triangle   A triangle having at least two congruent sides.

propiedad de identidad del cero   La suma de un sumando y cero es igual al sumando. Ejemplo: $5 + 0 = 5$

eventos independientes   Dos o más eventos en los cuales el resultado de uno de ellos no afecta el resultado de los otros eventos.

variable independiente   Variable en una función cuyo valor está sujeto a elección.

medición indirecta   Hallar una medición usando figuras semejantes para calcular el largo, ancho o altura de objetos que son difíciles de medir directamente.

desigualdad   Enunciado abierto que usa $<$, $>$, $\neq$, $\leq$ o $\geq$ para comparar dos cantidades.

entero   Cualquier número del conjunto $\{..., -4, -3, -2, -1, 0, 1, 2, 3, 4, ...\}$, donde ... significa que continúa sin fin.

rango intercuartil   Una medida de la variación en un conjunto de datos numéricos. Es la distancia entre el primer y el tercer cuartiles del conjunto de datos.

variación inversa   Relación en la cual el producto de x y y es una constante k. A medida que aumenta el valor de x, disminuye el valor de y o a medida que disminuye el valor de y, aumenta el valor de x.

número irracional   Número que no se puede expresar como el razón de dos enteros.

triángulo isósceles   Triángulo que tiene por lo menos dos lados congruentes.

Kk

kilogram   The base unit of mass in the metric system. One kilogram equals 1,000 grams.

kilogramo   Unidad básica de masa del sistema métrico. Un kilogramo equivale a 1,000 gramos.

Ll

lateral face   In a polyhedron, a face that is not a base.

cara lateral   En un poliedro, las caras que no forman las bases.

lateral surface area   The sum of the areas of all of the lateral faces of a solid.

área de superficie lateral   Suma de las áreas de todas las caras de un sólido.

least common denominator (LCD)   The least common multiple of the denominators of two or more fractions. You can use the LCD to compare fractions.

mínimo común denominador (mcd)   El menor de los múltiplos de los denominadores de dos o más fracciones. Puedes usar el mínimo común denominador para comparar fracciones.

like fractions   Fractions that have the same denominators.

fracciones semejantes   Fracciones que tienen los mismos denominadores.

like terms   Terms that contain the same variables raised to the same power. Example: $5x$ and $6x$ are like terms.

términos semejante   Términos que contienen las mismas variables elevadas a la misma potencia. Ejemplo: $5x$ y $6x$ son *términos semejante*.

line graph   A type of statistical graph using lines to show how values change over a period of time.

gráfica lineal   Tipo de gráfica estadística que usa segmentos de recta para mostrar cómo cambian los valores durante un período de tiempo.

linear expression   An algebraic expression in which the variable is raised to the first power, and variables are not multiplied nor divided.

expresión lineal   Expresión algebraica en la cual la variable se eleva a la primera potencia.

linear function   A function for which the graph is a straight line.

función lineal   Función cuya gráfica es una recta.

linear relationship   A relationship for which the graph is a straight line.

relación lineal   Una relación para la cual la gráfica es una línea recta.

liter   The base unit of capacity in the metric system. The amount of dry or liquid material an object can hold.

litro   Unidad básica de capacidad del sistema métrico. La cantidad de materia líquida o sólida que puede contener un objeto.

Glossary/Glosario

markdown   An amount by which the regular price of an item is reduced.

markup   The amount the price of an item is increased above the price the store paid for the item.

mean   The sum of the data divided by the number of items in the data set.

mean absolute deviation   A measure of variation in a set of numerical data, computed by adding the distances between each data value and the mean, then dividing by the number of data values.

measures of center   Numbers that are used to describe the center of a set of data. These measures include the mean, median, and mode.

measures of variation   A measure used to describe the distribution of data.

median   A measure of center in a set of numerical data. The median of a list of values is the value appearing at the center of a sorted version of the list—or the mean of the two central values, if the list contains an even number of values.

meter   The base unit of length in the metric system.

metric system   A decimal system of measures. The prefixes commonly used in this system are kilo-, centi-, and milli-.

mode   The number or numbers that appear most often in a set of data. If there are two or more numbers that occur most often, all of them are modes.

monomial   A number, variable, or product of a number and one or more variables.

Multiplication Property of Equality   If you multiply each side of an equation by the same nonzero number, the two sides remain equal.

Multiplication Property of Inequality   When you multiply each side of an inequality by a negative number, the inequality symbol must be reversed for the inequality to remain true.

rebaja   Una cantidad por la cual el precio regular de un artículo se reduce.

margen de utilidad   Cantidad de aumento en el precio de un artículo por encima del precio que paga la tienda por dicho artículo.

media   La suma de los datos dividida entre el número total de artículos en el conjunto de datos.

desviación media absoluta   Una medida de variación en un conjunto de datos numéricos que se calcula sumando las distancias entre el valor de cada dato y la media, y luego dividiendo entre el número de valores.

medidas del centro   Números que se usan para describir el centro de un conjunto de datos. Estas medidas incluyen la media, la mediana y la moda.

medidas de variación   Medida usada para describir la distribución de los datos.

mediana   Una medida del centro en un conjunto de dados númericos. La mediana de una lista de valores es el valor que aparace en el centro de una versíon ordenada de la lista, o la media de dos valores centrales si la lista contiene un número par de valores.

metro   Unidad fundamental de longitud del sistema métrico.

sistema métrico   Sistema decimal de medidas. Los prefijos más comunes son kilo-, centi- y mili-.

moda   El número o números que aparece con más frecuencia en un conjunto de datos. Si hay dos o más números que ocurren con más frecuencia, todosellos son modas.

monomio   Número, variable o producto de un número y una o más variables.

propiedad de multiplicación de la igualdad
Si multiplicas ambos lados de una ecuación por el mismo número no nulo, lo lados permanecen iguales.

propiedad de desigualdad en la multiplicación
Cuando se multiplica cada lado de una desigualdad por un número negativo, el símbolo de desigualdad debe invertirse para que la desigualdad siga siendo verdadera.

Multiplicative Identity Property The product of any number and one is the number.

Multiplicative Property of Zero The product of any number and zero is zero.

multiplicative inverse Two numbers with a product of 1. For example, the multiplicative inverse of $\frac{2}{3}$ is $\frac{3}{2}$.

propiedad de identidad de la multiplicación El producto de cualquier número y uno es el mismo número.

propiedad del cero en la multiplicación El producto de cualquier número y cero es cero.

inverso multiplicativo Dos números cuyo producto es 1. Por ejemplo, el inverso multiplicativo de $\frac{2}{3}$ es $\frac{3}{2}$.

Nn

negative exponent Any nonzero number to the negative n power. It is the multiplicative inverse of its nth power.

negative integer An integer that is less than zero. Negative integers are written with a — sign.

net A two-dimensional figure that can be used to build a three-dimensional figure.

exponente negativo Cualquier número que no sea cero a la potencia negative de n. Es el inverso multiplicativo de su *en*ésimo potencia.

entero negativo Número menor que cero. Se escriben con el signo —.

red Figura bidimensional que sirve para hacer una figura tridimensional.

nonagon A polygon having nine sides.

nonlinear function A function for which the graph is *not* a straight line.

nonproportional The relationship between two ratios with a rate or ratio that is not constant.

numerical expression A combination of numbers and operations.

enágono Polígono que tiene nueve lados.

nonlinear function Función cuya gráfica *no* es una línea recta.

no proporcional Relación entre dos razones cuya tasa o razón no es constante.

expresión numérica Combinación de números y operaciones.

Oo

obtuse angle Any angle that measures greater than 90° but less than 180°.

ángulo obtuso Cualquier ángulo que mide más de 90° pero menos de 180°.

obtuse triangle A triangle having one obtuse angle.

triángulo obtusángulo Triángulo que tiene un ángulo obtuso.

octagon A polygon having eight sides.

opposites Two integers are opposites if they are represented on the number line by points that are the same distance from zero, but on opposite sides of zero. The sum of two opposites is zero.

order of operations The rules to follow when more than one operation is used in a numerical expression.
1. Evaluate the expressions inside grouping symbols.
2. Evaluate all powers.
3. Multiply and divide in order from left to right.
4. Add and subtract in order from left to right.

ordered pair A pair of numbers used to locate a point in the coordinate plane. An ordered pair is written in the form (*x*-coordinate, *y*-coordinate).

origin The point at which the *x*-axis and the *y*-axis intersect in a coordinate plane. The origin is at (0, 0).

outcome Any one of the possible results of an action. For example, 4 is an outcome when a number cube is rolled.

outlier A data value that is either much *greater* or much *less* than the median.

octágono Polígono que tiene ocho lados.

opuestos Dos enteros son opuestos si, en la recta numérica, están representados por puntos que equidistan de cero, pero en direcciones opuestas. La suma de dos opuestos es cero.

orden de las operaciones Reglas a seguir cuando se usa más de una operación en una expresión numérica.
1. Primero, evalúa las expresiones dentro de los símbolos de agrupación.
2. Evalúa todas las potencias.
3. Multiplica y divide en orden de izquierda a derecha.
4. Suma y resta en orden de izquierda a derecha.

par ordenado Par de números que se utiliza para ubicar un punto en un plano de coordenadas. Se escribe de la siguiente forma: (coordenada *x*, coordenada *y*).

origen Punto en que el eje *x* y el eje *y* se intersecan en un plano de coordenadas. El origen está ubicado en (0, 0).

resultado Cualquiera de los resultados posibles de una acción. Por ejemplo, 4 puede ser un resultado al lanzar un cubo numerado.

valor atípico Valor de los datos que es mucho *mayor* o mucho *menor* que la mediana.

Pp

parallel lines Lines in a plane that never intersect.

parallelogram A quadrilateral with opposite sides parallel and opposite sides congruent.

rectas paralelas Rectas en un plano que nunca se intersecan.

paralelogramo Cuadrilátero cuyos lados opuestos son paralelos y congruentes.

pentagon   A polygon having five sides.

pentágono   Polígono que tiene cinco lados.

percent equation   An equation that describes the relationship between the part, whole, and percent.

$$\text{part} = \text{percent} \cdot \text{whole}$$

ecuación porcentual   Ecuación que describe la relación entre la parte, el todo y el por ciento.

$$\text{parte} = \text{por ciento} \cdot \text{todo}$$

percent error   A ratio that compares the inaccuracy of an estimate (amount of error) to the actual amount.

porcentaje de error   Una razón que compara la inexactitud de una estimación (cantidad del error) con la cantidad real.

percent of change   A ratio that compares the change in a quantity to the original amount.

$$\text{percent of change} = \frac{\text{amount of change}}{\text{original amount}}$$

porcentaje de cambio   Razón que compara el cambio en una cantidad a la cantidad original.

$$\text{porcentaje de cambio} = \frac{\text{cantidad del cambio}}{\text{cantidad original}}$$

percent of decrease   A negative percent of change.

porcentaje de disminución   Porcentaje de cambio negativo.

percent of increase   A positive percent of change.

porcentaje de aumento   Porcentaje de cambio positivo.

percent proportion   One ratio or fraction that compares part of a quantity to the whole quantity. The other ratio is the equivalent percent written as a fraction with a denominator of 100.

$$\frac{\text{part}}{\text{whole}} = \frac{\text{percent}}{100}$$

proporción porcentual   Razón o fracción que compara parte de una cantidad a toda la cantidad. La otra razón es el porcentaje equivalente escrito como fracción con 100 de denominador.

$$\frac{\text{parte}}{\text{todo}} = \frac{\text{porcentaje}}{100}$$

perfect cube   A rational number whose cube root is a whole number. 27 is a perfect cube because its cube root is 3.

cubo perfecto   Número racional cuya raíz cúbica es un número entero. 27 es un cubo perfecto porque su raíz cúbica es 3.

perfect squares   Numbers with square roots that are whole numbers. 25 is a perfect square because the square root of 25 is 5.

cuadrados perfectos   Números cuya raíz cuadrada es un número entero. 25 es un cuadrado perfecto porque la raíz cuadrada de 25 es 5.

permutation   An arrangement, or listing, of objects in which order is important.

permutación   Arreglo o lista de objetos en la cual el orden es importante.

perpendicular lines   Lines that meet or cross each other to form right angles.

rectas perpendiculares   Rectas que al encontrarse o cruzarse forman ángulos rectos.

pi   The ratio of the circumference of a circle to its diameter. The Greek letter π represents this number. The value of pi is 3.1415926. . . . Approximations for pi are 3.14 and $\frac{22}{7}$.

pi   Relación entre la circunferencia de un círculo y su diámetro. La letra griega π representa este número. El valor de pi es 3.1415926. . . . Las aproximaciones de pi son 3.14 y $\frac{22}{7}$.

plane   A two-dimensional flat surface that extends in all directions.

plano   Superficie bidimensional que se extiende en todas direcciones.

polygon A simple closed figure formed by three or more straight line segments.

polyhedron A three-dimensional figure with faces that are polygons.

population The entire group of items or individuals from which the samples under consideration are taken.

positive integer An integer that is greater than zero. They are written with or without a + sign.

powers Numbers expressed using exponents. The power 3^2 is read *three to the second power,* or *three squared.*

precision The ability of a measurement to be consistently reproduced.

principal The amount of money deposited or borrowed.

prism A polyhedron with two parallel congruent faces called bases.

probability The chance that some event will happen. It is the ratio of the number of favorable outcomes to the number of possible outcomes.

probability model A model used to assign probabilities to outcomes of a chance process by examining the nature of the process.

properties Statements that are true for any number or variable.

proportion An equation stating that two ratios or rates are equivalent.

proportional The relationship between two ratios with a constant rate or ratio.

pyramid A polyhedron with one base that is a polygon and three or more triangular faces that meet at a common vertex.

polígono Figura cerrada simple formada por tres o más segmentos de recta.

poliedro Una figura tridimensional con caras que son polígonos.

población El grupo total de individuos o de artículos del cual se toman las muestras bajo estudio.

entero positivo Entero que es mayor que cero; se escribe con o sin el signo +.

potencias Números que se expresan usando exponentes. La potencia 3^2 se lee *tres a la segunda potencia o tres al cuadrado.*

precisión Capacidad que tiene una medición de poder reproducirse consistentemente.

capital Cantidad de dinero que se deposita o se toma prestada.

prisma Un poliedro con dos caras congruentes paralelas llamadas bases.

probabilidad La posibilidad de que suceda un evento. Es la razón del número de resultados favorables al número de resultados posibles.

modelo de probabilidad Un modelo usado para asignar probabilidades a resultados de un proceso aleatorio examinando la naturaleza del proceso.

propiedades Enunciados que son verdaderos para cualquier número o variable.

proporción Ecuación que indica que dos razones o tasas son equivalentes.

proporcional Relación entre dos razones con una tasa o razón constante.

pirámide Un poliedro con una base que es un polígono y tres o más caras triangulares que se encuentran en un vértice común.

quadrant   One of the four regions into which the two perpendicular number lines of the coordinate plane separate the plane.

quadrilateral   A closed figure having four sides and four angles.

quartile   A value that divides the data set into four equal parts.

cuadrante   Una de las cuatro regiones en que dos rectas numéricas perpendiculares dividen el plano de coordenadas.

cuadrilátero   Figura cerrada que tiene cuatro lados y cuatro ángulos.

cuartil   Valor que divide el conjunto de datos en cuatro partes iguales.

Rr

radical sign   The symbol used to indicate a nonnegative square root, $\sqrt{}$.

radius   The distance from the center of a circle to any point on the circle.

random   Outcomes occur at random if each outcome occurs by chance. For example, rolling a number on a number cube occurs at random.

range   The set of output values for a function.

range   The difference between the greatest and least data value.

rate   A ratio that compares two quantities with different kinds of units.

rate of change   A rate that describes how one quantity changes in relation to another. A rate of change is usually expressed as a unit rate.

signo radical   Símbolo que se usa para indicar una raíz cuadrada no negativa, $\sqrt{}$.

radio   Distancia desde el centro de un círculo hasta cualquiera de sus puntos.

azar   Los resultados ocurren aleatoriamente si cada resultado ocurre por casualidad. Por ejemplo, sacar un número en un cubo numerado ocurre al azar.

rango   Conjunto de valores de salida para una función.

rango   La diferencia entre el número mayor y el menor en un conjunto de datos.

tasa   Razón que compara dos cantidades que tienen distintas unidades de medida.

tasa de cambio   Tasa que describe cómo cambia una cantidad con respecto a otra. Por lo general, se expresa como tasa unitaria.

rational numbers   The set of numbers that can be written in the form $\frac{a}{b}$, where a and b are integers and $b \neq 0$.

Examples: $1 = \frac{1}{1}, \frac{2}{9}, -2.3 = -2\frac{3}{10}$

real numbers   A set made up of rational and irrational numbers.

reciprocal   The multiplicative inverse of a number.

rectangle   A parallelogram having four right angles.

rectangular prism   A prism that has two parallel congruent bases that are rectangles.

reduction   An image smaller than the original.

regular polygon   A polygon that has all sides congruent and all angles congruent.

regular pyramid   A pyramid whose base is a regular polygon and in which the segment from the vertex to the center of the base is the altitude.

relation   Any set of ordered pairs.

relative frequency   A ratio that compares the frequency of each category to the total.

repeating decimal   The decimal form of a rational number.

rhombus   A parallelogram having four congruent sides.

right angle   An angle that measures exactly 90°.

---

números racionales   Conjunto de números que puede escribirse en la forma $\frac{a}{b}$ donde a y b son números enteros y $b \neq 0$.

Ejemplos: $1 = \frac{1}{1}, \frac{2}{9}, -2.3 = -2\frac{3}{10}$

números reales   Conjunto de números racionales e irracionales.

recíproco   El inverso multiplicativo de un número.

rectángulo   Paralelogramo con cuatro ángulos rectos.

prisma rectangular   Un prisma con dos bases paralelas congruentes que son rectángulos.

reducción   Imagen más pequeña que la original.

polígono regular   Polígono con todos los lados y todos los ángulos congruentes.

pirámide regular   Pirámide cuya base es un polígono regular y en la cual el segmento desde el vértice hasta el centro de la base es la altura.

relación   Cualquier conjunto de pares ordenados.

frecuencia relativa   Razón que compara la frecuencia de cada categoría al total.

decimal periódico   La forma decimal de un número racional.

rombo   Paralelogramo que tiene cuatro lados congruentes.

ángulo recto   Ángulo que mide exactamente 90°.

right triangle   A triangle having one right angle.

triángulo rectángulo   Triángulo que tiene un ángulo recto.

Ss

sales tax   An additional amount of money charged on items that people buy.

impuesto sobre las ventas   Cantidad de dinero adicional que se cobra por los artículos que se compran.

sample   A randomly selected group chosen for the purpose of collecting data.

muestra   Grupo escogido al azar o aleatoriamente que se usa con el propósito de recoger datos.

sample space   The set of all possible outcomes of a probability experiment.

espacio muestral   Conjunto de todos los resultados posibles de un experimento probabilístico.

scale   The scale that gives the ratio that compares the measurements of a drawing or model to the measurements of the real object.

escala   Razón que compara las medidas de un dibujo o modelo a las medidas del objeto real.

scale drawing   A drawing that is used to represent objects that are too large or too small to be drawn at actual size.

dibujo a escala   Dibujo que se usa para representar objetos que son demasiado grandes o demasiado pequeños como para dibujarlos de tamaño natural.

scale factor   A scale written as a ratio without units in simplest form.

factor de escala   Escala escrita como una razón sin unidades en forma simplificada.

scale model   A model used to represent objects that are too large or too small to be built at actual size.

modelo a escala   Réplica de un objeto real, el cual es demasiado grande o demasiado pequeño como para construirlo de tamaño natural.

scalene triangle   A triangle having no congruent sides.

triángulo escaleno   Triángulo sin lados congruentes.

scatter plot   In a scatter plot, two sets of related data are plotted as ordered pairs on the same graph.

diagrama de dispersión   Diagrama en que dos conjuntos de datos relacionados aparecen graficados como pares ordenados en la misma gráfica.

selling price   The amount the customer pays for an item.

precio de venta   Cantidad de dinero que paga un consumidor por un artículo.

semicircle   Half of a circle. The formula for the area of a semicircle is $A = \frac{1}{2}\pi r^2$.

semicírculo   Medio círculo La fórmula para el área de un semicírculo es $A = \frac{1}{2}\pi r^2$.

sequence   An ordered list of numbers, such as 0, 1, 2, 3 or 2, 4, 6, 8.

sucesión   Lista ordenada de números, como 0, 1, 2, 3 ó 2, 4, 6, 8.

similar figures   Figures that have the same shape but not necessarily the same size.

figuras semejantes   Figuras que tienen la misma forma, pero no necesariamente el mismo tamaño.

similar solids   Solids with the same shape. Their corresponding linear measures are proportional.

sólidos semejantes   Sólidos con la misma forma. Sus medidas lineales correspondientes son proporcionales.

simple event   One outcome or a collection of outcomes.

eventos simples   Un resultado o una colección de resultados.

simple interest   The amount paid or earned for the use of money. The formula for simple interest is $I = prt$.

interés simple   Cantidad que se paga o que se gana por el uso del dinero. La fórmula para calcular el interés simple es $I = prt$.

simple random sample   An unbiased sample where each item or person in the population is as likely to be chosen as any other.

muestra aleatoria simple   Muestra de una población que tiene la misma probabilidad de escogerse que cualquier otra.

simplest form   An expression is in simplest form when it is replaced by an equivalent expression having no like terms or parentheses.

expresión mínima   Expresión en su forma más simple cuando es reemplazada por una expresión equivalente que no tiene términos similares ni paréntesis.

simplify   Write an expression in simplest form.

simplificar   Escribir una expresión en su forma más simple.

simulation   An experiment that is designed to model the action in a given situation.

simulación   Un experimento diseñado para modelar la acción en una situación dada.

skew lines   Lines that do not intersect and are not coplanar.

rectas alabeadas   Rectas que no se intersecan y que no son coplanares.

slant height   The height of each lateral face.

altura oblicua   Altura de cada cara lateral.

slope   The rate of change between any two points on a line. It is the ratio of vertical change to horizontal change. The slope tells how steep the line is.

pendiente   Razón de cambio entre cualquier par de puntos en una recta. Es la razón del cambio vertical al cambio horizontal. La pendiente indica el grado de inclinación de la recta.

solution   A replacement value for the variable in an open sentence. A value for the variable that makes an equation true. Example: The *solution* of $12 = x + 7$ is 5.

solución   Valor de reemplazo de la variable en un enunciado abierto. Valor de la variable que hace que una ecuación sea verdadera. Ejemplo: La *solución* de $12 = x + 7$ es 5.

square   The product of a number and itself. 36 is the square of 6.

cuadrado   Producto de un número por sí mismo. 36 es el cuadrado de 6.

square   A parallelogram having four right angles and four congruent sides.

cuadrado   Paralelogramo con cuatro ángulos rectos y cuatro lados congruentes.

square root   The factors multiplied to form perfect squares.

al cuadrado   Factores multiplicados para formar cuadrados perfectos.

squared   The product of a number and itself. 36 is the square of 6.

raíz cuadrada   El producto de un número por sí mismo. 36 es el cuadrado de 6.

standard form   Numbers written without exponents.

forma estándar   Números escritos sin exponentes.

statistics   The study of collecting, organizing, and interpreting data.

estadística   Estudio que consiste en recopilar, organizar e interpretar datos.

straight angle   An angle that measures exactly 180°.

ángulo llano   Ángulo que mide exactamente 180°.

Subtraction Property of Equality   If you subtract the same number from each side of an equation, the two sides remain equal.

propiedad de sustracción de la igualdad   Si restas el mismo número de ambos lados de una ecuación, los dos lados permanecen iguales.

Subtraction Property of Inequality   If you subtract the same number from each side of an inequality, the inequality remains true.

propiedad de desigualdad en la resta   Si se resta el mismo número a cada lado de una desigualdad, la desigualdad sigue siendo verdadera.

supplementary angles   Two angles are supplementary if the sum of their measures is 180°.

ángulos suplementarios   Dos ángulos son suplementarios si la suma de sus medidas es 180°.

∠1 and ∠2 are supplementary angles.

∠1 y ∠2 son suplementarios.

surface area   The sum of the areas of all the surfaces (faces) of a three-dimensional figure.

área de superficie   La suma de las áreas de todas las superficies (caras) de una figura tridimensional.

survey   A question or set of questions designed to collect data about a specific group of people, or population.

encuesta   Pregunta o conjunto de preguntas diseñadas para recoger datos sobre un grupo específico de personas o población.

systematic random sample   A sample where the items or people are selected according to a specific time or item interval.

muestra aleatoria sistemática   Muestra en que los elementos o personas se eligen según un intervalo de tiempo o elemento específico.

Tt

---

term   Each number in a sequence.

término   Cada número en una sucesión.

term   A number, a variable, or a product or quotient of numbers and variables.

término   Número, variable, producto o cociente de números y de variables.

terminating decimal   A repeating decimal which has a repeating digit of 0.

decimal finito   Un decimal periódico que tiene un dígito que se repite que es 0.

theoretical probability   The ratio of the number of ways an event can occur to the number of possible outcomes. It is based on what *should* happen when conducting a probability experiment.

probabilidad teórica   Razón del número de maneras en que puede ocurrir un evento al número de resultados posibles. Se basa en lo que *debería* pasar cuando se conduce un experimento probabilístico.

three-dimensional figure   A figure with length, width, and height.

figura tridimensional   Figura que tiene largo, ancho y alto.

third quartile   For a data set with median M, the third quartile is the median of the data values greater than M.

tercer cuartil   Para un conjunto de datos con la mediana M, el tercer cuartil es la mediana de los valores mayores que M.

tip   Also known as a gratuity, it is a small amount of money in return for a service.

propina   También conocida como gratificación; es una cantidad pequeña de dinero en recompensa por un servicio.

total surface area   The sum of the areas of the surfaces of a solid.

área de superficie total   La suma del área de las superficies de un sólido.

transversal   The third line formed when two parallel lines are intersected.

transversal   Tercera recta que se forma cuando se intersecan dos rectas paralelas.

transversal

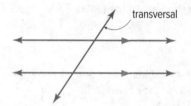
transversal

trapezoid   A quadrilateral with one pair of parallel sides.

trapecio   Cuadrilátero con un único par de lados paralelos.

tree diagram   A diagram used to show the sample space.

diagrama de árbol   Diagrama que se usa para mostrar el espacio muestral.

triangle   A figure with three sides and three angles.

triángulo   Figura con tres lados y tres ángulos.

triangular prism   A prism that has two parallel congruent bases that are triangles.

prisma triangular   Un prisma que tiene dos bases congruentes paralelas que triángulos.

two-step equation   An equation having two different operations.

ecuación de dos pasos   Ecuación que contiene dos operaciones distintas.

two-step inequality   An inequality than contains two operations.

desigualdad de dos pasos   Desigualdad que contiene dos operaciones.

Uu

unbiased sample   A sample representative of the entire population.

muestra no sesgada   Muestra que se selecciona de modo que se representativa de la población entera.

unfair game   A game where there is not a chance of each player being equally likely to win.

juego injusto   Juego donde cada jugador no tiene la misma posibilidad de ganar.

uniform probability model   A probability model which assigns equal probability to all outcomes.

modelo de probabilidad uniforme   Un modelo de probabilidad que asigna igual probabilidad a todos los resultados.

unit rate   A rate that is simplified so that it has a denominator of 1 unit.

tasa unitaria   Tasa simplificada para que tenga un denominador igual a 1.

unit ratio   A unit rate where the denominator is one unit.

razón unitaria   Tasa unitaria en que el denominador es la unidad.

unlike fractions   Fractions with different denominators.

fracciones con distinto denominador   Fracciones cuyos denominadores son diferentes.

Vv

variable   A symbol, usually a letter, used to represent a number in mathematical expressions or sentences.

variable   Símbolo, por lo general una letra, que se usa para representar un número en expresiones o enunciados matemáticos.

vertex   A vertex of an angle is the common endpoint of the rays forming the angle.

vértice   El vértice de un ángulo es el extremo común de los rayos que lo forman.

vertex   The point where three or more faces of a polyhedron intersect.

vértice   El punto donde tres o más caras de un poliedro se cruzan.

vertex   The point at the tip of a cone.

vértice   El punto en la punta de un cono.

vertical angles   Opposite angles formed by the intersection of two lines. Vertical angles are congruent.

ángulos opuestos por el vértice   Ángulos opuestos formados por la intersección de dos rectas. Los ángulos opuestos por el vértice son congruentes.

∠1 and ∠2 are vertical angles.

∠1 y ∠2 son ángulos opuestos por el vértice.

visual overlap   A visual demonstration that compares the centers of two distributions with their variation, or spread.

superposición visual   Una demostración visual que compara los centros de dos distribuciones con su variación, o magnitud.

volume   The number of cubic units needed to fill the space occupied by a solid.

voluntary response sample   A sample which involves only those who want to participate in the sampling.

volumen   Número de unidades cúbicas que se requieren para llenar el espacio que ocupa un sólido.

muestra de respuesta voluntaria   Muestra que involucra sólo aquellos que quieren participar en el muestreo.

---

x-axis   The horizontal number line in a coordinate plane.

x-coordinate   The first number of an ordered pair. It corresponds to a number on the x-axis.

eje x   La recta numérica horizontal en el plano de coordenadas.

coordenada x   El primer número de un par ordenado. Corresponde a un número en el eje x.

---

y-axis   The vertical number line in a coordinate plane.

y-coordinate   The second number of an ordered pair. It corresponds to a number on the y-axis.

eje y   La recta numérica vertical en el plano de coordenadas.

coordenada y   El segundo número de un par ordenado. Corresponde a un número en el eje y.

---

zero pair   The result when one positive counter is paired with one negative counter. The value of a zero pair is 0.

par nulo   Resultado de hacer coordinar una ficha positiva con una negativa. El valor de un par nulo es 0.

Chapter 5 Expressions

1. 16   **3.** 16   **5.** −50   **7.** −25

1. 34   3   **5.** 3   **7.** 2   **9.** −1   **11** 50 + 0.17m; $75.50
13. 9.1   **15.** 37.85   **17.** Sample answer: The fee to rent a bicycle is $10 plus $5 for each hour. The expression 5x + 10 represents the total cost for renting a bicycle for x hours.
19. Sample answer: 2n + 4; 2(n + 2)

21. 4   **23.** −12   **25.** 5   **27.** $8.75   **29a.** True   **29b.** False
29c. True   **31.** Let p = the number of hours Paida worked; p + 8   **33.** Let n = Nathan's age; n − 3

1. 7 is added to the previous term; 28, 35, 42   **3** 8 is added to the previous term; 58, 66, 74   **5.** 0.8 is added to the previous term; 5.6, 6.4, 7.2   **7** 3n; 36 in.

9a.

x	1	2	3	4	5
y	3	6	9	12	15

9b. 3n

9c.

Number of Minutes

Sample answer: The number of boxes increases by 3 each minute. The points appear to fall in a straight line passing through the origin.   **9d.** 135 boxes   **11.** + 1, + 2, + 3, + 4, ...; 16, 22, 29   **13.** 81; Sample answer: The multiples of 6 from 41 to 523 can be represented by the sequence 42, 48, 54, ... 522. The expression 6n + 36 represents this sequence. When n = 81, the value of the expression is 522. So, the 81st term of the sequence is 522. There are 81 multiples of 6 between 41 and 523.

15. 10 is added to the previous term; 46, 56, 66   **17.** 1.5 is added to the previous term; 10.5, 12.0, 13.5   **19.** 4 is added to the previous term; 20.6, 24.6, 28.6   **21.** 25 is added to the previous term; 120, 145, 170   **23a.** Each figure is 8 less than the previous figure.   **23b.** 40, 32   **25.** 33, 30, 27   **27a.** True
27b. True   **27c.** False   **29.** 1   **31.** 64   **33.** 5   **35.** $1.50

1. Commutative (+)   **3** Associative (+)   **5.** false; Sample answer: (24 ÷ 4) ÷ 2 ≠ 24 ÷ (4 ÷ 2)
7. = (15 + 12) + 8a   Associative (+)
    = 27 + 8a   Simplify.

9   = 3x · (x · 7)   Commutative (×)
    = (3x · x) · 7   Associative (×)
    = 3x² · 7   Simplify.
    = 3 · 7 · x²   Commutative (×)
    = (3 · 7) · x²   Associative (×)
    = 21x²   Simplify.

11. [7 + (47 + 3)][5 · (2 · 3)], Associative (+); (7 + 50)[5 · (2 · 3)], Simplify; 57[5 · (2 · 3)], Simplify; 57[(5 · 2) · 3], Associative (×); 57 · 10 · 3, Simplify; (57 · 10) · 3, Associative (×); 570 · 3, Simplify; 1,710   **13.** Blake incorrectly multiplied both the 5 and m by 4. He should have used the Associative Property to group the 5 and 4 together, simplify, and then multiply by m. 4 · (5 · m) = 20m   **15a.** no; Sample answer: 2 − 3 = −1 and −1 is not a whole number   **15b.** no; Sample answer: 1 + 1 = 2 and 2 is not a member of the set.

17. Commutative (×)   **19.** Associative (+)   **21.** 48 s; Sample answer: 12.4 + 12.6 = 25 and 11.8 + 11.2 = 23, 25 + 23 = 48
23. = (18 + 5) + 6m   Associative (+)
    = 23 + 6m   Simplify.

25. = 10 · 7 · y   Commutative (×)
    = (10 · 7) · y   Associative (×)
    = 70y   Simplify.
27. 2(2.29) + 2(2.21) + 2.50; 2(2.29) + 2.50 + 2(2.21); 2.50 + 2(2.21 + 2.29)   **29.** 36   **31.** 226   **33.** 74
35. $1.25(3) + $0.45(2); $4.65

1. 33   **3** −30   **5.** 4   **7.** −12x + 24   **9.** 30 − 6q
11. −15 + 3b   **13** $27.40; 4($7.00 − $0.15) = 4 · 7 − 4 · 0.15
15. 315;
$$9(30 + 5) = 9(30) + 9(5)$$
$$= 270 + 45$$

17. 672;

$$(100 + 12)6 = 100(6) + 12(6)$$
$$= 600 + 72$$

19. 488;

$$4(120 + 2) = 4(120) + 4(2)$$
$$= 480 + 8$$

21. Sample answer: $6(2a + 3b - c)$ **23.** $2a + ay + 2b + by$
25. No; $3 + (4 \cdot 5) = 23$ but $(3 + 4) \cdot (3 + 5) = 56$

Pages 381–382   Lesson 5-4   Extra Practice

27. 24   **29.** $-8a - 8b$ **31.** $-2p - 14$ **33.** $n(4.75 + 2.50) +$
30; $7.25n + 30$ **35.** $-12ab - 30ac$ **37.** $6y + 12z$
39. $-72p + 48n$ **41.** $3 \times (\$18.95 + \$14.95 + \$9.95)$; $131.55;
Sample answer: The ticket prices can be added first and then
the sum can be multiplied by 3. This requires fewer steps and
easier computations than multiplying each price by 3 and then
adding the resulting products.   **43.** -46 **45.** -47

Page 385   Problem-Solving Investigation   Make a Table

Case 3. 26 containers   **Case 5.** $2n + 2$; 18 toothpicks

Pages 391–392   Lesson 5-5   Independent Practice

1. terms: 2, $3a$, $9a$; like terms: $3a$, $9a$; coefficients: 3, 9; constant:
2   **3.** terms: 9, $-z$, 3, $-2z$; like terms: 9 and 3, $-z$ and $-2z$;
coefficients: -1, -2; constants: 9, 3   **5.** $11c$ **7.** $1.03t$; $74.16
9 $2x + 30$ **11** a. $7 + 5x + 4y + 2z$ b. $43   **13.** $16a +$
$8b + 4$ **15.** Sample answer: $3x + x - 7$; coefficients: 3, 1;
constant: -7 **17.** $18x - 3$; $18x - 3 = 18(2) - 3 = 33$ and
$8x - 2x + 12x - 3 = 8(2) - 2(2) + 12(2) - 3 = 33$

Pages 393–394   Lesson 5-5   Extra Practice

19. terms: 4, $5y$, $-6y$, y; like terms: $5y$, $-6y$, y; coefficients: 5,
-6, 1; constant: 4   **21.** terms: $-3d$, 8, $-d$, -2; like terms: $-3d$
and $-d$, 8 and -2; coefficients: -3, -1; constants: 8, -2
23. $2 + 4d$ **25.** $2m - 2$ **27.** $7m - 20$ **29.** $20x + 9$
31. $38g + 36h - 38$ **33.** $5a + 9b$ **35.** $t =$ hours Tricia
volunteered; $t + 9$ **37.** 10   **39.** 13

Pages 399–400   Lesson 5-6   Independent Practice

1. $11x + 11$ **3** $4x - 16$ **5.** $4x + 14$ **7.** $(22x + 10)$ mm;
230 mm   **9** $-x + 2$ **11.** $8.7x - 1.6$ **13.** Sample answer:
$(10x + 2)$ and $(-15x + 2)$ **15.** $2x + 1$; The expression $2x + 1$
will always be odd when x is an integer because when an
integer is doubled, the result is always even. Adding one to
the result will give an odd number.

Pages 401–402   Lesson 5-6   Extra Practice

17. $-4x + 16$ **19.** $-2x - 2$ **21.** $-6x + 5$ **23.** $(24x + 9)$ yd;
177 yd   **25a.** False   **25b.** False   **25c.** True   **27.** 35   **29.** 85

Pages 407–408   Lesson 5-7   Independent Practice

1 $5x + 2$ **3.** $2x + 2$ **5.** $8x - 12$ **7.** $5x - 2$;
248 customers   **9** $x + 0.51$ **11.** Sample answer: The
additive inverse of $(2x + 1)$ is $(-2x - 1)$.
$$(5x + 3) - (2x + 1) = (5x + 3) + (-2x - 1)$$
$$= 5x + 3 + (-2x) + (-1)$$
$$= 5x + (-2x) + 3 + (-1)$$
$$= 3x + 2$$
13. $-x + 5$ **15.** Sample answer: The rule is to add the inverse
when subtracting integers, and is applied to each term in the
linear expression that is subtracted.

Pages 409–410   Lesson 5-7   Extra Practice

17. $-3x + 6$ **19.** $-16x + 2$ **21.** $-4x - 7$ **23.** $0.8x + 0.6$
25. $-x + 2$ **27.** $12 + 1.50t - (10 + 1.25t) = 2 + 0.25t$
29. $(12x - 4)$ ft; 32 ft   **31.** $-\frac{1}{4}$ **33.** $\frac{1}{8}$ **35.** $\frac{2}{3}$

Pages 419–420   Lesson 5-8   Independent Practice

1. 24   **3** $36k$ **5.** cannot be factored   **7** 4 units by
$(x - 2)$ units   **9.** $(x + 2)$ dollars   **11.** $5(x + 4)$ units^2
13. $4(5x + 19)$ units^2 **15.** Sample answer: $20m$ and $12mn$
17. $6(4x - y)$

Pages 421–422   Lesson 5-8   Extra Practice

19. $6rs$ **21.** $20x$ **23.** $25xy$ **25.** $6(3x + 1)$ **27.** $5(2x - 7)$
29. $10(3x - 4)$ **31.** $(2x + 5)$ in.   **33.** $\frac{2}{3}(x + 9)$ **35.** $\frac{5}{6}(x - 36)$
37. $\frac{3}{8}(x + 48)$ **39.** $16ab$, $12a$; $28a$, $20a$ **41.** $3a + 30$
43.

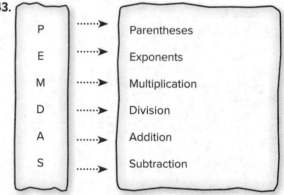

P	·······>	Parentheses
E	·······>	Exponents
M	·······>	Multiplication
D	·······>	Division
A	·······>	Addition
S	·······>	Subtraction

Page 425   Chapter Review   Vocabulary Check

Across
3. simplest form   **7.** sequence   **11.** counterexample
13. define
Down
1. equivalent   **5.** variable   **9.** term

Page 426   Chapter Review   Key Concept Check

1. $1 + 3$ **3.** $2x + 4$ **5.** $3(x + 7)$

Chapter 6 Equations and Inequalities

1. $p + 3$ **3.** $g + 10$ **5.** 17   **7.** 1   **9.** 35

Pages 441–442   Lesson 6-1   Independent Practice

1. 7   17   **5.** −1

7.

$7 = h + 2$; 5 h   **9a.** $s − 65 = 5$; 70 mph

9b.

$d + 22 = 176$; 154 ft   **9c.** The solution of each equation is 197; Colossos is 197 feet tall.   **11.** $115 + 115 + 65 + x = 360$; 65   **13.** She should have subtracted 5 from each side; −13   **15.** $x + 2 = 8$; The solution for the other equations is −6.

Pages 443–444   Lesson 6-1   Extra Practice

17. −9   **19.** −12   **21.** 7

23.

$x − 13 = 79$; 92 points   **25.** $−1 + (−3) + s + 2 = 0$; +2   **27.** −1.25   **29.** 12.3   **31.** 5.8   **33.** $-\frac{1}{12}$ **35a.** True   **35b.** False   **35c.** True   **37.** −20   **39.** 60   **41.** −36   **43.** $3h = −3$; $h = −1$

Pages 451–452   Lesson 6-2   Independent Practice

1. 7   **3.** 8   **5.** 80   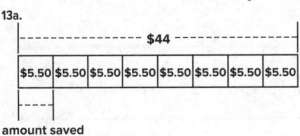 −5   **9.** −90   **11** $205 = \frac{d}{3}$; 615 mi

13a.

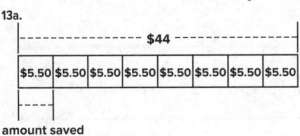

amount saved
in 1 hour

13b. $5.5x = 44$ **13c.** Sample answer: Divide each side by 5.5. Then simplify. $x = 8$ **15.** True; Sample answer: Multiply each side of the equation by $\frac{1}{5}$ instead of dividing each side by 5.

17. Sample answer: Multiply both sides by x, then divide both sides of the equation by 6; −5.

Pages 453–454   Lesson 6-2   Extra Practice

19. 4   **21.** 70   **23.** −120   **25.** $50 = 25t$; 2 s   **27.** 8 in.   **29.** $3\frac{1}{3}$ **31.** $1\frac{1}{100}$ **33.** $\frac{13}{4}$ **35.** 4   **37.** 2.1   **39.** $\frac{21}{4}$ or $5\frac{1}{4}$

Pages 461–462   Lesson 6-3   Independent Practice

1. 5   3   **5.** $\frac{20}{3}$ or $6\frac{2}{3}$ **7** $\frac{3}{4}p = 46.50$; $62   **9.** Emily's homeroom class; Sample answer: Write and solve the equations $0.75e = 15$ and $\frac{2}{3}s = 12$; $e = 20$ and $s = 18$; Since $20 > 18$, Emily's homeroom class has more students.   **11.** 20; Sample answer: Solve $8 = \frac{m}{4}$ to find that $m = 32$. So, replace m with 32 to find $32 − 12 = 20$.   **13.** Sample answer: Multiply each side by 2. Then divide each side by $(b_1 + b_2)$. So, $\frac{2A}{b_1 + b_2} = h$.

Pages 463–464   Lesson 6-3   Extra Practice

15. 7   **17.** −3.8   **19.** $-\frac{125}{12}$ or $-10\frac{5}{12}$

21.

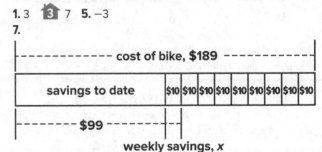

$140 = \frac{7}{15}x$; 300 ft   **23.** a train that travels 100 miles in $\frac{2}{3}$ hour; a train that travels 90 miles in $\frac{3}{5}$ hour   **25.** 22   **27.** 2   **29.** $3 \times \$0.25 + 5 \times \$0.50$; $3.25

Pages 473–474   Lesson 6-4   Independent Practice

1. 3   7   **5.** −3

7.

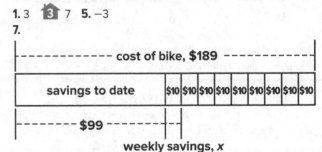

weekly savings, x

$189 = 10x + 99$; 9 weeks

9. 2.25   **11** **a.** −9°C   **b.** 92.2°F   **13.** No, none of the Fahrenheit temperatures convert to the same temperature in Celsius. Only −40°F = −40°C.   **15.** Sample answer: Cameron found the area of a trapezoid to be 52 square inches. One base was 12 inches long and the other was 14 inches long. What is the height h of the trapezoid?; 4 in.

Pages 475–476   Lesson 6-4   Extra Practice

17. −4   **19.** 4   **21.** 36

23a.

perimeter, 48 cm			
width	width	16	16

23b. 48 = 32 + 2*w*; 8 cm   **23c.** Sample answer: Using either method, you would subtract first and then divide
25. *c* = 30 + 0.05*m*; 395 mi   **27.** 6 · 10 + 6 · *n* or 60 + 6*n*
29. 5(*x* + 7)   **31.** 10(*t* + 3)

Pages 485–486   Lesson 6-5   Independent Practice

1. 6   **3** −14   **5.** −3.2   **7** 3(ℓ + 5) = 60; 15 in.
9a. 12(*m* − 2.57) = 0.36   **9b.** Sample answer: I first divided each side by 12 and then added 2.57 to each side; $2.60.
11. Sample answer: Marisol should have divided by six before subtracting three; 6(*x* + 3) = 21, *x* + 3 = 3.5, *x* = 3.5 − 3, *x* = 0.5   **13.** 3(*x* − 8) = 12; Sample answer: Valeria bought a new collar for each of her three dogs. She paid $8 for each necklace. Suppose she had $12 left. How much money did Valeria have initially to spend on each dog collar?; $12 per collar

Pages 487–488   Lesson 6-5   Extra Practice

15. 16   **17.** −2   **19.** 78   **21.** $5\frac{3}{4}$ or 5.75
23. $1.20\left(n + 2\frac{1}{2}\right)$ = 4.50; 1.25 or $1\frac{1}{4}$ pounds   **25.** Divide both sides by *p*; Add *q* to both sides.   **27.** −4   **29.** 4   **31.** −3
33. 2   **35.** −3, −2, −1, 0

Page 491   Problem-Solving Investigation   Work Backward

Case 3. 1,250 ft   **Case 5.** 6:25 A.M.

Pages 501–502   Lesson 6-6   Independent Practice

1. *h* ≤ −8   **3** 5 < *n*   **5.** *x* > −1
7. *m* ≥ −6;

9 *n* + 4 > 13; *n* > 9   **11.** *p* + 17 ≤ 26; *p* ≤ 9; Nine additional players or fewer can make the team.
13a. 42 + *x* ≥ 74; *x* ≥ 32   **13b.** 74 + *y* ≥ 110; *y* ≥ 36
15. Sample answer: *x* + 3 < 25   **17.** no; Sample answer: The solution is *x* ≥ −1, so the graph should have a closed dot above −1 and the arrow should point to the right, not the left.

Pages 503–504   Lesson 6-6   Extra Practice

19. *m* ≤ 4.3
21. −5 < *a*

23. *n* − 8 < 10; *n* < 18   **25.** 68 + *c* ≤ 125; *c* ≤ 57; The salesman has 57 cars or less left to sell.

27. $2\frac{2}{3} > x$ or $x < 2\frac{2}{3}$

29. $m \geq 11\frac{1}{5}$

31. $n \geq -4\frac{3}{16}$

33. *x* + 4 ≤ 7; −7 ≥ *x* − 10   **35.** −4; See answer 39 for graph.   **37.** −2; See answer 39 for graph.   **39.** −6;

Pages 509–510   Lesson 6-7   Independent Practice

1. *y* < 3   **3** 180 ≤ *m*   **5.** *m* ≥ 56   **7.** *n* ≤ 4.5
9. *w* ≤ −45
11 4 < *t*

13. *x* ≤ −32

15. Sample answer: The inequalities −2*x* > 12, $\frac{x}{2}$ < −3, and −7 > *x* −1 are equal to *x* < −6. The inequality −2 < *x* + 4 is equal to *x* > −6.   **17.** 5*n* ≤ 30; *n* ≤ 6   **19.** at least a 15
21a.

3 4 5 6 7 8 9 10 11 12 13 14

21b. yes; It represents the solutions that satisfy both inequalities.   **21c.** 4 ≤ *b* ≤ 13
21d.

3 4 5 6 7 8 9 10 11 12 13 14

Pages 511–512   Lesson 6-7   Extra Practice

23. *y* > −5   **25.** *p* ≥ −6   **27.** −40 < *y* or *y* > −40
29. *w* > 13

11 12 13 14 15

31. −20 ≥ *t* or *t* ≤ −20

−22 −21 −20 −19 −18

33. 4*n* ≥ −12; *n* ≥ −3   **35a.** False   **35b.** True   **35c.** False
37. 2   **39.** −2.5   **41.** 12

Pages 517–518 Lesson 6-8 Independent Practice

1. $x \geq 1$;

 $x > 12$

 $30 + 7x \geq 205$; $x \geq 25$ hours; He will have to work at least 25 hours   **7.** $\frac{x}{-5} + 1 \leq 7$; $x \geq -30$ **9.** $-2x - 6 > -18$; $x < 6$
11. Sample answer: $-2x + 5 > -7$ **13.** Sample answer: $\frac{x}{2} + 5 \geq 30$ **15.** $\frac{73 + x}{6} \geq 15$; $x \geq 17$; at least 17 points
17. Sample answer: At the electronics store, CDs were marked down $2.80 from their regular price. Orlando has $45 to spend on 4 CDs. How much can he spend on each CD?; $14.05

Pages 519–520 Lesson 6-8 Extra Practice

19. $x \leq -8$

21. $x \geq 42$

23. $75 + 5s \geq 125$; $s \geq 10$; Audrey needs to make at least 10 sales for her pay to be $125.   **25.** Add 5 to both sides; Divide both sides by -2; Reverse the inequality symbol.
27. $n > -3$

29. $t < 2$

31. -12 **33.** $4m + 2 = 30$; 7 years

Page 524 Chapter Review Key Concept Check

1. solution   **3.** equivalent equations

Chapter 7 Geometric Figures

Page 534 Chapter 7 Are You Ready?

1. 40°   **3.** 90°   **5.** 6.72 yd²

Pages 539–540 Lesson 7-1 Independent Practice

1. $\angle ABC$, $\angle CBA$, $\angle B$, $\angle 4$; acute $\angle MNP$, $\angle PNM$, $\angle N$, $\angle 1$; obtuse   neither   **7.** adjacent   **9.** vertical   **11.** 11
15. True; Sample answer:

17. Sample answer: Each pair of angles is adjacent and forms a straight angle. So $(2x + 8) + (5x - 10) = 180$ and $(3x + 42) + (x + 34) = 180$. When you solve both equations, $x = 26$. The angle measures are 60°, 120°, 120°, and 60°.

Pages 541–542 Lesson 7-1 Extra Practice

19. $\angle HKI$, $\angle IKH$, $\angle K$, $\angle 8$; obtuse   **21a.** Sample answer: $\angle 1$ and $\angle 3$; Since $\angle 1$ and $\angle 3$ are opposite angles formed by the intersection of two lines, they are vertical angles.
21b. Sample answer: $\angle 1$ and $\angle 2$; Since $\angle 1$ and $\angle 2$ share a common vertex, a common side, and do not overlap, they are adjacent angles.   **23.** 9   **25a.** vertical   **25b.** adjacent
25c. adjacent   **25d.** vertical   **27.** 134°   **29.** 38°
31. rectangle

Pages 547–548 Lesson 7-2 Independent Practice

1. neither   supplementary   **5.** 20   23
9. Sample answer: $\angle CGK$, $\angle KGJ$ **11a.** adjacent; adjacent; vertical   **11b.** $m\angle 1 + m\angle 2 = 180°$; $m\angle 2 + m\angle 3 = 180°$
11c. $m\angle 1 = 180° - m\angle 2$; $m\angle 3 = 180° - m\angle 2$; Sample answer: $m\angle 1$ and $m\angle 3$ are equal.   **11d.** Sample answer: Vertical angles are congruent.   **13a.** $m\angle E = 39°$; $m\angle F = 51°$ **13b.** $m\angle B = 60°$; $m\angle C = 120°$ **15.** Sample answer: Right angles have a measure of 90°, so two right angles will always have a sum of 180°. This is the definition of supplementary angles.

Pages 549–550 Lesson 7-2 Extra Practice

17. complementary   **19.** 15   **21.** never; Sample answer: Since an obtuse angle is greater than 90°, the sum of two obtuse angles must be greater than, not equal to, 180°.
23a.

[coordinate graph showing points (−3, 4), (1, 4), (−4, −1), (2, −1) with two intersecting lines]

23b. The lines appear to be perpendicular.   **23c.** line a: 1; line b; -1 **25.** $x°$; 90°; 180°; 45°; 45°

27.

square

Pages IN29–IN30   Indiana Lesson   Independent Practice

1. The triangles are not similar.   **3.** 200 ft   **5.** 37.5 m

7. $\frac{136}{34} = \frac{h}{1.5}$; 6 feet tall   **11.** Sample answer: The length of the tall object's shadow, the length of the shadow of a nearby object with a height that is directly measurable, and the height of the nearby object.

Pages IN31–IN32   Indiana Lesson   Extra Practice

13. 90 ft   **15.** 6 m   **17a.** $\frac{h}{ED} = \frac{BC}{DC}$ **17b.** The distance from the mirror to the person, the distance from the mirror to the base of the flag, the height of the person's eyes.
19. Sample answer: $\frac{6\text{ ft}}{3\text{ ft}} = \frac{h\text{ ft}}{25\text{ ft}}$; 50   **21.** Yes; the corresponding angles are congruent and $\frac{5}{10} = \frac{4}{8}$.

Pages 559–560   Lesson 7-3   Independent Practice

1. acute equilateral; Sample answer:

3. acute equilateral   **5.** obtuse isosceles   **7.** 118
9. acute isosceles   **11.** $125 + a = 180$, so $a = 55$; $a + b + 60 = 180$, so $b = 65$; $60 + d = 90$, so $d = 30$; $c + d + 90 = 180$, so $c = 60$ **13a.** never; Sample answer: The sum of the interior angles of a triangle is 180°. Two right angles have a sum of 180°. This means the third angle would equal 0°, which is not possible.   **13b.** never; Sample answer: The sum of the interior angles of a triangle is 180°. The measure of an obtuse angle is greater than 90°. So, a triangle cannot have more than one obtuse angle.

Pages 561–562   Lesson 7-3   Extra Practice

15. acute isosceles   **17.** right scalene   **19.** obtuse isosceles; Sample answer:

21. 90   **23.** 53°   **25.** 30   **27a.** False   **27b.** True   **27c.** False
29. 25 in^2 **31.** 35 cm^2 **33.** 9 yd^2

Page 569   Problem-Solving Investigation   Make a Model

Case 3. 15 tables; 2 people can sit on the ends. Then divide the remaining people by 2. $(32 - 2) \div 2 = 15$.   **Case 5.** Faith: Spanish; Sarah: German; Guadalupe: French

Pages 579–580   Lesson 7-4   Independent Practice

1. 102.6 mi   **3.** 12 cm; $\frac{1}{300}$ **5.** 108 ft^2 **9.** always;
Sample answer: A scale factor of $\frac{3}{1}$ means that 3 units of the drawing is equal to 1 unit of the object, so the scale drawing or model will be larger than the actual object.

Pages 581–582   Lesson 7-4   Extra Practice

11. 30 km   **13.** 102.5 km   **15.** $109\frac{3}{8}$ ft   **17.** 3,420 ft^2
19. 40 ft by 60 ft; Sample answer: Set up and solve proportions to find the actual length and width: $\frac{1\text{ in.}}{20\text{ ft}} = \frac{2\text{ in.}}{w\text{ ft}}$ and $\frac{1\text{ in.}}{20\text{ ft}} = \frac{3\text{ in.}}{\ell\text{ ft}}$ **21.** 10   **23.** 22

Pages 589–590   Lesson 7-5   Independent Practice

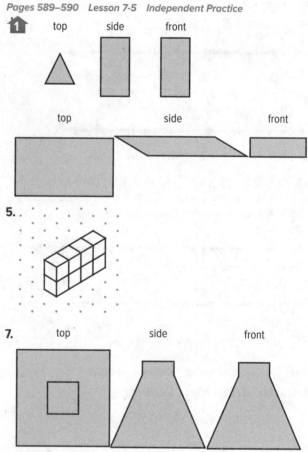

9. triangle; It is the only two-dimensional figure.   **11a.** never
11b. never   **11c.** sometimes

Pages 591–592   Lesson 7-5   Extra Practice

13.   top   side   front

15.

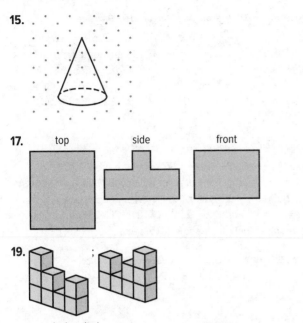

17.

top	side	front

19.

21. line; $\overleftrightarrow{WX}$ or $\overleftrightarrow{XW}$ **23.** line segment; $\overline{EF}$ or $\overline{FE}$ **25.** parallel

Pages 597–598   Lesson 7-6   Independent Practice

1 **figure name:** triangular pyramid
   bases: *ACD*
   faces: *ACD, ABD, ABC, DBC*
   edges: $\overline{AB}, \overline{BC}, \overline{CD}, \overline{AD}, \overline{AC}, \overline{BD}$
   vertices: *A, B, C, D*
   skew lines: Sample answer: $\overline{BD}$ and $\overline{AC}$

3 rectangle   **5.** triangle   **7.** False; two planes intersect at a line, which is an infinite number of points.   **11.** sometimes; A rectangular prism has 2 bases and 4 faces, but a triangular prism has 2 bases and 3 faces.   **13.** sometimes; A triangular pyramid has a triangle for its base.

Pages 599–600   Lesson 7-6   Extra Practice

15. **figure name:** rectangular prism
   bases: *ABCD, EFGH, ABFE, DCGH, ADHE, BCGF*
   faces: *ABCD, EFGH, ABFE, DCGH, ADHE, BCGF*
   edges: $\overline{AB}, \overline{BC}, \overline{CD}, \overline{AD}, \overline{EF}, \overline{FG}, \overline{GH}, \overline{EH}, \overline{AE}, \overline{BF}, \overline{CG}, \overline{DH}$
   vertices: *A, B, C, D, E, F, G, H*
   skew lines: Sample answer: $\overline{DH}$ and $\overline{GF}$

17. curve   **19.** Because there are two parallel, congruent triangular bases, it is a triangular prism.   **21a.** Figure 2   **21b.** Figure 1   **21c.** Figure 3   **23.** hexagon   **25.** 90°

Page 603   Chapter Review   Vocabulary Check

Across
11. equilateral   **15.** complementary
Down
1. adjacent   **3.** supplementary   **5.** triangle   **7.** vertical
9. acute   **13.** right

Page 604   Chapter Review   Key Concept Check

1. vertex   **3.** 90°   **5.** scale drawing

Chapter 8 Measure Figures

Page 610   Chapter 8   Are You Ready?

1. 42 sq m   **3.** 76.5 sq mm

Pages 617–618   Lesson 8-1   Independent Practice

1. 2.5 mm   **3.** 34 cm   **5** $3.14 \times 13 = 40.8$ cm
7 19 people   **9a.** 30 mm   **9b.** 31.4 mm   **9c.** 31.4159 mm
9d. Sample answer: The more decimal places of the estimate of π, the more precise the circumference.   **11.** 18 in.   **13.** 257 cm
15. Greater than; Sample answer: Since the radius is 4 feet, the diameter is 8 feet. Since π is a little more than 3, the circumference will be a little more than 3 times 8, or 24 feet.
17. The circumference would double. For example, with a diameter of 4 feet, the circumference is about 12.6 feet. With a diameter of 8 feet, the circumference is about 25.1 feet.

Pages 619–620   Lesson 8-1   Extra Practice

19. 3.5 in.   **21.** 72 ft   **23.** $\frac{22}{7} \times 21 = 66$ ft   **25.** $\frac{22}{7} \times 42 =$
132 mm   **27.** 37.7 cm   **29.** Each is π, or about 3.14, units longer than the previous circle.   **31a.** False   **31b.** True
31c. False   **33.** 12.74 m^2 **35.** 36,976 ft^2

Pages 627–628   Lesson 8-2   Independent Practice

1. $3.14 \times 6 \times 6 = 113.0$ cm^2 **3** $3.14 \times 5.5 \times 5.5 =$
95.0 ft^2 **5.** $3.14 \times 6.3 \times 6.3 = 124.6$ mm^2 **7.** 254.3 ft^2
9 226.1 in^2 **11.** 163.3 yd^2 **13.** The large pizza; the medium pizza's area is 78.5 square inches and costs $0.102 per square inch. The large pizza's area is 153.86 square inches and costs $0.097 per square inch.   **15.** When the radius of a circle is doubled, the circumference doubles and the area is 4 times as large. In the formula for area of a circle, the radius is squared, so when the radius of a circle is doubled, the area is 2^2 or 4 times as large.   **17.** 5.9 in^2 **19.** Sample answer: To find the area of the quarter circle, multiply the area of the entire circle by 14; $A = \frac{1}{4}\pi r^2$; 19.6 in^2

Pages 629–630   Lesson 8-2   Extra Practice

21. $3.14 \times 6.3 \times 6.3 = 124.6$ cm^2 **23.** $3.14 \times 5.4 \times 5.4 =$
91.6 yd^2 **25.** $3.14 \times 9.3 \times 9.3 = 271.6$ mm^2 **27.** 144.7 ft^2
29. 64.3 in^2 **31.** circle; $\frac{1}{2} \cdot 100 \cdot 100 < 3 \cdot 50 \cdot 50$
33. 154 in^2; Sample answer: Using $\frac{22}{7}$ makes the computation easier since the radius is 7. The 7s cancel out in the multiplication.   **35.** 210 in^2 **37.** 39.5 cm^2

Pages 635–636   Lesson 8-3   Independent Practice

1. 64 cm^2 **3.** 220.5 cm^2 **5** 38.6 ft^2 **7** 119.5 ft^2
9. 77 cm^2 **11.** 44.6 ft^2; 30.3 ft   **13.** 110.8 ft^2

Pages 637–638   Lesson 8-3   Extra Practice

15. 87.5 m^2 **17.** 180 cm^2 **19.** 9 cm^2 **21.** 240 ft^2
23a. 36   **23b.** 14.14   **23c.** 92.56   **25.** 3.7 cm^2 **27.** 4.7 m

Pages 643–644 Lesson 8-4 Independent Practice

1 192 m^3 **3** 108 m^3 **5a.** 96 ft^3; 128 ft^3; 168 ft^3; 160 ft^3; 120 ft^3 **5b.** The height must allow the water to be deep enough for someone to get wet and the length and width must allow a person to fit. So the first and last sets of dimensions would not work. **7a.** Sample answer: There is a direct relationship between the volume and the length. Since the length is doubled, the volume is also doubled. **7b.** The volume is eight times greater. **7c.** Neither; Sample answer: doubling the height will result in a volume of 4 · 4 · 10 or 160 in^3; doubling the width will result in a volume of 4 · 8 · 5 or 160 in^3.

Pages 645–646 Lesson 8-4 Extra Practice

11. 236.3 cm^3 **13.** 20.4 mm^3 **15.** 306.52 = 19.4h; 15.8 m **17.** 166$\frac{1}{4}$ yd^3 **19.** 2 in. by 1.5 in. by 0.5 in.; 3 in. by 1 in. by 0.5 in. **21.** 25.8 m **23.** 29.2 cm

Page 649 Problem-Solving Investigation Solve a Simpler Problem

Case 3. 80 chairs **Case 5.** 7,763,270.6 mi^2; Sample answer: The area of Asia is about 17,251,712.4 mi^2 and the area of North America is about 9,488,441.8 mi^2. 17,251,712.4 − 9,488,441.8 = 7,763,270.6

Pages 657–658 Lesson 8-5 Independent Practice

1 80 ft^3 **3.** 42 ft^3 **5.** 14 in. **7** 10 in^3 **9.** The volume is eight times greater; Sample answer: Since each dimension is two times greater, the volume is 2 × 2 × 2 or eight times greater. **11.** Sample answer: first set: area of the base, 40 ft^2; height of the pyramid, 12 ft; second set: area of the base, 30 ft^2; height of the pyramid, 16 ft **13.** The volumes are the same.

Pages 659–660 Lesson 8-5 Extra Practice

15. 60 in^3 **17.** 195 yd^3 **19.** 11 ft **21.** 22 in. **23.** 1,234.2 m^3 **25.** 24 in.; Sample answer: Replace V with 1,560 and B with 13 × 15 in the formula $V = \frac{1}{3}Bh$. Then solve for h. **27.** 1.5 ft^2 **29.** 28.75 ft^2

Pages IN37–IN38 Indiana Lesson Independent Practice

1 88.0 mm^2 **3.** 272.0 mm^2 **5.** 113.1 in^2 **7.** 1,068.1 yd^2 **9** 241.3 in^2 **11.** No, the surface area of the side of the cylinder will double, but the area of the bases will not. **13.** $A = 2\pi rh + \pi r^2$; Sample answer: The baker will not ice the bottom of the cake, so you only need to include the area of one of the bases in the equation.

Pages IN39–IN40 Indiana Lesson Extra Practice

15 1,105.8 cm^2; 1,508.0 cm^2 **17.** 763.4 in^2 **19.** Sample answer: 2 · 3 · 4^2 + 2 · 3 · 4 · 4 or 192 m^2 **21.** about 85.7% **23a.** 562 **23b.** 653 **23c.** II; 91; I **25.** 23.08 ft^2 **27.** 3.5 in^3

Pages 669–670 Lesson 8-6 Independent Practice

1 314 cm^2 **3** 207 in^2 **5.** 180 in^2 **7.** S.A. = 6x^2 **9.** False; Sample answer: A 9 × 7 × 13 rectangular prism has a surface area of 2(9 × 13) + 2(9 × 7) + 2(13 × 7) or 542 square units. Doubling the length, the surface area is 2(18 × 13) + 2(18 × 7) + 2(13 × 7) or 902 square units. 2 × 542 ≠ 902 **11.** 1,926 cm^2

Pages 671–672 Lesson 8-6 Extra Practice

13. 833.1 mm^2 **15.** 96 ft^2 **17.** Yes; there are 2,520 ft^2 of fencing. Since 8 gallons of paint will cover 350 · 8 or 2,800 ft^2 and 2,800 ft^2 > 2,520 ft^2, 8 gallons is enough paint. **19.** 64.5 in^2 **21a.** 12.5 **21b.** 50 **21c.** 71 **21d.** 196 **23.** triangle; triangle; triangle **25.** rectangle; circle; oval

Pages 681–682 Lesson 8-7 Independent Practice

1 95 in^2 **3.** 328 in^2 **5.** 0.52 ft^2 **7** 78 in^2 **9.** 6.5 cm **11.**

Sample answer: Both a square pyramid and a rectangular pyramid have isosceles triangles as their lateral faces. All the lateral faces are congruent on a square pyramid but, on a rectangular pyramid, the opposite pairs of lateral faces are congruent.

Pages 683–684 Lesson 8-7 Extra Practice

13. 197.1 m^2 **15.** 765 cm^2 **17.** 26.1 ft^2 **19.**

21a. True **21b.** True **21c.** False **23.** 456 ft^2 **25.** 10 ft

Pages 693–694 Lesson 8-8 Independent Practice

1 2.3 m^3 **3.** 2,600 ft^2 **5** 0.5 ft^3 **7.** 10.4 m^2 **9.** 100 in^3 **13.** less than; Sample answer: The combined surface area of the two prisms is 180 in^2. Since they share a common surface, the area of that surface is not included in the total surface area.

Pages 695–696 Lesson 8-8 Extra Practice

15. 100 in³ **17.** 280.2 cm² **19a.** 1.68 ft³ **19b.** 19.28 ft²

21.

23.

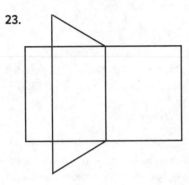

Page 699 Chapter Review Vocabulary Check

1. diameter **3.** circle **5.** circumference **7.** semicircle
9. volume **11.** lateral

Page 700 Chapter Review Key Concept Check

1. twice **3.** height

Chapter 9 Probability

Page 710 Chapter 9 Are You Ready?

1. $\frac{1}{3}$ **3.** $\frac{2}{3}$ **5.** 30 **7.** 24

Pages 715–716 Lesson 9-1 Independent Practice

1. $\frac{1}{4}$, 25%, or 0.25 **3** $\frac{1}{1}$, 100%, or 1 **5** $\frac{1}{5}$, 0.2, or 20%;
Sample answer: Since 80% arrive on time, that means that
20% do not arrive on time. **7.** Picking a black jelly bean is
impossible since the probability of picking a black jelly bean is
0%. **9a.** $\frac{1}{8}$, 0.125, 12.5%; $\frac{1}{2}$, 0.5, 50% **9b.** $\frac{3}{4}$, 0.75, 75%

11. 70%, $\frac{1}{3}$; Sample answer: 70% and $\frac{1}{3}$ are probabilities that
are not complementary because $0.7 + 0.\overline{3} \neq 1$. The other sets
of probability are complementary.

Pages 717–718 Lesson 9-1 Extra Practice

13. $\frac{1}{5}$, 20%, or 0.2 **15.** $\frac{7}{10}$, 70%, or 0.7 **17.** $\frac{1}{2}$, 50%, or 0.5

19. $\frac{3}{5}$, 60%, or 0.6 **21.** The complement of selecting a girl is
selecting a boy. The probability of the complement is $\frac{37}{100}$, 0.37,
or 37%. **23.** $\frac{124}{125}$, 99.2%, or 0.992; It is very likely that card 13
will *not* be chosen. **25.** P(orange) = $\frac{1}{5}$; P(green) = $\frac{2}{5}$ **27.** >
29. $\frac{3}{25}$; $\frac{1}{5}$; Bryan misses more foul shots than Dwayne.

Pages 725–726 Lesson 9-2 Independent Practice

1 **a.** $\frac{1}{5}$; The experimental probability is close to the
theoretical probability of $\frac{1}{6}$. **b.** $\frac{9}{10}$; The experimental
probability is close to the theoretical probability of $\frac{5}{6}$.
3a. 162 people **3b.** about 134 people **5** **a.** $\frac{1}{3}$
b. $\frac{6}{25}$; $\frac{13}{50}$
c.

Sample answer: Section B should be one half of the spinner
and sections A and C should each be one fourth of the spinner.
7. Yes; Sample answer: $\frac{5\text{ sharpened}}{10\text{ unsharpened}} = \frac{20\text{ sharpened}}{x\text{ unsharpened}}$. So,
$x = 40$.

Pages 727–728 Lesson 9-2 Extra Practice

9. $\frac{9}{20}$; The experimental probability of $\frac{9}{20}$ is close to the
theoretical probability of $\frac{1}{2}$. **11.** 50 customers

13. experimental; 40; less **15.** P(not red) **17.** vanilla sundae,
vanilla cone, chocolate sundae, chocolate cone, strawberry
sundae, strawberry cone; equally likely

Pages 737–738 Lesson 9-3 Independent Practice

1. H1, H2, H3, H4, H5, T1, T2, T3, T4, T5
3 purple 10, purple 18, purple 21, purple 24,
green 10, green 18, green 21, green 24,
black 10, black 18, black 21, black 24,
silver 10, silver 18, silver 21, silver 24

5. $\frac{1}{36}$;

1, 1	1, 2	1, 3	1, 4	1, 5	1, 6
2, 1	2, 2	2, 3	2, 4	2, 5	2, 6
3, 1	3, 2	3, 3	3, 4	3, 5	3, 6
4, 1	4, 2	4, 3	4, 4	4, 5	4, 6
5, 1	5, 2	5, 3	5, 4	5, 5	5, 6
6, 1	6, 2	6, 3	6, 4	6, 5	6, 6

7 P(Player 1) = $\frac{6}{8}$ or $\frac{3}{4}$; P(Player 2) = $\frac{2}{8}$ or $\frac{1}{4}$; RRB, RYB,
RRY, RYY, BRB, BYB, BYY, BRY **9.** The first outcome in the
I bracket should be IC.

Pages 739–740 Lesson 9-3 Extra Practice

11.

| Appetizer | Entree | Dessert | Sample Space |

13a. 16 combinations **13b.** $\frac{1}{16}$

13c.

| Shoes | Socks | Sample Space |

8 combinations

15. (Ava, Brooke); (Greg, Brooke); (Antoine, Mario) **17.** $\frac{1}{8}$
19. $\frac{1}{2}$ **21.** $\frac{1}{3}$; There are 2 numbers out of 6 on a number cube that are greater than 4. $\frac{2}{6} = \frac{1}{3}$

Pages 745–746 Lesson 9-4 Independent Practice

1 Sample answer: Spin a spinner with 4 equal-size sections 50 times. **3** Sample answer: Spin a spinner divided into 3 equal sections and roll a number cube. Repeat the simulation until all types of cookies are obtained. **5.** Sample answer: Use 3 red marbles to represent winning and 7 blue marbles to represent losing. Draw 1 marble 4 times, replacing the marble each time. **7.** Sample answer: a survey of 100 people voting on whether or not to enact a tax increase, where each person is equally likely to vote yes or no. Toss a coin 100 times. **9.** Sample answer: sometimes; The spinner must have equal-sized sections.

Pages 747–748 Lesson 9-4 Extra Practice

11. Sample answer: Use a spinner with 5 equal sections to represent the 5 discounts. Spin 4 times to represent 4 customers receiving cards. **13.** Sample answer: Toss a coin. Heads represents one color and tails represents the other color. Repeat until both colors are selected. **15.** Sample answer: Spin a spinner with 4 equal sections. Each section represents one of the magazines. Repeat the simulation until all possible magazines are selected. **17.** Spin a spinner with

equal size spaces labeled A, B, C, D, E, and F. Let spinning A represent winning a prize and let spinning other letters represent not winning a prize; Roll a number cube. Let rolling a 1 represent winning a prize and let rolling a 2, 3, 4, 5, or 6 represent not winning a prize.

Page 755 Problem-Solving Investigation Act It Out

Case 3. 31 **Case 5.** unfair; Sample answer: There are 20 out of 36 outcomes that are multiples of 3 and only 15 that are multiples of 4. Jason has a greater chance of winning.

Pages 761–762 Lesson 9-5 Independent Practice

1 12 **3.** 84 **5.** 6 possible routes; $\frac{1}{6}$ or about 17%
7. $\frac{1}{50}$; very unlikely **9** No; the number of selections is 32 · 11 or 352, which is less than 365. **11.** 10 groups, 8 activities have 80 outcomes; the other two have 72 outcomes. **13.** 6^x

Pages 763–764 Lesson 9-5 Extra Practice

15. 8 **17.** 27 **19.** 16 **21.** $\frac{4}{48}$ or $\frac{1}{12}$; Sample answer: There are 3 · 4 · 4 or 48 different possible outcomes of a phone plan. There are 1 · 4 · 1 or 4 different possible outcomes of a phone plan that includes Brand B and has a headset. **23.** $108 = 9 \times c \times 2$; 6 colors **25.** $\frac{1}{2}$ **27.** Sample answer: Assign each number of a number cube to a toy. Roll the number cube. Repeat until all numbers are rolled.

Pages 769–770 Lesson 9-6 Independent Practice

1 24 **3.** 840 **5.** 40,320 **7.** 120 ways **9** 6
11. Sample answer: The number of ways you can order 3 books on a shelf is 3 · 2 · 1 or 6. **13a.** 15 **13b.** 120
13c. 10 **13d.** 28

Pages 771–772 Lesson 9-6 Extra Practice

15. 60 **17.** 120 **19.** $\frac{1}{90}$ **21.** $\frac{1}{120}$ **23a.** False **23b.** True
23c. True **25.** $\frac{29}{30}$ **27.** WB, WG, RB, RG, GB, GG

Pages 779–780 Lesson 9-7 Independent Practice

1. $\frac{1}{24}$ **3** $\frac{1}{8}$ **5.** $\frac{1}{144}$ **7** $\frac{7}{95}$ **9.** $\frac{1}{19}$ **11.** $\frac{3}{8}$;
dependent event; after the first piece of paper is chosen, there is one less from which to choose. **13.** Sample answer: Spinning the spinner twice represents two independent events. The probability of getting an even number is $\frac{2}{5}$ each time; $\frac{2}{5} \cdot \frac{2}{5}$ or $\frac{4}{25}$. **15a.** 0.0004 or 0.04% **15b.** about 400 packages

Pages 781–782 Lesson 9-7 Extra Practice

17. $\frac{5}{14}$ **19.** $\frac{92}{287}$ **21.** $\frac{3}{20}$ **23.** $\frac{7}{60}$ **25.** $\frac{3}{55}$ **27.** $\frac{6}{55}$
29a. True **29b.** True **29c.** False **31.** 18 **33.** 51
35. $9 = 0.15x$; 60

Page 785 Chapter Review Vocabulary Check

1. sample space **3.** theoretical

Page 786 Chapter Review Key Concept Check

1. experimental probability **3.** compound event

Chapter 10 Statistics

Page 792   Chapter 10   Are You Ready?

1. Rihanna   **3.** 75

Pages 797–798   Lesson 10-1   Independent Practice

1. $\frac{3}{10}$, 0.3, or 30%   **3** $\frac{2}{25}$, 0.08, or 8%   **5** 9 students

7. About 143 students prefer humor books, and the number of students that prefer nonfiction is 88. So, there are about 55 more students who prefer humor books to nonfiction books.
9. about 100 times   **11.** Sample answer: Randomly select a part of the group to get a sample. Determine their preferences and use the results to determine the percent of the total group. It makes sense to use a sample when surveying the population of a city.

Pages 799–800   Lesson 10-1   Extra Practice

13. $\frac{3}{5}$, 0.6, or 60%   **15a.** about 60,000   **15b.** about 72,500
15c. about 7,200   **17.** $\frac{27}{238} = \frac{n}{100}$ **19.** $\frac{27}{100} = \frac{p}{238}$
21. $\frac{54}{20} = \frac{405}{x}$; 150 minutes or 2.5 hours   **23.** $\frac{1}{25}$

Pages 805–806   Lesson 10-2   Independent Practice

1 The conclusion is valid. This is an unbiased systematic random sample.   **3** This is a simple random sample. So, the sample is valid; about 205 people.   **5.** Sample answer: Questions should be asked in a neutral manner. For example, the question "You really don't like Brand X, do you?" might not get the same answer as the question "Do you prefer Brand X or Brand Y?"   **7.** Sometimes; Sample answer: The sample needs to represent the entire population to be valid.   **9.** Sample answer: The sample will be biased because it is a convenience sample. Marisol will be asking only basketball fans.

Pages 807–808   Lesson 10-2   Extra Practice

11. This is an unbiased, simple random sample because randomly selected Californians were surveyed. So, the conclusion is valid.   **13.** This is an unbiased, systematic random sample. So, the conclusion is valid; 304 students.
15. The survey results in a convenience sample; Sample answer: The school district should survey every tenth family living within the school district's boundaries.   **17a.** Invalid
17b. Valid   **17c.** Valid   **19.** median; Sample answer: She scored better than the mean on four of the tests. She scored lower than the mode on four of the tests.

Pages 817–818   Lesson 10-3   Independent Practice

1 Graph B; Sample answer: The ratio of the area of the gas pumps in the graph on the right are not proportional to the cost of gas.   **3** The median or the mode because they are much closer in value to most of the data.

5.

7. Sample answer: Since the graph makes it seem as if rent has been stable, a person may choose to become a tenant.
9. Sample answer: The graph makes it appear that the Fall section is greater than the Spring section. This is because the perspective of the graph makes it appear greater, when, in fact, they are equal in size.

Pages 819–820   Lesson 10-3   Extra Practice

11. Sample answer: The scale of the graph is not divided into equal intervals, so differences in heights appear less than they actually are.   **13.** Sample answer: The mode is 100, but she only received 100 two times out of 6 tests.   **15.** The intervals on the vertical scale are inconsistent.

Page 823   Problem-Solving Investigation   Use a Graph

Case 3. Sample answer: 2017

Case 5. $36.20

Pages 833–834   Lesson 10-4   Independent Practice

1 Sample answer: The times at Lucy's Steakhouse have a median of 20 minutes with an interquartile range of 20 minutes. The times at Gary's Grill have a median of 15 minutes with an interquartile range of 10 minutes. In general, a customer will wait longer at Lucy's Steakhouse.
3a. Plant A: 2.75, 0.75; Plant B: 3.1; 0.7
3b.

3c. Sample answer: Both populations have similar interquartile ranges. The median for Plant B is greater. So, Plant B generally showed more growth.   **5.** The data shown in the histograms are only shown in intervals. Specific values are not shown.

Pages 835–836   Lesson 10-4   Extra Practice

9. this season; Sample answer: Both seasons' scores have a median of 20 points, but last season's scores have an interquartile range of 15 points while this season's interquartile range is 10 points. So, the football team's performance was more consistent this season.   **11.** Sample answer: 2, 4, 4, 5, 8, 9, 10   **13a.** False   **13b.** False   **13c.** True   **15.** 1.74 million   **17.** Sample answer: The shape of the distribution is not symmetric since the lengths of each box and whisker are not the same. There are no outliers.

Pages IN45–IN46   Indiana Lesson   Independent Practice

1 The mean best represents the data. There are no extreme values. mean: 56.4 minutes   **3** **a.** 1,148   **b.** With the outlier, the mean is 216.83 ft, the median is 33.5 ft, there is no mode, and the range is 1,138 ft. Without the outlier, the mean is 30.6 ft, the median is 24 ft, there is no mode, and the range is 52 ft.   **c.** With the outlier, the best measure is the median depth; without the outlier, the best measure is the mean.   **5.** Pilar did not include the outlier. The mean is 20. The median, which is 15.5, best describes the data because the outlier affects the mean more than it affects the median.   **7.** Sample answer: 125, 32, and 19

Pages IN47–IN48   Indiana Lesson   Extra Practice

9. Since the set of data has no extreme values or numbers that are identical, the mean or median, 6 songs, would best represent the data.   **11a.** 62°   **11b.** With the outlier, the mean is 32.71°, the median is 29°, the mode is 29° and the range is 37°. Without the outlier, the mean is 27.83°, the median is 28.5°, the mode is 29°, and the range is 4°.   **11c.** Sample answer: With the outlier, the best measure is the mode; without the outlier, the best measure is the mode; the outlier does not affect the mode, but affects the mean and median.   **13a.** median   **13b.** mean   **13c.** mode   **15.** 260   **17.** 154   **19.** 203 tickets

Pages 843–844   Lesson 10-5   Independent Practice

1 box plot; shows the median
3. A box plot is an appropriate graph because there is a large set of data and it will show the measures of variation of the data set. This graph has a median of 41.

Number of Push-ups

35 36 37 38 39 40 41 42 43 44 45 46 47 48 49 50

5a. Situation B; Sample answer: A bar graph can show the number of customers who made a purchase by each individual age.   **5b.** Yes; Sample answer: line plot; A line plot shows the frequency of data on a number line.   **7.** always; Sample answer: The sections of the circle graph can be taken from the

bars of the graph and the percents can be found by dividing each bar's value by the total number of data values.
9. Sample answer: Both use bars to show how many things are in each category. A histogram shows the frequency of data that has been organized into equal intervals, so there is no space between the bars. It would be appropriate to use a histogram instead of a bar graph when the data can be organized into equal intervals.

Pages 845–846   Lesson 10-5   Extra Practice

11. circle graph; compares parts to a whole
13a.

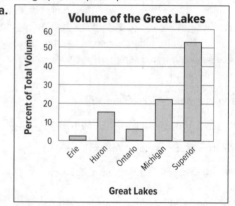

13b. Sample answer: The circle graph is most appropriate because it shows how each lake compares to the whole.
15.

A histogram is an appropriate graph because the data is given in intervals. The graph shows people ages 26–30 text the least amount.   **17.** line graph; circle graph; bar graph
19. 65 men; 65 women

Page 849   Chapter Review   Vocabulary Check

Across
5. population   **9.** sample
Down
1. systematic   **3.** simple   **7.** unbiased

Page 850   Chapter Review   Key Concept Check

1. survey   **3.** biased sample

Index

Dd

Ee

Qq

Rr

Ss

Index

Ww

Xx

Yy

Zz

Index

$=$

Name _____

Work Mats

0
1
2
3
4
5
6
7
8
9

−11
−10
−9
−8
−7
−6
−5
−4
−3
−2
−1
0
1
2
3
4
5
6
7
8
9
10
11

What Are Foldables and How Do I Create Them?

Foldables are three-dimensional graphic organizers that help you create study guides for each chapter in your book.

Step 1 Go to the back of your book to find the Foldable for the chapter you are currently studying. Follow the cutting and assembly instructions at the top of the page.

Step 2 Go to the Key Concept Check at the end of the chapter you are currently studying. Match up the tabs and attach your Foldable to this page. Dotted tabs show where to place your Foldable. Striped tabs indicate where to tape the Foldable.

How Will I Know When to Use My Foldable?

When it's time to work on your Foldable, you will see a Foldables logo at the bottom of the **Rate Yourself!** box on the Guided Practice pages. This lets you know that it is time to update it with concepts from that lesson. Once you've completed your Foldable, use it to study for the chapter test.

How Do I Complete My Foldable?

No two Foldables in your book will look alike. However, some will ask you to fill in similar information. Below are some of the instructions you'll see as you complete your Foldable. **HAVE FUN** learning math using Foldables!

Instructions and what they mean

Best Used to...	Complete the sentence explaining when the concept should be used.
Definition	Write a definition in your own words.
Description	Describe the concept using words.
Equation	Write an equation that uses the concept. You may use one already in the text or you can make up your own.
Example	Write an example about the concept. You may use one already in the text or you can make up your own.
Formulas	Write a formula that uses the concept. You may use one already in the text.
How do I ...?	Explain the steps involved in the concept.
Models	Draw a model to illustrate the concept.
Picture	Draw a picture to illustrate the concept.
Solve Algebraically	Write and solve an equation that uses the concept.
Symbols	Write or use the symbols that pertain to the concept.
Write About It	Write a definition or description in your own words.
Words	Write the words that pertain to the concept.

Meet Foldables Author Dinah Zike

Dinah Zike is known for designing hands-on manipulatives that are used nationally and internationally by teachers and parents. Dinah is an explosion of energy and ideas. Her excitement and joy for learning inspires everyone she touches.

Linear Expressions

add or subtract

factor

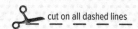 cut on all dashed lines   fold on all solid lines   tape to page 426

Examples

Examples

page 426

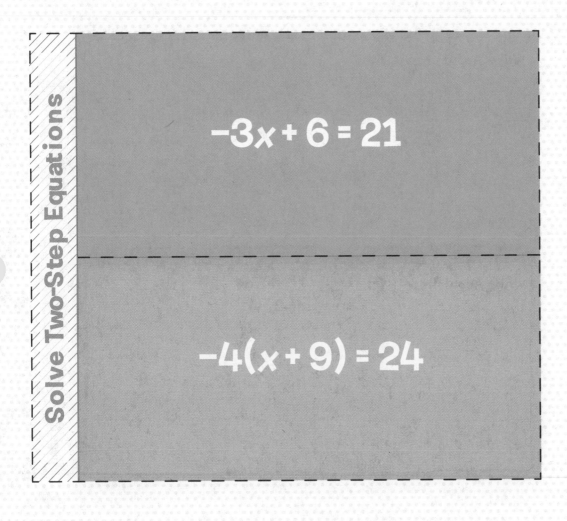

Solve Two-Step Equations

$$-3x + 6 = 21$$

$$-4(x + 9) = 24$$

cut on all dashed lines   fold on all solid lines   tape to page 524   FOLDABLES®

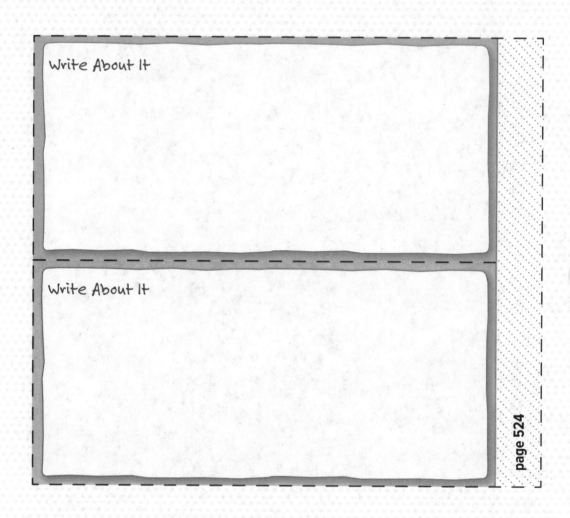

Write About It

Write About It

page 524

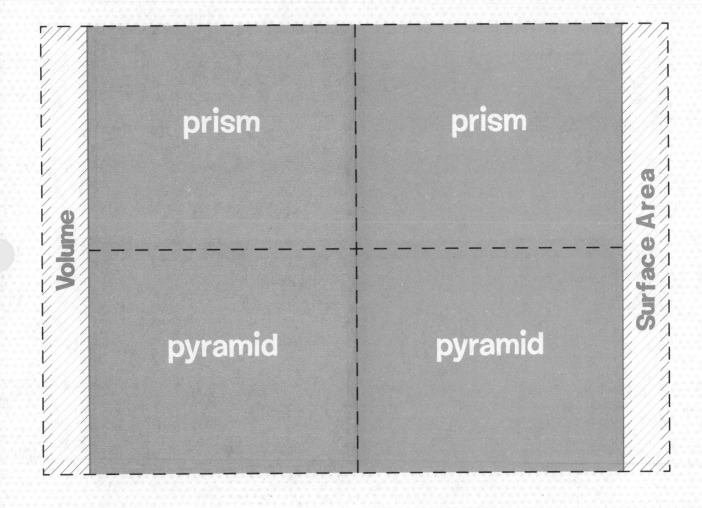

Volume

prism

prism

pyramid

pyramid

Surface Area

Probability

simple event

compound event

Foldables

page 786

Definition

Definition